# BIOACTIVE MOLECULES IN PLANT FOODS

# AGRICULTURE ISSUES AND POLICIES

Additional books in this series can be found on Nova's website
under the Series tab.


Additional e-books in this series can be found on Nova's website
under the e-book tab.

# BIOACTIVE MOLECULES IN PLANT FOODS

## FLORENCE OJIUGO URUAKPA
### EDITOR

Nova Science Publishers, Inc.
*New York*

**Library of Congress Cataloging-in-Publication Data**

Bioactive molecules in plant foods / editor: Florence Ojiugo Uruakpa.
    p. cm.
  Includes index.
  ISBN 978-1-62081-515-1 (hardcover)
  1. Plant bioactive compounds. 2. Phytonutrients. I. Uruakpa, Florence Ojiugo.
  QK898.B54B 563 2012
  580--dc23

                    2012010676

*Published by Nova Science Publishers, Inc. † New York*

# CONTENTS

# PREFACE

In this functional foods era, when people prefer disease prevention to treatment (people are more interested in getting their medication from kitchen cabinets than from hospitals), there is a need for a book that provides insight in the components of plant foods that enhance our health and longevity. As products of the functional foods and nutraceuticals era unleash into everyday life, people need to be more educated in what science can and cannot do. Further, the current rising healthcare costs in most countries underscores the need for a preventive rather than treatment approach by consumers, researchers, health professionals and government agencies. The link between diet, moderate physical activity and wellness has been a prime focus in recent times. Although earlier report for the link was based on epidemiological findings but developments in the area of functional foods attest to the claims by preclinical and clinical studies.

The herbal supplements market has been on the rise in the past years, with more than 500 herbs marketed in the United States and sales in excess of $3 billion/year. Consumers' enthusiasm comes from potential benefits derived from the use of various herbs (plants or plant parts such as leaf, stem, root, bark, seed, and flower) which are rich sources of phytochemicals – a large group of non-nutrient compounds that perform physiological functions in the body. Phytochemiclas are found in plants such as fruits, veggies, legumes, grains, herbs, tea, and spices. Of the many plant molecules, polyphenols make up the largest group with its intake estimated at about 1 g daily.

Over the past decade, there has been a surge in the publication of research findings and developments in the field of functional foods, but often in fragmented and non-targeted manner. Thus the need to fill the existing gap by writing a book that focuses on plant bioactive molecules. The book highlights bioactive compounds from plant sources (e.g. antioxidants, bioactive peptides of plant origin, lignans). It covers aspects such as their methods of isolation/extraction and purification; mechanisms of action, functional and/or health benefits to consumers; basic principles, theories, concepts and applications that explain the effectiveness of plant bioactive components; why we need to know what plant bioactives are, their significance and relevance; the distinct characteristics and strengths of bioactive molecules in performing/achieving their roles in foods before and/or after use/consumption; their role and importance in maintaining good health; their commercial availability; the practical implications of plant bioactive molecules in foods; future status/impact of plant bioactives on health and economy. The area of functional foods, nutraceuticals and natural health products is very dynamic and our lives will continue to be influenced by the increasing rate at which new advances occur in this area of food and nutritional sciences.

In: Bioactive Molecules in Plant Foods
Editor: Florence Ojiugo Uruakpa

ISBN: 978-1-62081-515-1
© 2012 Nova Science Publishers, Inc.

*Chapter I*

# PLANT BIOACTIVES IN CHINESE DIETARY HERBS

## *Junzeng Zhang[1] and Zhimin Wang[2]*

[1]Institute for Nutrisciences and Health, National Research Council Canada,
Charlottetown, PE, Canada
[2]Research Center of Chemistry and Quality Evaluation for Chinese Materia Medica,
Institute of Chinese Materia Medica, China Academy of Chinese Medical Sciences,
Beijing, P. R. China

## ABSTRACT

For traditional Chinese medicine (TCM), the food system is indispensable to general wellness and healing. The properties and uses of many Chinese herbs in various forms of food systems have been documented and discussed in TCM literature spanning thousands of years. As functional foods and nutraceuticals are gaining attention nowadays, the knowledge of the healing power of food and TCM practices are attracting much interest. In this chapter, 87 Chinese herbs, authorized for use as foods under the current Chinese regulatory system, are briefly introduced along with information on their historical use. Additionally, some highlights are presented from the past ten plus years (1998-2010) of the progress of bioactives research from selected dietary herbs.

## INTRODUCTION

In traditional Chinese medicine (TCM), the food system is an essential component for the prevention and treatment of many diseases. The integration of diet, herbal medicine, acupuncture and physical exercise techniques, such as Tai Ji (or Tai Chi), has been an important aspect of Chinese history and civilization.

The concept of disease prevention as the preferred approach was first introduced in the earliest TCM literature, "Huang Di Nei Jing" (400 B.C.), with the statement that "the best doctor is the one who prevents diseases." The earliest TCM herbal drug book, "Shen Nong Ben Cao Jing" (A.D. 200), described 365 ingredients (minerals, herbs and animals) across 3 categories—the top-, middle-, and low-grades, referring not to quality, but rather to the therapeutic or health-maintaining properties. There are more than a hundred materials listed in the top-grade group, including many herbal drugs, which are suggested to be consumed for various health benefits without toxicity concerns. Since then, many other classic TCM publications have also provided information specifically on the wellness-maintaining applications of Chinese dietary herbs in the medicated food system.

At present in China, usage of dietary herbs is as common in home cooking as in commercial, medicated diet settings. In the Chinese regulatory framework, approximately 200 herbs are listed as either foods or source materials for producing healthy food products [1]. This means these herbs can be legally consumed in any food applications, or used for commercial healthy food product development and marketing. A further subset of 87 of these is categorized as dietary herbs.

In this chapter, the historical uses and applications of the aforementioned 87 dietary herbs will be introduced, followed by a brief review of the chemistry, biological and pharmacological effects of the bioactive compounds of the most commonly used dietary herbs from this list. Background information and a list of guideline documents of the current Chinese regulatory system for health foods or novel foods are also provided.

Due to space limitations, the discussion will focus on bioactive research conducted using representative examples of the dietary herbs during the past decade or so (1998-2010). This chapter aims to serve as an introduction to the bioactives present in this particular food system.

# 1. DIETARY HERBS COMMONLY USED AS SPICES AND FLAVOURING INGREDIENTS IN CHINESE FOOD

In Chinese medicine, herbs that are used as spices are warm or hot in nature. They are commonly used to warm internal organs and expel coldness.

## 1.1. *Zingiber officinale* Rosc. (Common Name: Ginger; Chinese Name: Jiang)

Ginger is one of the key flavouring ingredients in Chinese cooking, and is also a commonly prescribed herb in Chinese medicine. Both the fresh and the dried rhizome of ginger are used. The fresh variety is mainly used for colds, coughing and vomiting, while the dried ginger is used for stomach and abdominal pain as well as diarrhea [2].

The 6-gingerol (1) and 6-shogaol (2) are two representatives of the major bioactive components in ginger. Both 1 and 2, as well as their natural analogs, such as 6-gingerdiol (3) and ginger extracts, are strong antioxidants [3-7]. Ginger also contains other phenolic compounds, such as dehydrogingerone (4, exists in dried ginger only), 5- [4-hydroxy-6-(4-hydroxyphenethyl)-tetrahydro-2$H$-pyran-2-yl]-3-methoxybenzene-1,2-diol (5) (Figure 1) and other common phenolic acids (i.e., syringic, gallic, cinnamic, $p$-coumaric, and caffeic acids) [5, 8, 9].

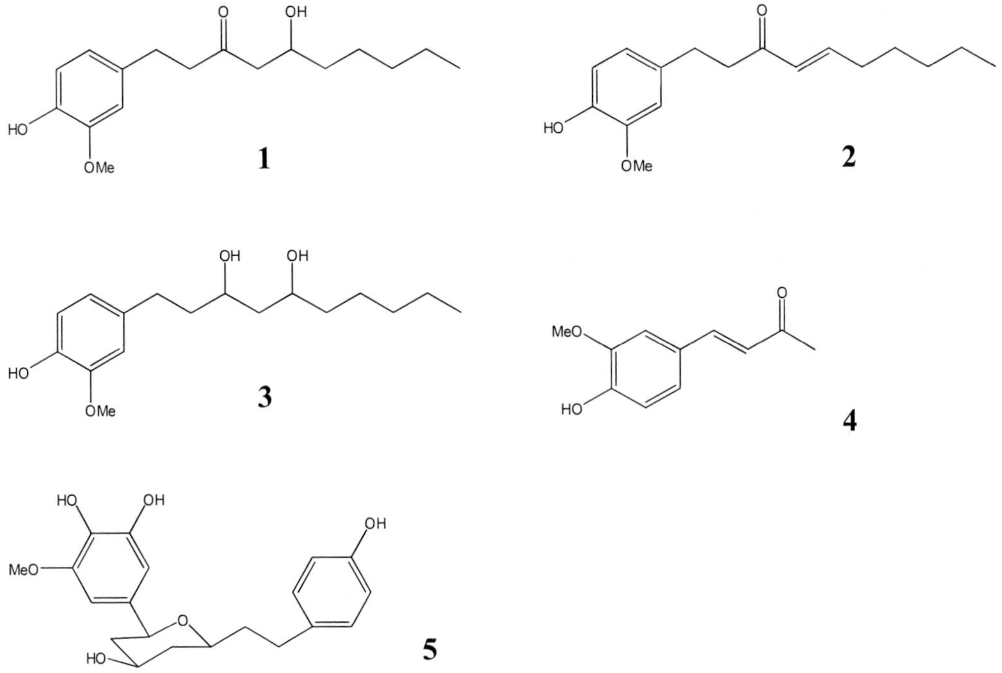

Figure 1. Structures of compounds from *Zingiber officinale* Rosc.

Ginger has been historically used as a remedy for nausea and vomiting. Recently, the beneficial effects of ginger have been verified through experimental and clinical studies, primarily on motion sickness and pregnancy nausea [10-13]. However, ginger has not been shown to provide alleviation for all forms of nausea and vomiting, such as after laparoscopic surgery [14].

As a specific main ingredient in fresh ginger, 6-Gingerol has been identified as the major bioactive component responsible for the blood lipid-lowering effect of ginger methanol extract in a fructose induced hyperlipimedic and hyperinsulinemic rat model [15]. Aqueous and methanol extracts of ginger were also found to have anti-obesity effects in both high-fat and goldthioglucose induced obese mice [16, 17]. Additionally, several animal studies have revealed that ginger extracts not only modulate blood lipids, but also possess anti-diabetic properties [16, 18-21]. More recent studies in hypercholesterol and high fat diet fed rat models also demonstrated the beneficial effects of ginger aqueous and ethanolic extracts in metabolic syndrome [22, 23]. As well, 6-Gingerol and 6-shogaol were shown to significantly inhibit the tumor necrosis factor-alpha (TNF-alpha) mediated downregulation of adiponectin expression in 3T3-L1 adipocytes, but each through their own distinct mechanism [24].

Ginger and its main components also have anti-inflammatory and immune modulation activities, as evidenced in animal studies [20, 25-31]. As well, those components have shown to be beneficial against certain cancers or to be anticarcinogenic in several experimental studies [32-47].

Recently, ginger extract has been shown to be beneficial on morphine analgesia and suggested as potential adjunct for pain management [48]. Studies involving above 70 volunteers also revealed that the raw or heat-treated ginger supplementations reduced muscle pain caused by eccentric exercise [49].

The safety of ginger powder was assessed in a recent rat study. Rats were given daily doses of 500, 1000, and 2000 mg/kg body weight of ginger powder for 35 days, and no obvious organ abnormality was found. The high dose, however, led to slightly reduction of obsolute and relative body weights [50].

## 1.2. *Zanthoxylum schinifolium* Sieb. tt Zucc. or *Z. bungeanum* Maxim. (Common Name: Prickly-Ash; Chinese Name: Hua Jiao)

Hua Jiao, the dried pericarp of Chinese prickly-ash, has been used in Chinese medicine for warming internal organs, alleviating stomach and abdominal pain, as well as reducing vomiting and diarrhea [2]. Prickly-ash is also used in daily Chinese cooking, and is one of the key flavour ingredients for Sichuan or Szechuan style Chinese food. Essential oil composition analysis indicates that, in addition to some common terpenes, such as limonene, 4-terpineol, γ-terpinene, α-terpineol acetate, β-pinene, α-terpineol and β-linalool, the herb's unique pungent property is due to unsaturated alkylamides, primarily hydroxy-α-sanshool (**6**) and hydroxy-β-sanshool (**7**) [51, 52].

This spice's volatile oil was shown to decrease cell viability and induce apoptosis in HepG2 human hepatoma cells, suggesting that prickly-ash essential oil could be used for hepatocellular carcinoma therapy [53].

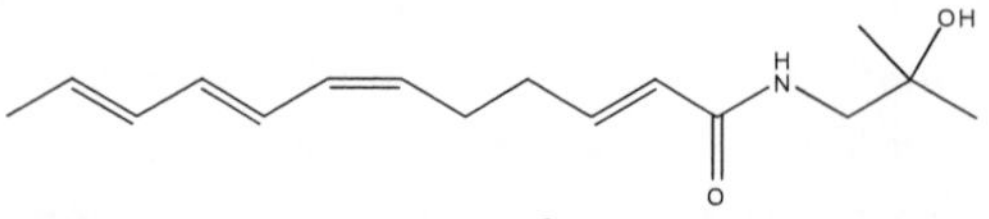

**6** 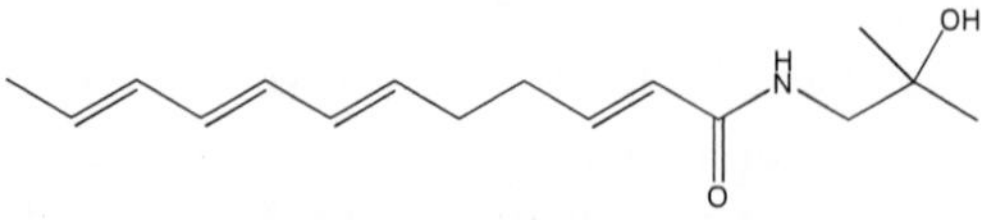                                    **7**

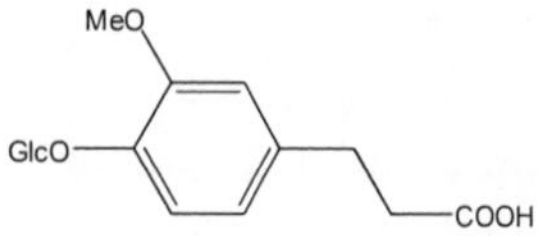

**8**

Figure 2. Structures of compounds from *Zanthoxylum schinifolium* Sieb. et Zucc. or *Z. bungeanum* Maxim.

On the other hand, methanol extract of *Z. bungeanum* was found to inhibit NO production in lipopolysaccharide-stimulated macrophages. The active compound was identified as 4-O-D-glucopyranosyldihydroferulic acid (*8*) (Figure 2) through a bioassay-guided fractionation and purification process [54]. *Z. schinifolium* extract was also revealed to suppress vascular inflammatory process in a TNF-alpha induced vascular inflammation in human umbilical vein endothelial cells [55].

Recently, oily extracts of *Zanthoxylum* pepers were investigated for chemosensory ion channel related mechanisms of pungent sensations. The results indicated that the pungent nature was mediated via interactions with transient receptor potential ankyrin 1 (TRPA1) and TRP vanilloid 1 (TRPV1) channels [56].

## 1.3. *Illicium verum* Hook. F. (Common Name: Star Anise; Chinese Name: Ba Jiao)

Chinese star anise is another popular spice commonly used in Chinese cuisine. In Chinese medicine, the dried fruit is used for warming the stomach and relieving pain and vomiting [2]. Its essential oil contains a dominant component, anethole (**9**), which was reported to have antimicrobial and antifungal properties [57-59]. The components obatained from supercritical extraction were also reported to be potent against antibiotic-resistant pathogens [60]. Phenylpropanoids, such as 1-(4'-Methoxyphenyl)-(1R,2S and 1S,2R)-propanediol (**10**) (Figure 3), were also identified from the fruit to possess preventive activity against lethality due to septic shock in an *in vivo* model [61].

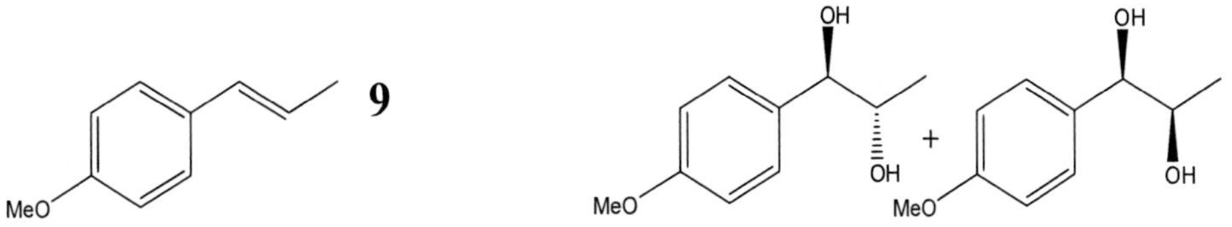

Figure 3. Structures of compounds from *Illicium verum* Hook. f.

## 1.4. *Cinnamomum cassia* Presl (Common Name: Chinese Cinnamon; Chinese Name: Rou Gui)

The dried bark of Chinese cinnamon has been used in Chinese medicine for impotence, relieving pain at the waist and knees, dizziness, vomiting and dysmenorrhea [2]. Chinese cinnamon is also frequently used in the preparation of soups. The main components in the essential oil are cinnamaldehyde (**11**) and 2-hydroxycinnamaldehyde (**12**), with **12** being the major one. The essential oil and cinnamaldehyde were both shown to be cytotoxic and to regulate hepatic enzymes for drug metabolism [62]. Cinnamaldehyde and the cinnamon extracts were also found to have *in vitro* anti-bacterial and anti-fungal activities [63-65].

An ethanol extract of Chinese cinnamon was found to have potent antioxidant properties *in vitro* using a rat liver homogenate lipid peroxidation model [66]. On the other hand, the water extract protected glutamate-induced neuronal death in a rat cerebellar granule cell model [67]. In addition, several studies have revealed the potential benefits of Chinese cinnamon and its cinnamaldehyde components, including 2-methoxycinnamaldehyde (**13**) (Figure 4), in anti-inflammation, anti-cancer and immune modulation [68-76].

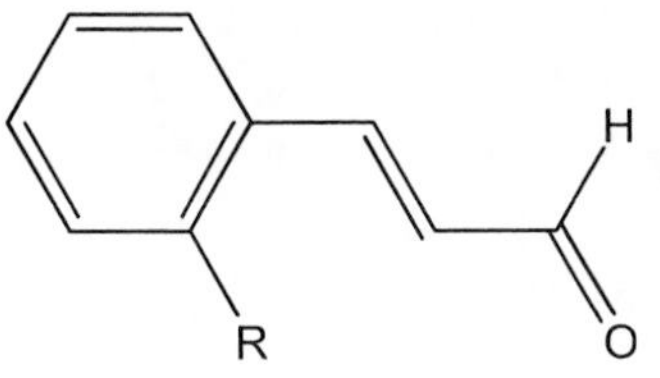

**11 R=H**
**12 R=OH**
**13 R=OMe**

Figure 4. Structures of compounds from *Cinnamomum cassia* Presl.

In rat models, Chinese cinnamon bark or its extract were shown to lower the blood glucose level in a glucose tolerance test. However, this effect was not found in rats that were not challenged with a high glucose load. This direct anti-diabetic effect was also confirmed in an insulin secreting cell model as the extract was found to have a stimulatory effect in insulin release [77]. Cinnamic acid, a compound presented in alcoholic extract of *C. Cassia* was also shown recently to inhibit protein tyrosine phosphatase 1B (PTP1B) and activate glucose transport by a phosphatidylinositol-3-kinase (PI3-K)-independent pathway [78]. A review examinating randomized and controlled clinical trials also indicated that cinnamon bark appeared to possess antihyperglycaemic properties [79].

Additionally, recent animal studies showed that *Cinnamomum cassia* may be beneficial to bone formation, skin whitening and anxiety [80-82].

## 1.5. *Piper nigrum L.* (Common Name: Black Pepper; Chinese Name: Hei Hu Jiao)

Black pepper (dried fruit) is one of world's most important spices, accounting for approximately 35% of the world trade in this category. In Chinese medicine, black pepper is for warming internal organs, relieving stomach pain, vomiting, diarrhea, seafood detoxification and improving appetite [2]. It has been widely used in China for its aroma and pungency, with 1% to 3% of volatile oil content responsible for such properties. The major components of black pepper volatile oil are terpenes, such as β-caryophyllene, limonene, sabinene, β-bisabolene and α-copaene [83].

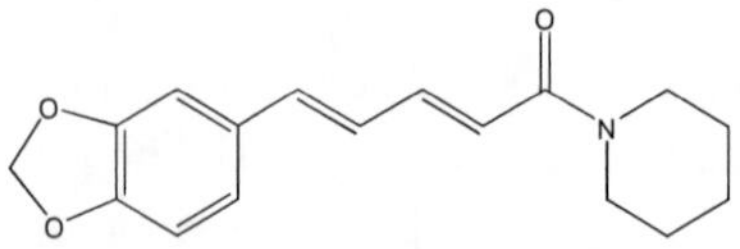

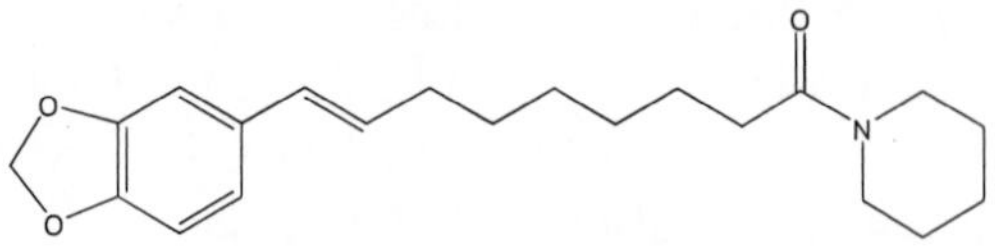

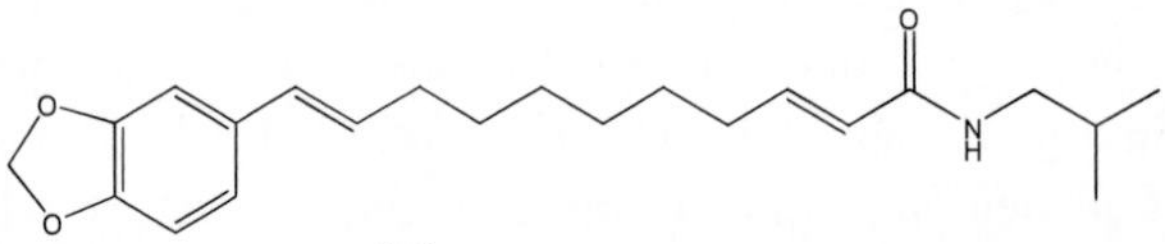

Figure 5. Structures of compounds from *Piper nigrum L.*

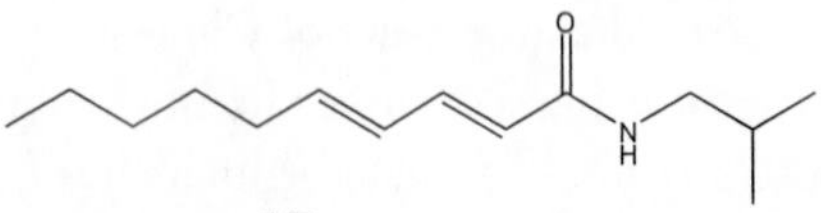

The characteristic components of black pepper, however, are the alkamides, such as piperine (**14**), piperrolein (**15**), piperchabamide (**16**) and pellitorin (**17**) (Figure 5) [84, 85]. Piperine, the major alkaloid present in black pepper, has been reported to have many health beneficial effects. These include: bioavailability-enhancing activity for some nutritional substances and drugs [86, 87]; melanocyte proliferation stimulatory effects for potential benefits in vitiligo [84, 88]; anti-oxidant/radical scavenging, anti-mutagenic and anti-carcinogenic effects [89-99]; acetylcholinesterase inhibitory, anti-depressive, cognition enhancing activity [100-103]; blood glucose- and lipid-lowering through hormone modulation [104-107]; immune modulation [108]; anti-inflammarion [109] and inhibitory effects on cell adhesion [85]. Black pepper and piperine were also shown to have spasmodic and antispasmodic effects for applications in gastrointestinal motibility disorders [110]. In a recent rat study, perperine was found to prevent blood pressure increase induced by L-nitro-L-arginine methyl ester [111].

Other components, such as polysaccharides, obtained from black pepper were also reported to have immune-enhancing effects [112]. Additionally, black pepper extracts were found to possess antioxidant and anti-diabetic activities in both *in vitro* and *in vivo* models [113-115].

## 1.6. Other Chinese Herbs Used as Spices and Flavouring Ingredients

*Agastache rugosa* (Fisch. et Mey.) O. ktze. (Chinese name: Huo Xiang): dried stem and leaf are used for colds, headache, vomiting and diarrhea [116].

*Allium macrostemon* Bge. or *A. chinensis* G. Don (Chinese name: Xie Bai): dried bulb is used for chest pain, coughing and diarrhea [2].

*Alpinia officinrum* Hance (Chinese name: Gao Liang Jiang): the dried rhizome is used for warming the stomach, helping digestion, relieving stomach and abdominal coldness and pain, diarrhea and eructation [2].

*Alpinia oxyphylla* Miq. (Chinese name: Yi Zhi Ren): dried fruit is used for diarrhea, abdominal pain, enuresis, micturition and spermatorrhea [2].

*Amomum villosum* Lour. or *A. villosum* Lour. var. *xanthioides* T. L. Wu et Senjen or *A. longiligulare* T. L. Wu (Chinese name: Sha Ren): dried fruit is used for warming internal organs, helping digestion, vomiting and diarrhea [2].

*Brassica juncea* (L.) Czern. et Coss. or *B. juncea* (L.) Czern. et Coss. var. *gracilis* Tsen et Lee (Chinese name: Huang Jie Zi): dried seed is used for warming internal organs, relieving stomach and abdominal coldness and pain, vomiting, coughing, rheumatic pain, numbness in limb and amenorrhea [116].

*Eugenia caryophyllata* Thunb. (Chinese name: Ding Xiang): dried flower bud is used for warming stomach and kidney, vomiting, hiccupping and abdominal pain [2].

*Foeniculum vulgare* Mill. (Chinese name: Xiao Hui Xiang): dried fruit is used for colds, abdominal pain, vomiting and dysmenorrhea [2].

*Mentha haplocalyx* Brig. (Chinese name: Bo He): dried stem and leaf are used for colds, headache, sore throat, dental ulcer and measles [2].

*Mosla chinensis* Maxim. or *M. chinensis* 'Jiangxiangru' (Chinese name: Xiang Ru): dried stem and leaf are used for fever, headache, abdominal pain, vomiting, diarrhea and difficulties with urination [2].

*Myristica fragrans* Houtt. (Chinese name: Rou Dou Kou): dried seed is used for diarrhea, abdominal pain and vomiting [2].

*Perilla frutescens* (L.) Britt. (Chinese name: Zi Su): dried stem and leaf are used for colds, coughing, stomach ache, vomiting and seafood detoxification; the dried seed is used for coughing, asthma and constipation [2].

## 2. DIETARY HERBS COMMONLY USED AS TONIC INGREDIENTS IN CHINESE FOOD

A key concept of traditional Chinese medicine and well-being practices is to prevent disease and maintain a strong defense capability against illness. Tonic herbal remedies have thus been an important component in TCM as well as in Chinese food. Recent progress on the research of bioactives in some common dietary tonic herbs are briefly reviewed below.

### 2.1. *Dioscorea opposita* Thunb. (Common Name: Yam; Chinese Name: Shan Yao)

Shan Yao has traditionally been used as a "top-grade" herb. Those grown in the province of Henan are viewed to be of the best quality and were usually offered to emperors in ancient times. The dried rhizome is used in Chinese medicine for diarrhea, nourishing the stomach and lung, and improving appetite [2]. In the past decade, small molecule bioactives reported from the tuber of this yam species include 3,4,6-trihydroxyphenanthrene-3-O-β-D-glucopyranoside (**18**), which was isolated from hexane and methanol extracts and tested for antifungal activities without effect [117]. Recent studies revealed that a number of phenolic compounds from the rhizome of *D. opposite* posess radical scavenging and cyclooxygenase-2 (COX-2) inhibitory activities, and the neuroprotective effect of these components was confirmed both in primary cultured neurons of rats and spatial learning and memory studies in mice [118, 119]. Also 6,7-dihydroxy-2-methoxy-1,4-phenanthrenedione (**19**) (Figure 6), another phenanthrene analog obtained from the aerial part of this plant, was found to have neuroprotective and antioxidant activities in *in vitro* experiments [120].

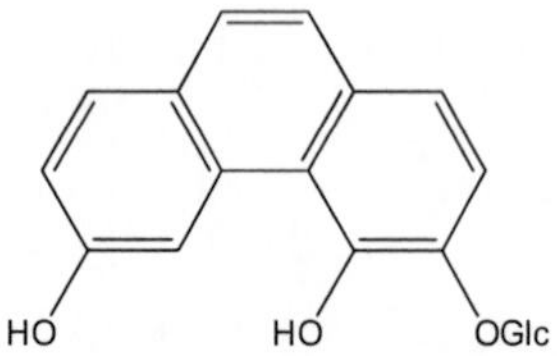

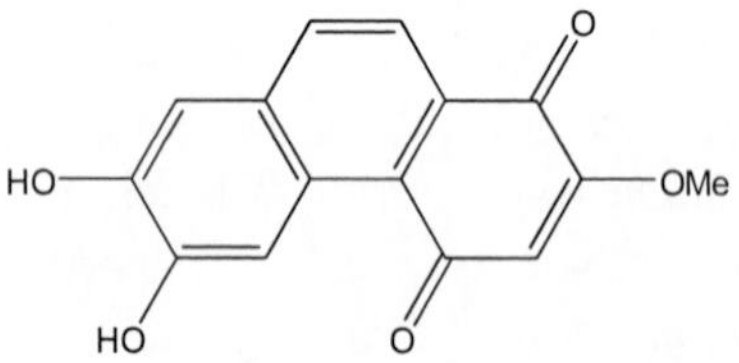

Figure 6. Structures of compounds from *Dioscorea opposita* Thunb.

Although the compositions were not disclosed, yam extracts were recently reported to modulate aquaporin 7 (AQP7) channel protein expression and activation in adipocytes for glycerol elimination, and to enhance insulin-stimulated glucose uptake in 3T3-L1 adipocytes via increasing mRNA expression of the GLUT4 glucose transporter. In a dexamethasone-induced diabetic rat model, yam extract significantly reduced blood insulin and glucose levels [121, 122].

Yam contains a large amount of starch and polysaccharides [123, 124], but the potential health benefit has not been well studied. Recently, a viscous protein, dioscorin, with molecular weight of about 200 kDa, was shown to have potent antioxidant and angiotensin I-converting enzyme (ACE) inhibitory activities [125].

## 2.2. *Ziziphus jujuba* Mill. (Common Name: Chinese Date; Chinese Name: Zao)

Chinese date is widely used in TCM practices and in food. The dried fruit is used as a tonic, which differs from the closely related herb of the same genus *Ziziphus jujuba* Mill. var. *spinosa* (Bunge) Hu ex H. F. Chou, where the seed is used for sedative and anxiolytic properties [2]. There are a number of cultivars for Chinese date that vary in their physical properties, sweetness and nutritional value.

There has been little research on the bioactives of Chinese date. Recently, cyclic adenosinemonophosphate (cAMP) was identified from the water extract [126]. HPLC-MS was also used to characterize some nucleosides and nucleobases, as well as triterpenic acids from the fruits [127, 128]. Some phenolic compounds such as protocatechuic acid from Chinese date have also been evaluated for their antioxidant capacities [129]. In a hamster model, water soluble carbohydrate concentrate prepared from Chinese date was found to improve gastrointestinal milieu and reduce the intestinal mucosa exposure to ammonia and other toxic or detrimental molecules [130].

In Europe, the fatty acids and carotene profiles of Chinese date varieties from southeast Spain were analyzed. The results showed that triacylglycerols having medium chain fatty acids were abundant in the tested samples, and carotene content was comparable to other fruits [131].

A placebo controlled clinical trial on *Ziziphus jujube* extract had demonstrated its effetiveness and safety for chronic constipation [132].

## 2.3. *Lycium barbarum* L. (Common Name: Wolfberry; Chinese Name: Gou Qi or Goji Berry)

In Chinese medicine, the dried fruit is used as a tonic for fatigue, soreness and pain at the waist and knees, dizziness, tinnitus and blurred vision [2]. As one of the most important dietary herbs in the Chinese food system, Goji berry has been widely used and studied [133]. In the past decade, research efforts on Goji berry bioactives have centered on the glycoconjugates or polysaccharide components and their bioactivities. For small molecules, scopoletin (20) (Figure 7) was isolated from the fruit and shown to inhibit the proliferation of PC3 cells (human prostate cancer cell) [134]. Total flavonoids extracted from the berry were tested *in vitro* and demonstrated potent protective effects against free radicals and lipid peroxidation in rat liver mitochondria and red blood cells [135, 136]. Study with MCF-7 cells revealed that Goji extract inhibited the growth of estrogen receptor positive human breast cancer cells by altering estradiol metabolism [137]. In mouse model, Goji berry juice taken orally also protected skin damage agaist UV radiation, likely through antioxidant pathways [138]. In addition, a recent rat study showed that the milk-based wolfberry preparation prevented prenatal stress-induced cognitive impairment [139].

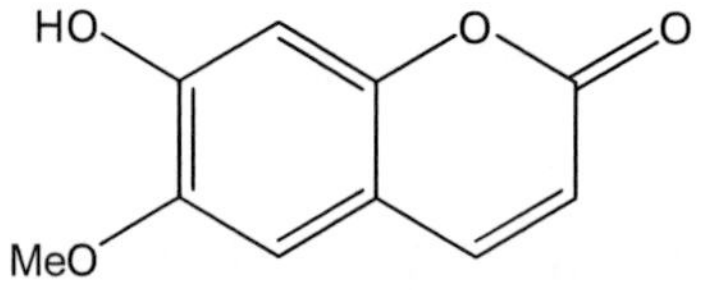

**20**

Figure 7. Structure of compound from *Lycium barbarum* L.

Glycoconjugates, polysaccharides, polysaccharide-protein complexes and glycopeptides obtained from Goji berry have been actively investigated for their immune enhancing [140-151], anti-cancer/tumor [144, 145, 152-155], anti-aging/oxidative stress [156-165] and neuroprotective [157, 158, 160, 161, 166-171] activities. In addition, Goji berry polysaccharides were also found to have beneficial effects for dyslipidemia, and diabetes and its complications in various models [159, 172-178]. A recent study also indicated that Goji polysaccharides may be beneficial in preventing the development of cardiovascular diseases by reducing myocardial injury in ischemia/reperfusion in rats [179].

A recent randomized, double-blind, placebo-controlled clinical trial in North America demonstrated that consumption of a standardized Goji beverage (with polysaccharide as the bioactive component) for 14 days could significantly increase ratings for energy level, athletic performance, quality of sleep, ease of awakening, ability to focus on activities, mental acuity, calmness, feelings of health, contentment and happiness. It also markedly reduced fatigue and stress, and improved gastrointestinal function [180]. In another controlled clinical studies with the standarized Goji berry juice in 60 older Chinese healthysubjects, significant incease in general feelings of well-being, short-term memory and focus between pre- and post-intervention, in comparing with the control group [181].

## 2.4. *Sesamum indicum* L. (Common Name: Black Sesame; Chinese Name: Hei Zhi Ma)

Black sesame seed is a tonic food widely used in China, and a cultivar variety of the white sesame, which is consumed in many Western societies. In Chinese medicine, the dried seed is for dizziness, blurred vision, tinnitus, deafness, poliosis, hair loss and constipation [2]. The lignans, such as sesamin (**21**), sesamolin (**22**), sesamolinol (**23**), sesaminol (**24**) and sesaminol triglucoside (**25**), have been reported to be the major bioactive components in both the white and black sesames [182, 183]. Recently, an anthraquinone compound, anthrasesamone F (**26**) (Figure 8), was isolated from black sesame seed [184].

Being a type of phenolic compounds, lignans from sesame seeds were revealed to be strong antioxidants in scavenging free radicals [185-188]. Supercritical carbon dioxide extract of black sesame seed was shown to have strong antioxidant properties in both 1,1-diphenyl-2-picrylhydrazyl (DPPH) radical and linoleic acid assays [189]. These phenolic lignans were recently found to have neuroprotective activities against 3-nitropropionic acid and β-amyloid induced cognitive dysfunction or ischemic neuronal damage from animal studies [190-193].

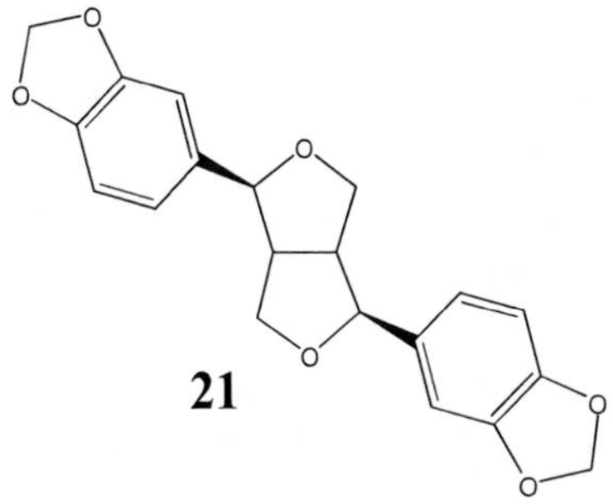

**21**

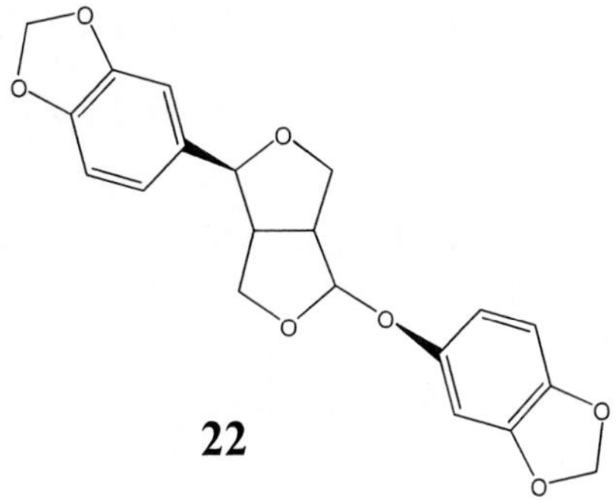

**22**

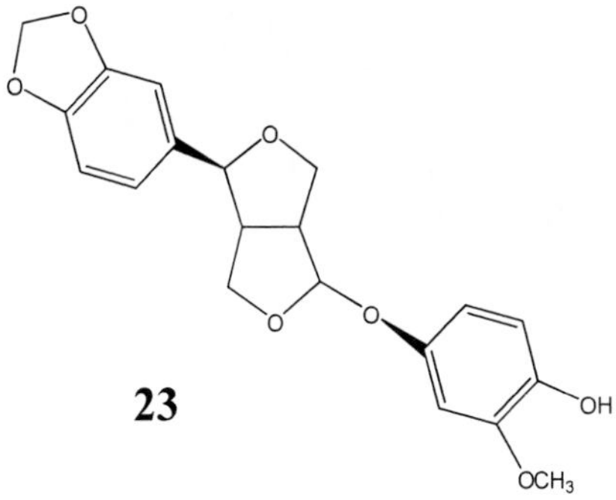

**23**

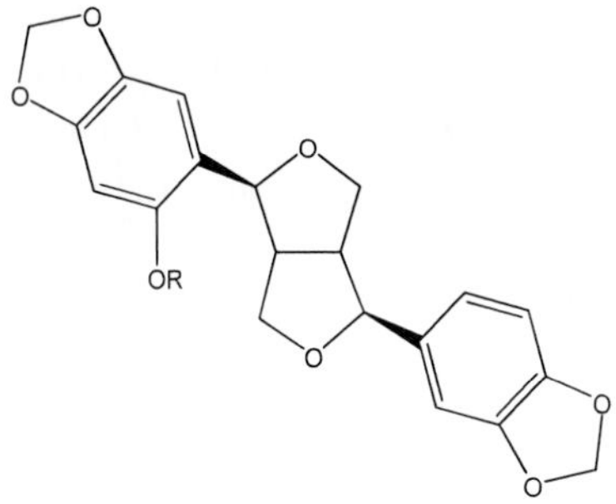

**24** R=H
**25** R=2'-O-β-D-glucopyranosyl (1->2)-O-
[β-D-glucopyranosyl (1->6)]-β-D-
glucopyranoside

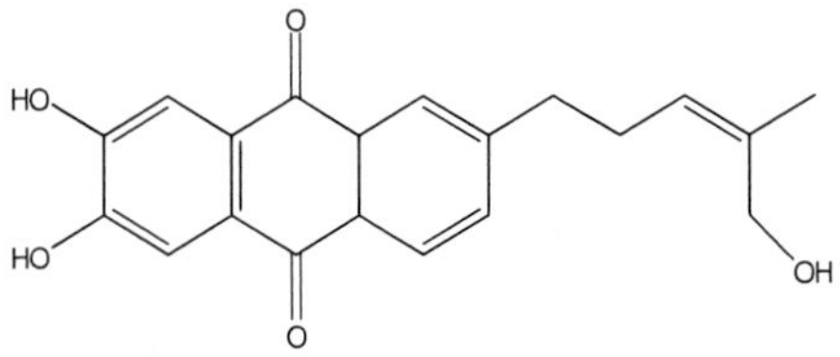

**26**

Figure 8. Structures of compounds from *Sesamum indicum* L.

Sesame seed extract, particularly the lignans, have increasingly been shown to have anti-dyslipidemia and anti-diabetic activities [194-196]. Also, the alcohol extract was found to possess anti-tumor properties against mice sarcoma 180 and Heps 22 [197], and the compound sesamin seemed to have chemopreventive effect through suppression of NF-kappa B signaling pathway [198]. More recent studies also showed the fertility promoting effect of ethanolic extract of sesame seed, alone, or in combination with Vitamin C [199], and the anti-inflammatory property of lignan compound sesaminol triglucoside [200].

In addition, sesamin, one of the major lignans in the seed, was also confirmed to be a precursor of mammalian lignans *in vitro* and in rat models [182]. This further demonstrated that the sesame seed is a good source of bioactive and bioavailable dietary lignans.

## 2.5. Other Dietary Herbs Used as Tonic Ingredients

*Apis cerana* Fabricius or *A. mellifera* Linnaeus (Chinese name: Feng Mi): the honey is used for stomach and abdominal pain, coughing, and constipation [2].

*Dimocarpus longan* Lour. (Chinese name: Long Yan Rou or Gui Yuan): dried aril is a tonic for the cardiovascular system, specifically for palpitations, in addition to improving memory [2].

*Equus asinus* L. (Chinese name: E Jiao): the gelatin produced from the skin is used to treat abnormalities of the blood, as well as for dizziness and palpitations, fatigue, insomnia and coughing [2].

*Morus alba* L. (Chinese name: Sang Shen): dried fruit is a tonic for blood, and used for dizziness, tinnitus, palpitations, insomnia, poliosis and constipation. The dried leaf (Chinese name: Sang Ye) is used for fever, coughing, dizziness, headache and blurred vision [2].

*Polygonatum kingianum* Coll. et Hemsl. or *P. sibiricum* Red. or *P. cyrtonema* Hua (Chinese name: Huang Jing): dried rhizome is used for fatigue, dry mouth, coughing, and improving appetite [2].

*Rubus chingii* Hu (Chinese name: Fu Pen Zi): dried fruit is used for enuresis, frequent urination, impotence, prospermia and spermatorrhea [2].

# 3. DIETARY HERBS THAT HELP DIGESTION

## 3.1. *Crataegus pinnatifida* Bge. Var. *major* N.E.Br. or *C. pinnatifida* Bge. (Common Name: Chinese Hawthorn Fruit; Chinese Name: Shan Zha)

Chinese hawthorn fruit and its products are popular snack foods and one of the most commonly prescribed herbs in China. Its dried fruit is used for helping digestion, particularly of meat, and strengthening the stomach [2]. The fruit contains polyphenolics, including procyanidins and flavonoids, such as procyanidin B2 (**27**), procyanidin B5 (**28**) and hyperoside (**29**). Chlorogenic acid (**30**) and triterpenoids such as ursolic acid (**31**) are also present in the fruit [201]. These phenolics, although not directly related to digestive function, were demonstrated to contribute to the lipid-regulating, anti-tumor and anti-inflammatory effects of Chinese hawthorn fruit [202-205]. The fruit supplementation was found to reduce both brown and white adipose tissues and improve blood biochemical profiles in high fat diet induced obese hamster model, likely through activation of PPAR-alpha [206]. A recent study on the 3-hydroxy-3-methylglutaryl coenzyme A reductase (HMGR) inhibitory effect of C. pinnatifida had led to isolation of quercetin, hyperoside, rutin, and chlorogenic acid. It was revealed that these compounds also have synergic action in HMGR inhibition [207]. Additionally, two furo-1, 2-naphthoquinones, crataequinone A (**32**) and crataequinone B (**33**) (Figure 9) were also characterized from the fruit for anti-inflammatory activity via the inhibition of intercellular adhesion molecule-1 (ICAM-1) [208].

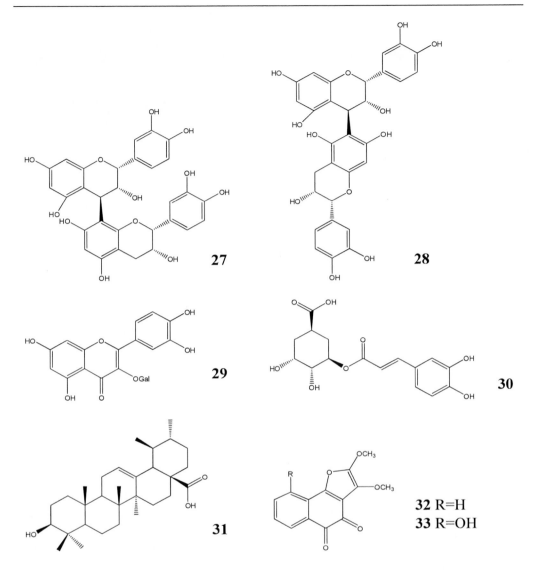

Figure 9. Structures of compounds from *Crataegus pinnatifida* Bge. var. *major* N.E.Br. or *C. pinnatifida* Bge.

## 3.2. *Hordeum vulgare* L. (Common Name: Malt, Germinated Barley; Chinese Name: Mai Ya)

Malt or germinated barley has been used in TCM to help digestion [2]. Traditionally, both the raw and processed malts (stir-fried or charred) are used for somewhat different applications such as stimulating or reducing milk secretion. For small molecular bioactives, the research has been very limited; two compounds, a flavone tricin (**34**) and an amino acid/peptide derivative N-benzoyl-phenylalanine-2-benzoylamino-3-phenyl propyl ester (**35**) (Figure 10) were isolated and characterized, along with several other common small molecules such as β-sitosterol, daucosterol, 7-oxositosterol and 5-hydroxymethyl-2-furaldehyde [209, 210].

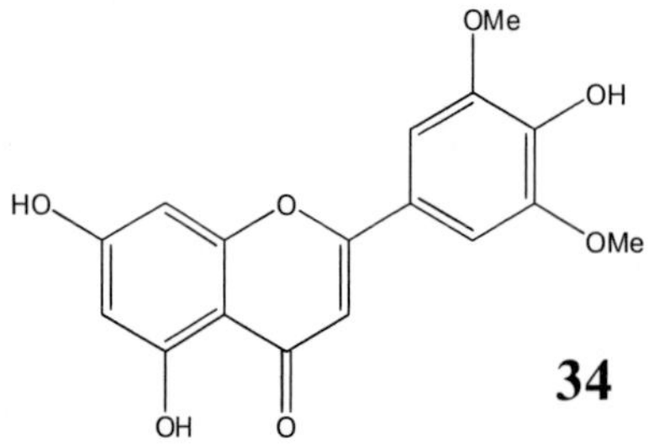

Figure 10. Structures of compounds from *Hordeum vulgare* L.

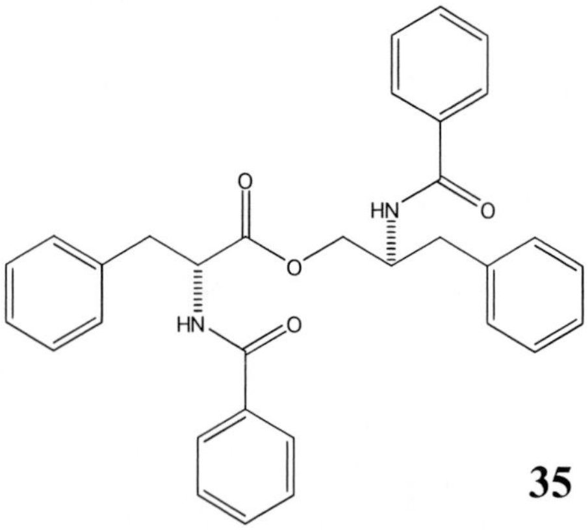

Germinated barley contains hemicellulose-rich dietary fibre and this component may be the main bioactive for its beneficial effects in promoting the growth of intestinal microflora, ameliorating inflammation of colitis and treating ulcerative colitis, and improving constipation, as observed in *in vitro* and animal studies [211-226] as well as in human trials [214, 217, 221, 227-232].

An aqueous ethanol extract of Mai Ya was also found to have anti-hyperprolactinemia effects in rats, and this finding is in agreement with its traditional use for reducing milk secretion [233].

## 3.3. Other Herbs that Regulate Digestion

*Cichorium glandulosum* Bioss. et Huet or *C. intybus* L. (Chinese name: Ju Ju): dried stem and leaf, or root are used to help digestion as well as for jaundice, stomach ache, edema and oliguresis [2].

*Citrus aurantium* L. var. *amara* Engl. (Chinese name: Dai Dai Hua): dried unripe fruit is used to help digestion [2].

*Citrus medica* L. var. *sarcodactylis* Swingle (Chinese name: Fu Shou): dried fruit is used to assist digestion [2].

*Citrus reticulata* Blanco (Chinese name: Ju Hong): dried exocarp is used for coughing, vomiting, and helps digestion [2].

*Dolichos lablab* L. (Chinese name: Bai Bian Dou): dried seed is used to help digestion [2].

*Gallus gallus domesticus* Brisson (Chinese name: Ji Nei Jin): dried inner is used to assist digestion, and also for vomiting, diarrhea, unuresis and spermatorrhea [2].

*Phyllanthus emblica* L. (Chinese name: Yu Gan Zi): dried fruit is used for blood stasis, cough, sore throat, dry mouth, and also to help digestion [2].

*Raphanus sativus* L. (Chinese name: Lai Fu Zi): dried seed is used to assist digestion, and also for relief of stomach distension, abdominal pain, constipation, diarrhea and coughing [2].

# 4. Dietary Herbs Commonly Used as Tea for Flu and Fever

Two flower herbs are highlighted here due to the popularity of their uses in China for preventing or fighting flu, cold, and reducing fever.

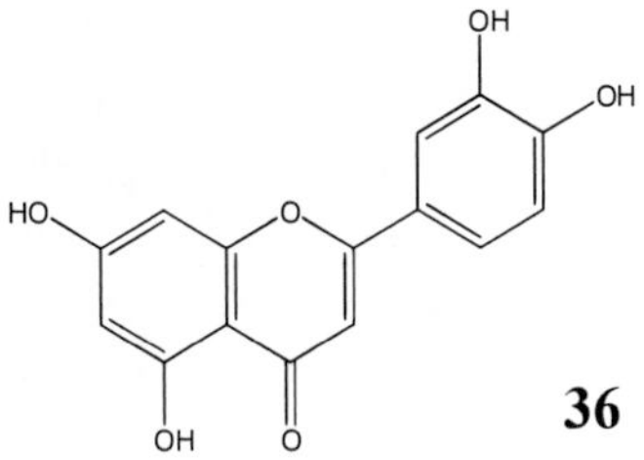


**36**

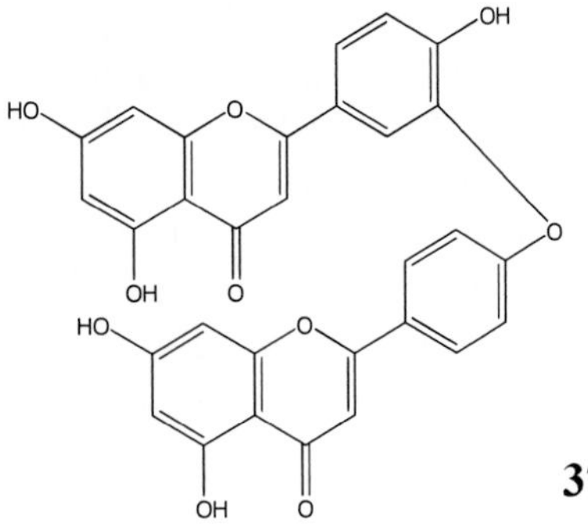


**37**

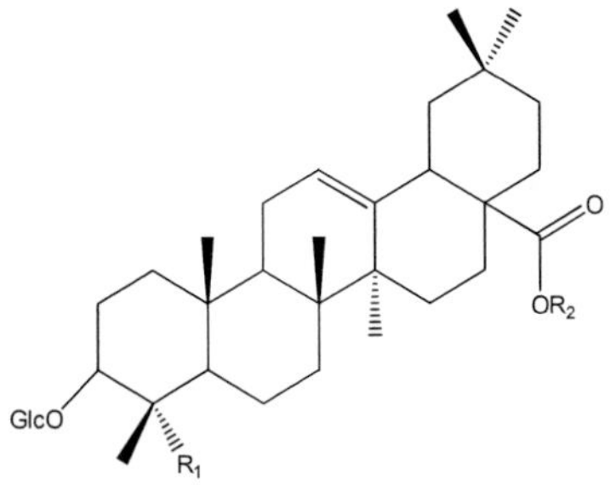


**38** R1=$CH_2OH$; R2=Glc(1->2)[Xyl(1->6)]Glc
**39** R1=Me; R2=Rha(1->2)[Xyl(1->6)]Glc

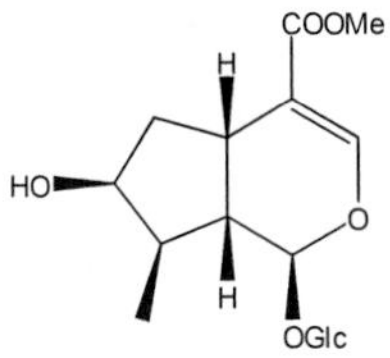


**40**

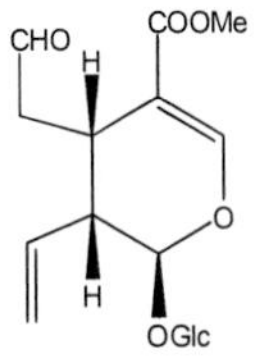


**41**

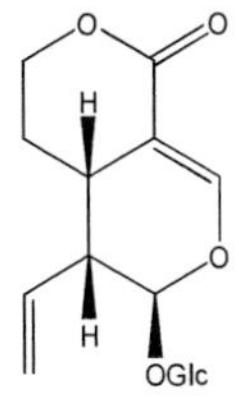


**42**

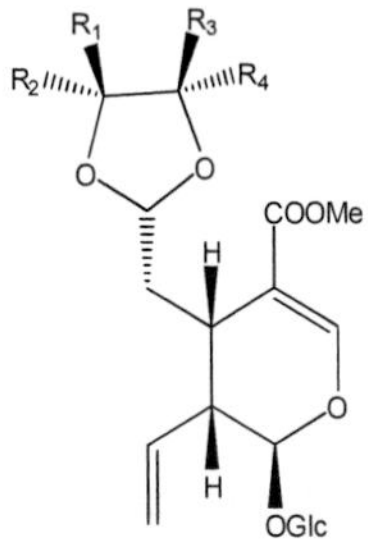


**43** R1=R3=Me; R2=R4=H
**44** R1=R3=H; R2=R4=Me

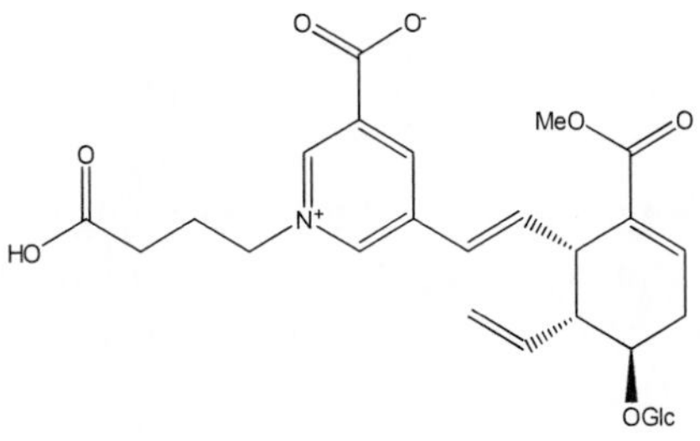


**45**

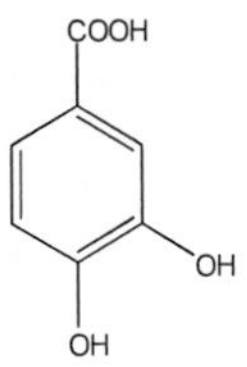


**46**

Figure 11. Structures of compounds from *Lonicera japonica* Thunb.

## 4.1. *Lonicera japonica* Thunb. (Common Name: Japanese Honeysuckle; Chinese Name: Jin Yin Hua, Er Hua)

In Chinese medicine, the dried flower bud or new flower of the plant is commonly used for fever relief [2]. Jin Yin Hua contains caffeoyl derivatives such as chlorogenic acid (**30**) [234], flavonoids such as luteolin (**36**) and ochnaflavone (**37**) [235-238], triterpene saponins such as lonicerosides D (**38**) and E (**39**) [239], iridoids such as loganin (**40**), secologanin (**41**), sweroside (**42**), longiceracetalides A (**43**) and B (**44**), and lonijaposide A (**45**) [240, 241], and benzoic acid derivative protocatechuic acid (**46**) (Figure 11) [242].

Luteolin was found to induce human lung carcinoma CH27 cell apoptosis [235, 236], while the biflavonoid ochnaflavone demonstrated anti-inflammatory activity by inhibiting LPS-induced nitric oxide gene expression in RAW264.7 cells [237, 238]. More recently, lueolin was found to have beneficial effects against lipopolysaccharide-induced acute lung injury, emeliorate lung fibrosis, and suppress inflammatory mediator [243-245]. Compounds **30**, **36** and **46** isolated from Jin Yin Hua were found to be cytotoxic for HepG2 hepatocellular carcinoma cells, but only **46** was capable of inducing hepatocellular carcinoma cell death [242]. The flavonoid rutin from it showed protective effect against oxidative stress-medicated myocardial damage in cell and rat models [246].

In addition, aqueous and alcohol extracts of Japanese honeysuckle have been revealed to have anti-inflammatory, anti-angiogenic, and anti-nociceptive activities in different testing models in the past decade [247-253].

## 4.2. *Chrysanthemum morifolium* Ramat. (Common Name: Chrysanthemum; Chinese Name: Ju Hua)

The dried flower of the plant is used in Chinese medicine for cold, headache, dizziness, redness, swelling, eye pain and blurred vision [2]. Chrysanthemum tea is part of the common diet in China; its prevalence extends as far as the Chinese communities of many other countries. Chrysanthemum extract has been shown to inhibit apoptosis of vascular smooth muscle cells, and also possesses cardioprotective effects during ischemia/anoxia and reperfusion/reoxygenation in isolated rat heart and ventricular myocytes [254-256]. It also protects rats against cerebral ischemia and reperfusion injury [257], and also possesses potent neuroprotective activities in SH-SY5Y cells [258]. Several triterpene diols and triols isolated from Ju Hua, such as faradiol (**47**), heliantriol (**48**) and arnidiol (**49**), were found to have cytotoxic and anti-tumor promoting effects against human cancer cell lines [259-261]. Anti-HIV and antimutagenic activities were reported for flavonoid components, such as luteolin (**36**), apigenin 7-O-β-D-(4'-caffeoyl)-glucuronide (**50**), acacetin (**51**) and apigenin (**52**) [262, 263].

In a recent rat study, oral administration of luteolin and apigenin indicated that apigenin was more efficiently absorbed than luteolin. Both of them can be absorbed quickly with a slow elimination rate [264]. In addition, two new dicaffeoylquinic acids, 3,5-dicaffeoyl-quinic acid (**53**) and 3,5-*epi*-dicaffeoyl-quinic acid (**54**) (Figure 12), were isolated from chrysanthemum and exhibited strong antioxidant activities [265].

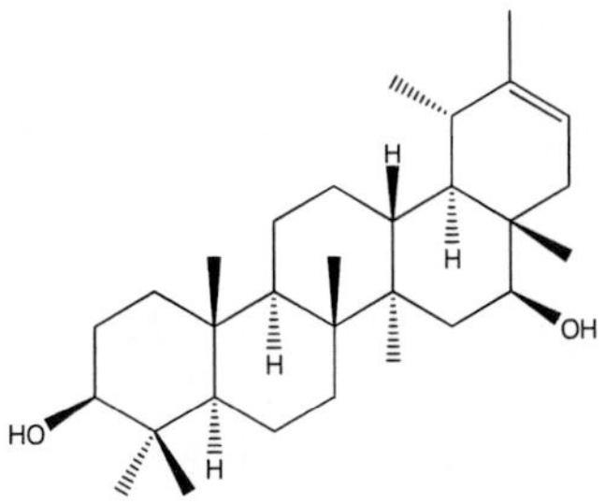

**47**

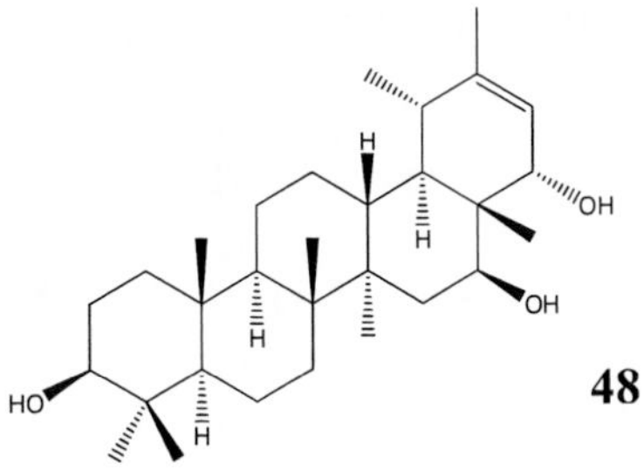

**48**

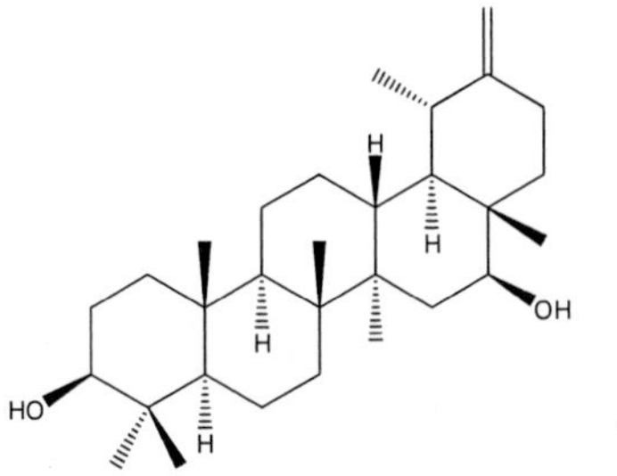

**49**

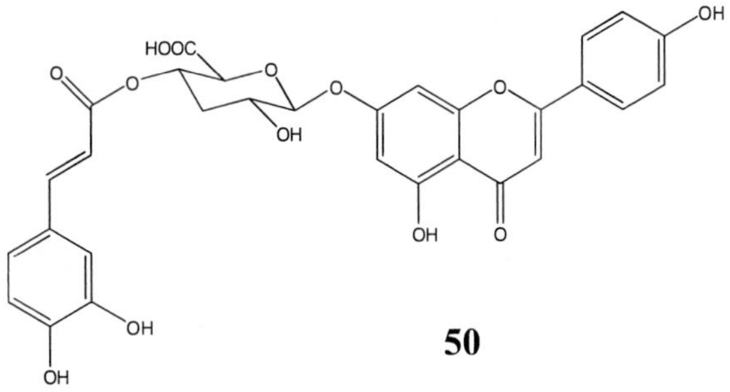

**50**

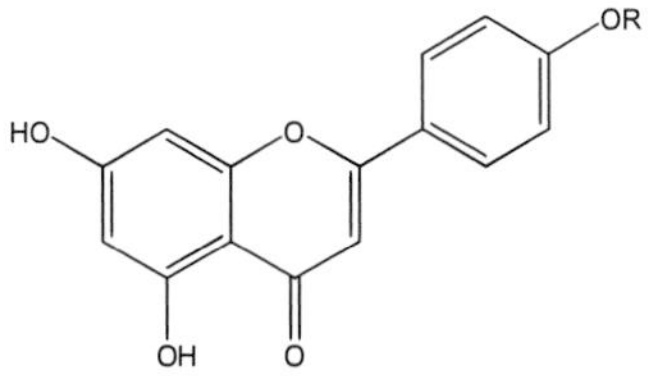

**51** R=Me
**52** R=H

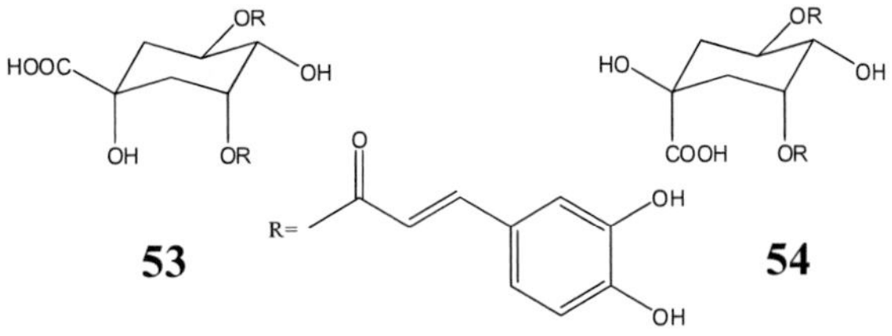

**53** **54**

Figure 12. Structures of compounds from *Chrysanthemum morifolium* Ramat.

Chrysanthemum extract was shown to be safe when tested in a recent rat studies with daily dose levels of 320 to 1280 mg/kg body weight. There was no toxicological changes observed [266].

## 4.3. Other Herbs Used as Tea Ingredients

*Citrus reticulata* Blanco (Chinese name: Ju Pi): dried pericarp is commonly used to improve appetite, and for vomiting, diarrhea, and coughing with excessive phlegm [2].

*Momordica grosvenori* Swingle (Chinese name: Luo Han Guo): dried fruit is used for coughing, sore throat, aphonia and constipation [2].

*Prunus mume* (Sieb.) Sieb. et Zucc. (Chinese name: Wu Mei): dried fruit is used for coughing and diarrhea [2].

*Sterculia lychnophora* Hance (Chinese name: Pang Da Hai): dried seed is used for coughing, sore throat, celostomia, constipation and headache [2].

# 5. OTHER HERBS IN THE CHINESE FOOD SYSTEM

## 5.1. *Poria cocos* (Schw.) Wolf (Chinese Name: Fu Ling)

The scleorotia of *Poria cocos* has been used in both Chinese food and medicine. As a Chinese herb, it is used for edema, oliguria, diarrhea, pavor and insomnia [2]. Its flour has a bland taste and improves appetite, and historically has been used for snack foods or healthy foods for China's royal family. It has also been used in commercial snack food products in China, particularly in Beijing.

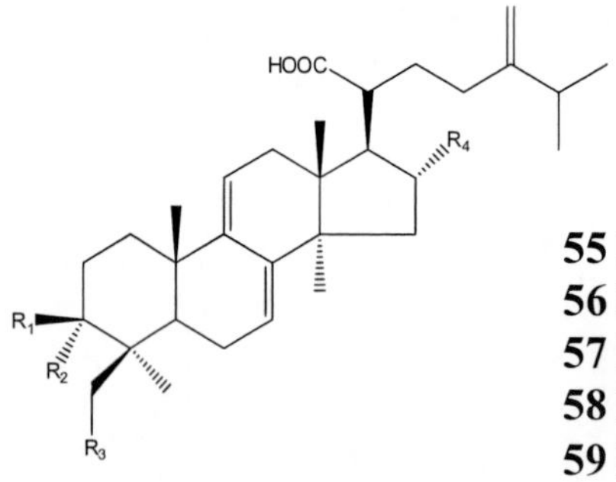

**55** R1=O-p-hydroxybenzoyl; R2=R3=H; R4=OH
**56** R1=OAc; R2=R3=H; R4=OH
**57** R1,R2=O; R3=H; R4=OH
**58** R1,R2=O; R3=OH; R4=OH
**59** R1,R2=O; R3=R4=H

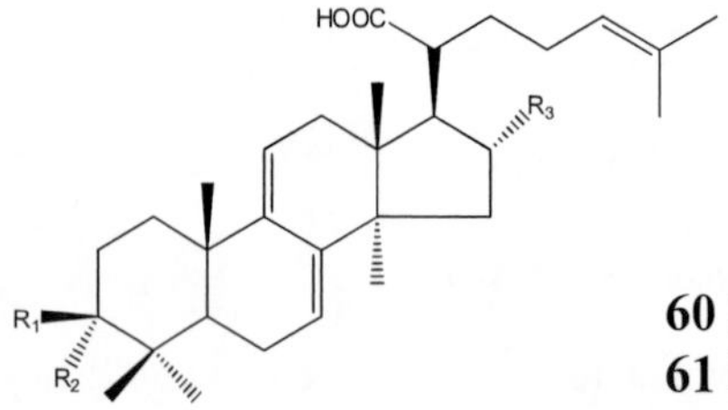

**60** R1=OH; R2=H; R3=OH
**61** R1,R2=O; R3=H

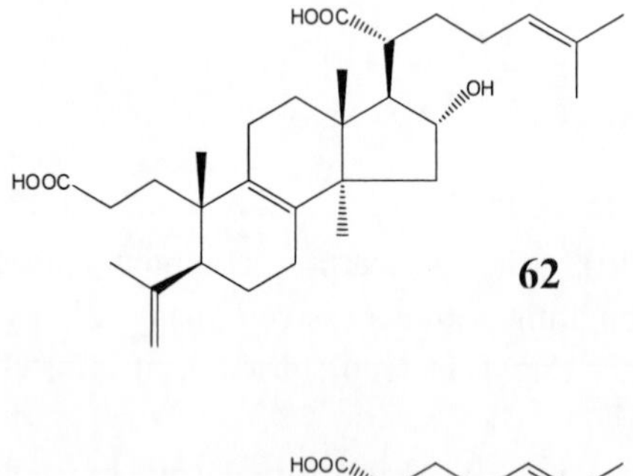

**62**

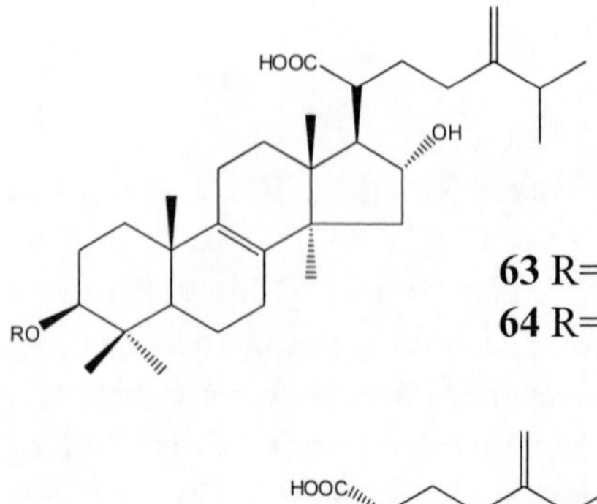

**63** R=Ac
**64** R=H

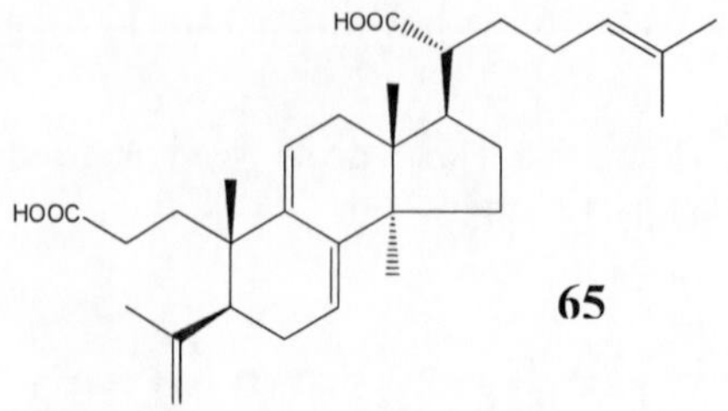

**65**

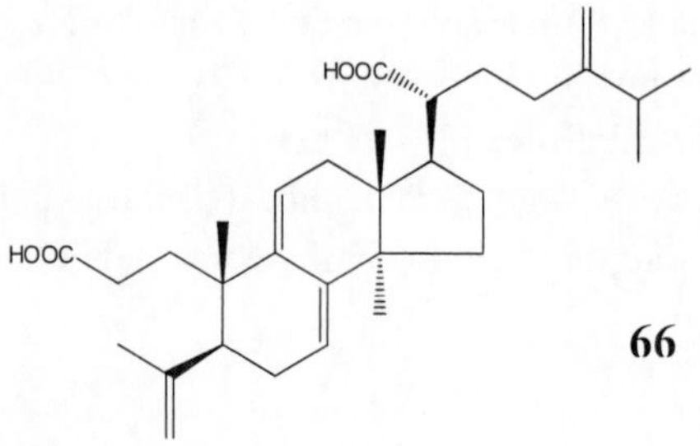

**66**

Figure 13. Structures of compounds from *Poria cocos* (Schw.) Wolf.

Polysaccharides, such as β-glucans, are the dominant components of this herb, and their anti-tumor activities have been well investigated during the past decade [267-275]. A novel immunomodulatory protein was also reported from Poria [276]. Another group of bioactives in Poria, lanostane-type triterpenoids, has also been actively studied for anti-tumor and anti-inflammatory benefits [277-288]. These components include: 3β-hydroxybenzoyl-dehydrotumulosic acid (**55**), dehydropachymic acid (**56**), polyporenic acid C (**57**), 29-hydroxypolyporenic acid C (**58**), dehydroeburiconic acid (**59**), dehydrotrametenolic acid (**60**), dehydrotrametenonic acid (**61**), poricoic acid G (**62**), pachymic acid (**63**), tumulosic acid (**64**), 16-deoxyporicoic acid B (**65**) and poricoic acid C (**66**) (Figure 13). Interestingly, compound **60** was found to promote adipocyte differentiation *in vitro* and acts as an insulin sensitizer *in vivo* [289], and 63 showed recently to stimulate glucose uptake by enhancing GLUT-4 expression and translocation in 3T3-L1 adipocytes [290].

In addition, *Poria cocos* water extract was shown to protect PC12 neuronal cells against β-amyloid induced cell death by suppressing oxidative stress and apoptosis [291].

## 5.2. *Nelumbo nucifera* Gaertn. (Common Name: Lotus Seed; Chinese Name: Lian Zi)

In Chinese cooking, particularly for porridge or conjee, lotus seed is commonly used with other grain materials. The seed is used for diarrhea, spermatorrhea, palpitations and insomnia. The seed is also a tonic ingredient in Chinese medicine, while the leaf (Chinese name: He Ye) is for polydipsia, diarrhea, nose bleeds, hemafecia, metrorrhagia and metrostaxis [2]. Alkaloids and phenolic compounds appear to be the main bioactives reported.

The hepaprotective, free radical scavenging, or antioxidant effects of lotus seed may primarily come from its phenolics, such as oligomeric procyanidins [292-294] or phenolic alkaloids, such as bisbenzylisoquinoline alkaloids. For example, alkaloid isoliensinine (**67**) was revealed to inhibit pulmonary fibrosis likely due to its antioxidant and/or anti-inflammatory activities [295]. It also showed inhibitory effects on the proliferation of porcine coronary arterial smooth muscle cells by suppressing the over-expression of several growth factors [296]. Another bisbenzylisoquinoline alkaloid, neferine (**68**), along with the lotus seed extract and the total alkaloids fraction, were reported to have relaxation effects on rabbit corpus cavernosum tissue by enhancing the concentration of cAMP in the tissue and inhibiting phosphodiesterase activity [297]. Recently, compound **68** was also demonstrated to be the bioactive component for lotus seed's sedative activity. The sedative effects were revealed to be different from that of diazepam [298]. In addition, bioactivities such as insulin sensitivity enhancing, antioxidant, anti-inlfammatory, cholinesterase and beta-site APP cleaving enzyme 1 (BACE 1) inhibitory, and anti-depressant were reported lately for neferine [299-301]. The acetylcholinesterase and butyrylcholinesterase inhibitory effects were revealed for a monoterpene glycoside from the stamens as well [302]. In rat model, the extract of lotus seed was shown to improve scopolamine-induced dementia through inhibiting acetylcholinesterase activity and inducing choline acetyltransferase expression [303].

In addition, isoquinoline alkaloid (S)-armepavine (**69**) (Figure 14), as well as the see and rhizome extracts have been shown to have immune modulatory functions [304-307].

Lotus seed extract has also been found to inhibit herpes simplex virus type 1 (HSV-1) replication [308], but the bioactive components responsible have yet to be characterized.

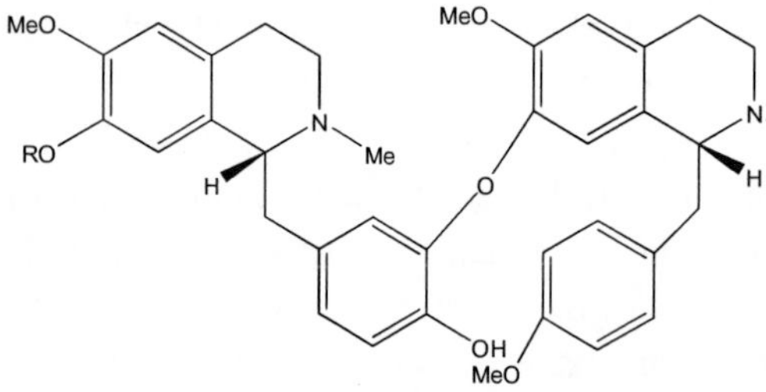

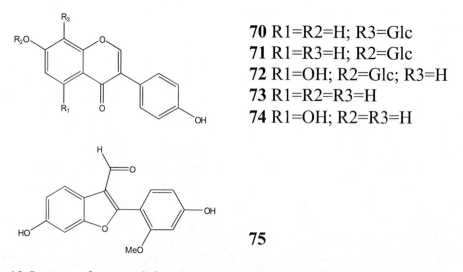

**67** R=H
**68** R=Me
**69** 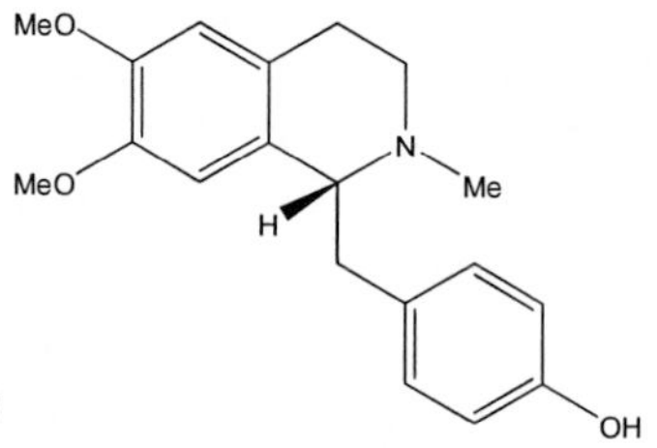

Figure 14. Structures of compounds from *Nelumbo nucifera* Gaertn.

## 5.3. *Pueraria lobata* (Willd.) Ohwi (Common Name: Kudzu; Chinese Name: Ge Gen)

**70** R1=R2=H; R3=Glc
**71** R1=R3=H; R2=Glc
**72** R1=OH; R2=Glc; R3=H
**73** R1=R2=R3=H
**74** R1=OH; R2=R3=H

**75**

Figure 15. Structures of compounds from *Pueraria lobata* (Willd.) Ohwi

Ge Gen is commonly used in TCM for headache, neck and back pain, thirst, measles and diarrhea [2], while its flour has been consumed as a starchy food ingredient. In addition to starch, Kudzu contains mainly flavonoids, particularly isoflavones and saponins. During the past decade, a limited number of reports on triterpenoids and phytosterols have indicated anti-tumor and immune functions [309-311]. The active research has focused on the bioactivities of Kudzu isoflavones, such as puerarin (**70**), daidzin (**71**), genistin (**72**), daidzein (**73**) and genistein (**74**). Total isoflavones of Ge Gen were shown to significantly decrease serum total cholesterol and liver triacylglycerol in ovariectomized rats and to prevent secondary osteoporosis in rats induced by dexamethasome [312, 313]. Phenolic components were recently shown to protect PC12 cells against β-amyloid induced toxicity [314]. The major isoflavone compound, puerarin, has been studied with *in vitro* and *in vivo* models, as well as human clinical trials for its health promoting functions for diabetes and its complications [315-322], liver protection [323-327], neuroprotection and cognition improvement [328-338], bone formation [339, 340], antipyretic effects [341, 342], antioxidation [343, 344] and cardiovascular protection [345]. More recent study using breast cancer cells MCF-7/adr indicated that puerarin suppressed multidrug resistance by inhibiting MDR-1 experssion [346]. Additionally, a new 2-arylbenzofuran compound, puerariafuran (**75**) (Figure 15), was isolated from the root of *Pueraria lobata* and shown to have inhibitory activity against advanced glycation end products (AGEs) and inhibit aldose reductase and xylose-induced lens opacity [347, 348].

## 5.4. Other Miscellaneous Herbs in Chinese Food System

The following herbs are also regulated as food ingredients by Chinese health regulations; most of the ingredients are commonly used, but their bioactive components will not be discussed here due to limitation of space.

*Agkistrodon acutus* (Guenther) (Chinese name: Fu She): dried body (with viscera removed) is used for rheumatic arthritis, facial distortion due to stroke, hemiparalysis and hypersparsmia [2].

*Angelica dadurica* (Fisch. ex Hoffm.) Benth. et Hook. f. or *A. dahurica* (Fisch. ex Hoffm.) Benth. et Hook. f. var. *formosana* (Boiss.) Shan et Yuan (Chinese name: Bai Zhi): dried root is for headache due to cold and toothache [2].

*Canarium album* Raeusch. (Chinese name: Qing Guo): dried fruit is used for sore throat, coughing, and seafood detoxification [2].

*Canavalia gladiata* (Jacq.) DC. (Chinese name: Dao Dou): dried seed is used in warming internal organs and for vomiting [2].

*Cannabis sativa* L. (Chinese name: Huo Ma Ren): dried fruit is used for constipation [2].

*Cassia obtusifolia* L. (Chinese name: Jue Ming Zi): dried seed is used to improve vision, and for dizziness, headache and constipation [2].

*Chaenomeles speciosa* (Sweet) Nakai (Chinese name: Mu Gua): dried fruit is for rheumatic pain, vomiting and diarrhea [2].

*Cirsium setosum* (Wild.) MB. (Chinese name: Xiao Ji): dried stem and leaf are used to stop bleeding [2].

*Citrus medica* L. or *C. wilsonii* Tanaka (Chinese name: Xiang Yuan): dried fruit is used for chest and hypochondrium distending pain, vomiting and coughing [2].

*Coix lacryma-jobi* L. var. *mayuen* (Roman.) Stapf (Chinese name: Yi Yi Ren): dried seed is for edema, difficulties with urination, and rheumatic arthritis and diarrhea [2].

*Gardenia jasminoides* Ellis (Chinese name: Zhi Zi): dried fruit is for fever, jaundice, hematuria, nose bleeds and ulcerative carbuncle [2].

*Ginkgo biloba* L. (Chinese name: Bai Guo): dried seed is used for asthma, coughing, enuresis and frequent urination [2].

*Glycine max* (L.) Merr. (Chinese name: Dan Dou Chi): the fermented product from seed is used for cold, headache, dysphoria, chest distress and insomnia [2].

*Glycyrrhiza uralensis* Fisch. or *G. inflata* Bat. or *G. glabra* L. (Chinese name: Gan Cao): the dried rhizome and root are used for fatigue, short of breath, coughing and pain. It is the most popular Chinese herb and is usually prescribed with other herbs as it mediates other herbs by reducing toxicity [2].

*Hippophae rhamnoides* L. (Chinese name: Sha Ji): dried fruit is used for coughing, abdominal pain and helping digestion [2].

*Houttuynia cordata* Thunb. (Chinese name: Yu Xing Cao): dried aerial part or whole is used for fever, coughing, and ulcerative carbuncle [2].

*Hovenia dulcis* Thunb. or *H. acerba* Lindl. or *H. trichocarpa* Chun et Tsiang (Chinese name: Zhi Ju Zi): dried seed is used for hangovers, vomiting, and difficulties with urination and defecation [116].

*Imperata cylindrica* Beauv. var *major* (Nees) C. E. Hubb. (Chinese name: Bai Mao Gen): fresh or dried rhizome is used for hematemesis, hematuria, nose bleeds, thirst, jaundice, edema, and heat and pain during urination [2].

*Laminaria japonica* Aresch. or *Ecklonia kurome* Okam. (Chinese name: Kun Bu): dried thallus is used for cecidum and tumors [2].

*Lilium lancifolium* Thunb. or *L. brownie* F. E. Brown var. *viridulum* Baker or *L. pumilum* DC. (Chinese name: Bai He): dried bulb is for cough, palpitations due to fear, and insomnia and trances [2].

*Ostrea gigas* Thunberg or *O. talienwhanensis* Crosse or *O. rivularis* Gould (Chinese name: Mu Li): dried shell is used for palpitations due to fear, and insomnia, dizziness and tinnitus [2].

*Phaseolus calcaratus* Roxb. or *P. angularis* Wight (Chinese name: Chi Xiao Dou): dried seed for edema, jaundice and rheumatic pain [2].

*Phragmites communis* Trin. (Chinese name: Lu Gen): fresh or dried rhizome is used for fever, polydipsia, vomiting, coughing, and heat and pain during urination [2].

*Platycodon grandiflorum* (Jacq.) A. DC. (Chinese name: Jie Geng): dried root is for coughing with excessive phlegm, chest distress, sore throat and celostomia [2].

*Polygonatum odoratum* (Mill.) Druce (Chinese name: Yu Zhu): dried rhizome is used for coughing [2].

*Portulaca oleracea* L. (Chinese name: Ma Chi Xian): dried stem and leaf are used to stop bleeding [2].

*Prunus armeniaca* L. or *P. armeniaca* L. var. *ansu* Maxim or *P. sibirica* L. or *P. mandshurica* (Maxim.) Koehne (Chinese name: Xing Ren): dried seed is for coughing and constipation [116].

*Prunus humilis* Bge. or *P. japonica* Thunb. or *P. pedunculata* Maxim. (Chinese name: Yu Li Ren): dried seed is used for constipation, abdominal distention, edema, and difficulty in micturition [2].

*Prunus persica* (L.) Batsch or *P. davidiana* (Carr.) Franch. (Chinese name: Tao Ren): dried seed for amenia, dysmenorrhea, and constipation [2].

*Sophora japonica* L. (Chinese name: Huai Mi or Huai Hua): dried flower or flower bud is used for hemafecia, hemntodiarrhea, nose bleeding, hematemesis, headache, and dizziness [2].

*Taraxacum mongolicum* Hand.- Mazz. or *T. sinicum* Kitag. (Chinese name: Pu Gong Ying): dried whole plant for mammary abscess, sore throat, jaundice, heat and pain at urination [2].

*Torreya grandis* Fort. (Chinese name: Fei Zi): dried seed for expelling intestinal parasites and constipation [2].

*Zaocys dhumnades* (Cantor) (Chinese name: Wu Shao She): dried body for rheumatic pain [2].

# 6. HEALTHY FOOD AND NOVEL FOOD PRODUCTS IN CHINA

## 6.1. Healthy Food

Based on traditional use and Chinese dietary customs for maintaining health, and considering international regulatory practices, the China State Food and Drug Administration (SFDA) introduced a regulatory framework and related guidelines for healthy food products on July 1, 2005. The definition for healthy food is referred to as "a food product which has certain health-maintaining properties, or for the purpose of supplementing vitamins and minerals for appropriate groups of consumers with the aim of modulating body functions rather than treating diseases, with no acute, sub-acute, or chronic toxicity."

There are approximately 10,000 registered healthy food products on the Chinese market and 600 to 1,000 new ones approved each year. The China Ministry of Health requires manufacturers of healthy food products to comply with GMPs to ensure product quality and safety.

### 6.1.1. Permitted Health Claims for Healthy Food Products

Currently, 27 claims are allowed, but each product can only register for no more than 2 claims. The claims and experimental or clinical data requirements are listed in Table 1.

**Table 1. Health claims allowed for healthy food products in China**

| | |
|---|---|
| 1. Enhances immune system | 15. Anti-oxidant ★ |
| 2. Improves sleep | 16. Assists in improving memory ★ |
| 3. Assists liver protection against chemical damage | 17. Assists in lead excretion ★ |
| 4. Increases bone density | 18. Relieves sore throat ★ |
| 5. Increases tolerance against oxygen deficiency | 19. Assists in lowering blood pressure ★ |
| 6. Assists in protection against radiation | 20. Improves lactation ★ |
| 7. Relieves body fatigue # | 21. Lowers body weight ★# |
| 8. Relieves eye fatigue ☆ | 22. Improves growth and development ★# |
| 9. Removes acne ☆ | 23. Improves nutritional anemia ★ |
| 10. Removes chloasma ☆ | 24. Modulates intestinal microflora ★ |
| 11. Improves skin water content ☆ | 25. Enhances digestion ★ |
| 12. Improves skin lipid content ☆ | 26. Relaxes the bowels ★ |
| 13. Assists in lowering blood lipids ★ | 27. Assists in protection of gastric mucosa from damage ★ |
| 14. Assists in lowering blood glucose ★ | |

★ Health claim requires supporting data from animal studies and human trials.

☆ Health claim requires supporting data from human trials.

\# Data from stimulant drug test required.

### 6.1.2. List of Chinese Regulatory Guidelines Related to Healthy Food Products

The following current guidelines are legal documents in effect to regulate healthy food products in China: Regulation on Healthy Food Products Registration; Requirements for Healthy Food Products Registration and Approval; Naming Regulation for Healthy Food Products; Regulation on Registration and Examination of Amino Acids Conjugates as Health Food Products; Regulation on Registration and Examination of Nucleic Acids as Healthy Food Products; Regulation on Registration and Examination of Wild Animals and Plants as Healthy Food Products; Regulation on Registration and Examination of Probiotic Bacteria as Healthy Food Products; Regulation on Registration and Examination of Nutrients and Dietary Supplements; Regulation on Registration and Examination of Fungi as Healthy Food Products; Regulation on Healthy Food Products Sample Preparation and Site Inspection; and Regulation on Registration and Examination of Healthy Food Products Manufactured with Macroporous Adsorption Resin as Processing Aids in Isolation and Purification, etc. [349-352].

## 6.2. Novel Food Products

Based on the *Food Hygiene Act* of the P. R. China, a new regulation was introduced on December 1, 2007 for novel food products [353]. According to this Regulation on Novel Food Products, novel food products include: (1) Animals, plants, or microorganisms with no consumption history in China as food; (2) Food ingredients derived from animals, plants, or microorganisms, which have no consumption history in China; (3) New microorganism strains used for food processing; and (4) Food ingredients with composition or property changes due to new processing methods. Novel food products are regulated under the *Food Hygiene Act*, which stipulates that these products should have neither acute, sub-acute, or chronic toxicity nor other potential safety concerns. Since any novel food materials for making healthy food products will need to be registered and attain approval first, this provides companies from outside of China with a market entry point for new and specialty food materials. To date, most of the novel food products registered or being registered in China is from multinational food companies located within and outside of China.

## 7. Future Perspective

With China's rapid economic development during recent decades, quality and healthy lifestyle are becoming the key driving forces for the growing healthy foods market, estimated to be $10 billion (USD) in 2007, which is exceeding a 10% growth rate annually. China is also the home of many health and wellness practices, including the use of Chinese dietary herbs, dating back thousands of years. The combination of research and product development using cutting edge technologies, with TCM's healing and wellness-maintaining experiences and practices would accelerate the process for developing plant bioactives as new dietary supplements or as future healthy food/functional food ingredients.

## ACKNOWLEDGMENT

We appreciate Dr. Hui-Min Gao from the Institute of Chinese Materia Medica, China Academy of Chinese Medical Sciences for her help in collecting information. We are also very grateful to Dr. Stephen Ewart from the National Research Council of Canada (NRC) - Institute for Marine Biosciences for offering comments and making corrections, and Ms. Lise Lafontaine and Mr. Jun Wang from the NRC - Institute for Nutrisciences and Health for further revisions.

## REFERENCES

[1] China Ministry of Health. *Notice on the Further standardization of Dietary Food Materials Regulation China Ministry of Health;* 2002.

[2] CP Commission. China Pharmacopoeia. 2005 ed. *Beijing: Chemical Industry Press;* 2005.

[3] Sekiwa Y, Kubota K, Kobayashi A. Isolation of novel glucosides related to gingerdiol from ginger and their antioxidative activities. *J Agric Food Chem.* 2000 Feb;48(2):373-7.

[4] Masuda Y, Kikuzaki H, Hisamoto M, Nakatani N. Antioxidant properties of gingerol related compounds from ginger. *Biofactors.* 2004;21(1-4):293-6.

[5] Kuo PC, Damu AG, Cherng CY, Jeng JF, Teng CM, Lee EJ, et al. Isolation of a natural antioxidant, dehydrozingerone from Zingiber officinale and synthesis of its analogues for recognition of effective antioxidant and antityrosinase agents. *Arch Pharm Res.* 2005 May;28(5):518-28.

[6] Ansari MN, Bhandari U, Pillai KK. Ethanolic Zingiber officinale R. extract pretreatment alleviates isoproterenol-induced oxidative myocardial necrosis in rats. *Indian J Exp Biol.* 2006 Nov;44(11):892-7.

[7] Ajith TA, Hema U, Aswathy MS. Zingiber officinale Roscoe prevents acetaminophen-induced acute hepatotoxicity by enhancing hepatic antioxidant status. *Food Chem Toxicol.* 2007 Nov;45(11):2267-72.

[8] Siddaraju MN, Dharmesh SM. Inhibition of gastric H+, K+-ATPase and Helicobacter pylori growth by phenolic antioxidants of Zingiber officinale. *Mol Nutr Food Res.* 2007 Mar;51(3):324-32.

[9] Tao QF, Xu Y, Lam RY, Schneider B, Dou H, Leung PS, et al. Diarylheptanoids and a monoterpenoid from the rhizomes of Zingiber officinale: antioxidant and cytoprotective properties. *J Nat Prod.* 2008 Jan;71(1):12-7.

[10] Sharma SS, Gupta YK. Reversal of cisplatin-induced delay in gastric emptying in rats by ginger (Zingiber officinale). *J Ethnopharmacol.* 1998 Aug;62(1):49-55.

[11] Keating A, Chez RA. Ginger syrup as an antiemetic in early pregnancy. *Altern Ther Health Med.* 2002 Sep-Oct;8(5):89-91.

[12] Borrelli F, Capasso R, Aviello G, Pittler MH, Izzo AA. Effectiveness and safety of ginger in the treatment of pregnancy-induced nausea and vomiting. *Obstet Gynecol.* 2005 Apr;105(4):849-56.

[13]  Hickok JT, Roscoe JA, Morrow GR, Ryan JL. A Phase II/III Randomized, Placebo-Controlled, Double-Blind Clinical Trial of Ginger (Zingiber officinale) for Nausea Caused by Chemotherapy for Cancer: A Currently Accruing URCC CCOP Cancer Control Study. *Support Cancer Ther.* 2007 Sep 1;4(4):247-50.

[14]  Eberhart LH, Mayer R, Betz O, Tsolakidis S, Hilpert W, Morin AM, et al. Ginger does not prevent postoperative nausea and vomiting after laparoscopic surgery. *Anesth Analg.* 2003 Apr;96(4):995-8, table of contents.

[15]  Kadnur SV, Goyal RK. Beneficial effects of Zingiber officinale Roscoe on fructose induced hyperlipidemia and hyperinsulinemia in rats. *Indian J Exp Biol.* 2005 Dec;43(12):1161-4.

[16]  Bhandari U, Kanojia R, Pillai KK. Effect of ethanolic extract of Zingiber officinale on dyslipidaemia in diabetic rats. *J Ethnopharmacol.* 2005 Feb 28;97(2):227-30.

[17]  Goyal RK, Kadnur SV. Beneficial effects of Zingiber officinale on goldthioglucose induced obesity. *Fitoterapia.* 2006 Apr;77(3):160-3.

[18]  Akhani SP, Vishwakarma SL, Goyal RK. Anti-diabetic activity of Zingiber officinale in streptozotocin-induced type I diabetic rats. *J Pharm Pharmacol.* 2004 Jan;56(1):101-5.

[19]  Al-Amin ZM, Thomson M, Al-Qattan KK, Peltonen-Shalaby R, Ali M. Anti-diabetic and hypolipidaemic properties of ginger (Zingiber officinale) in streptozotocin-induced diabetic rats. *Br J Nutr.* 2006 Oct;96(4):660-6.

[20]  Ojewole JA. Analgesic, antiinflammatory and hypoglycaemic effects of ethanol extract of Zingiber officinale (Roscoe) rhizomes (Zingiberaceae) in mice and rats. *Phytother Res.* 2006 Sep;20(9):764-72.

[21]  Islam MS, Choi H. Comparative effects of dietary ginger (Zingiber officinale) and garlic (Allium sativum) investigated in a type 2 diabetes model of rats. *J Med Food.* 2008 Mar;11(1):152-9.

[22]  ElRokh el SM, Yassin NA, El-Shenawy SM, Ibrahim BM. Antihypercholesterolaemic effect of ginger rhizome (Zingiber officinale) in rats. *Inflammopharmacology.* 2010 Dec;18(6):309-15.

[23]  Nammi S, Sreemantula S, Roufogalis BD. Protective effects of ethanolic extract of Zingiber officinale rhizome on the development of metabolic syndrome in high-fat diet-fed rats. *Basic Clin Pharmacol Toxicol.* 2009 May;104(5):366-73.

[24]  Isa Y, Miyakawa Y, Yanagisawa M, Goto T, Kang MS, Kawada T, et al. 6-Shogaol and 6-gingerol, the pungent of ginger, inhibit TNF-alpha mediated downregulation of adiponectin expression via different mechanisms in 3T3-L1 adipocytes. *Biochem Biophys Res Commun.* 2008 Aug 29;373(3):429-34.

[25]  Grzanna R, Lindmark L, Frondoza CG. Ginger--an herbal medicinal product with broad anti-inflammatory actions. *J Med Food.* 2005 Summer;8(2):125-32.

[26]  Phan PV, Sohrabi A, Polotsky A, Hungerford DS, Lindmark L, Frondoza CG. Ginger extract components suppress induction of chemokine expression in human synoviocytes. *J Altern Complement Med.* 2005 Feb;11(1):149-54.

[27]  Aktan F, Henness S, Tran VH, Duke CC, Roufogalis BD, Ammit AJ. Gingerol metabolite and a synthetic analogue Capsarol inhibit macrophage NF-kappaB-mediated iNOS gene expression and enzyme activity. *Planta Med.* 2006 Jun;72(8):727-34.

[28]  Zhou HL, Deng YM, Xie QM. The modulatory effects of the volatile oil of ginger on the cellular immune response in vitro and in vivo in mice. *J Ethnopharmacol.* 2006 Apr 21;105(1-2):301-5.

[29] Ahui ML, Champy P, Ramadan A, Pham Van L, Araujo L, Brou Andre K, et al. Ginger prevents Th2-mediated immune responses in a mouse model of airway inflammation. *Int Immunopharmacol.* 2008 Dec 10;8(12):1626-32.

[30] Ghayur MN, Gilani AH, Janssen LJ. Ginger attenuates acetylcholine-induced contraction and Ca2+ signalling in murine airway smooth muscle cells. *Can J Physiol Pharmacol.* 2008 May;86(5):264-71.

[31] Imanishi N, Andoh T, Mantani N, Sakai S, Terasawa K, Shimada Y, et al. Macrophage-mediated inhibitory effect of Zingiber officinale Rosc, a traditional oriental herbal medicine, on the growth of influenza A/Aichi/2/68 virus. *Am J Chin Med.* 2006;34(1):157-69.

[32] Manju V, Nalini N. Chemopreventive efficacy of ginger, a naturally occurring anticarcinogen during the initiation, post-initiation stages of 1,2 dimethylhydrazine-induced colon cancer. *Clin Chim Acta.* 2005 Aug;358(1-2):60-7.

[33] Bidinotto LT, Spinardi-Barbisan AL, Rocha NS, Salvadori DM, Barbisan LF. Effects of ginger (Zingiber officinale Roscoe) on DNA damage and development of urothelial tumors in a mouse bladder carcinogenesis model. *Environ Mol Mutagen.* 2006 Oct;47(8):624-30.

[34] Rhode J, Fogoros S, Zick S, Wahl H, Griffith KA, Huang J, et al. Ginger inhibits cell growth and modulates angiogenic factors in ovarian cancer cells. *BMC Complement Altern Med.* 2007;7:44.

[35] Shukla Y, Prasad S, Tripathi C, Singh M, George J, Kalra N. In vitro and in vivo modulation of testosterone mediated alterations in apoptosis related proteins by [6]-gingerol. *Mol Nutr Food Res.* 2007 Dec;51(12):1492-502.

[36] Vijaya Padma V, Arul Diana Christie S, Ramkuma KM. Induction of apoptosis by ginger in HEp-2 cell line is mediated by reactive oxygen species. *Basic Clin Pharmacol Toxicol.* 2007 May;100(5):302-7.

[37] Ishiguro K, Ando T, Maeda O, Ohmiya N, Niwa Y, Kadomatsu K, et al. Ginger ingredients reduce viability of gastric cancer cells via distinct mechanisms. *Biochem Biophys Res Commun.* 2007 Oct 12;362(1):218-23.

[38] Chen CY, Liu TZ, Liu YW, Tseng WC, Liu RH, Lu FJ, et al. 6-shogaol (alkanone from ginger) induces apoptotic cell death of human hepatoma p53 mutant Mahlavu subline via an oxidative stress-mediated caspase-dependent mechanism. *J Agric Food Chem.* 2007 Feb 7;55(3):948-54.

[39] Kim JS, Lee SI, Park HW, Yang JH, Shin TY, Kim YC, et al. Cytotoxic components from the dried rhizomes of Zingiber officinale Roscoe. *Arch Pharm Res.* 2008 Apr;31(4):415-8.

[40] Lee HS, Seo EY, Kang NE, Kim WK. [6]-Gingerol inhibits metastasis of MDA-MB-231 human breast cancer cells. *J Nutr Biochem.* 2008 May;19(5):313-9.

[41] Pan MH, Hsieh MC, Kuo JM, Lai CS, Wu H, Sang S, et al. 6-Shogaol induces apoptosis in human colorectal carcinoma cells via ROS production, caspase activation, and GADD 153 expression. *Mol Nutr Food Res.* 2008 May;52(5):527-37.

[42] Tuntiwechapikul W, Taka T, Songsomboon C, Kaewtunjai N, Imsumran A, Makonkawkeyoon L, et al. Ginger extract inhibits human telomerase reverse transcriptase and c-Myc expression in A549 lung cancer cells. *J Med Food.* 2010 Dec;13(6):1347-54.

[43] Guahk GH, Ha SK, Jung HS, Kang C, Kim CH, Kim YB, et al. Zingiber officinale protects HaCaT cells and C57BL/6 mice from ultraviolet B-induced inflammation. *J Med Food.* 2010 Jun;13(3):673-80.

[44] Sang S, Hong J, Wu H, Liu J, Yang CS, Pan MH, et al. Increased growth inhibitory effects on human cancer cells and anti-inflammatory potency of shogaols from Zingiber officinale relative to gingerols. *J Agric Food Chem.* 2009 Nov 25;57(22):10645-50.

[45] Nigam N, George J, Srivastava S, Roy P, Bhui K, Singh M, et al. Induction of apoptosis by [6]-gingerol associated with the modulation of p53 and involvement of mitochondrial signaling pathway in B[a]P-induced mouse skin tumorigenesis. *Cancer Chemother Pharmacol.* 2010 Mar;65(4):687-96.

[46] Nigam N, Bhui K, Prasad S, George J, Shukla Y. [6]-Gingerol induces reactive oxygen species regulated mitochondrial cell death pathway in human epidermoid carcinoma A431 cells. *Chem Biol Interact.* 2009 Sep 14;181(1):77-84.

[47] Brown AC, Shah C, Liu J, Pham JT, Zhang JG, Jadus MR. Ginger's (Zingiber officinale Roscoe) inhibition of rat colonic adenocarcinoma cells proliferation and angiogenesis in vitro. *Phytother Res.* 2009 May;23(5):640-5.

[48] Sepahvand R, Esmaeili-Mahani S, Arzi A, Rasoulian B, Abbasnejad M. Ginger (Zingiber officinale Roscoe) elicits antinociceptive properties and potentiates morphine-induced analgesia in the rat radiant heat tail-flick test. *J Med Food.* 2010 Dec;13(6):1397-401.

[49] Black CD, Herring MP, Hurley DJ, O'Connor PJ. Ginger (Zingiber officinale) reduces muscle pain caused by eccentric exercise. *J Pain.* 2010 Sep;11(9):894-903.

[50] Rong X, Peng G, Suzuki T, Yang Q, Yamahara J, Li Y. A 35-day gavage safety assessment of ginger in rats. *Regul Toxicol Pharmacol.* 2009 Jul;54(2):118-23.

[51] Iseli V, Potterat O, Hagmann L, Egli J, Hamburger M. Characterization of the pungent principles and the essential oil of Zanthoxylum schinifolium pericarp. *Pharmazie.* 2007 May;62(5):396-400.

[52] Yang X. Aroma constituents and alkylamides of red and green huajiao (Zanthoxylum bungeanum and Zanthoxylum schinifolium). *J Agric Food Chem.* 2008 Mar 12;56(5):1689-96.

[53] Paik SY, Koh KH, Beak SM, Paek SH, Kim JA. The essential oils from Zanthoxylum schinifolium pericarp induce apoptosis of HepG2 human hepatoma cells through increased production of reactive oxygen species. *Biol Pharm Bull.* 2005 May;28(5):802-7.

[54] Tezuka Y, Irikawa S, Kaneko T, Banskota AH, Nagaoka T, Xiong Q, et al. Screening of Chinese herbal drug extracts for inhibitory activity on nitric oxide production and identification of an active compound of Zanthoxylum bungeanum. *J Ethnopharmacol.* 2001 Oct;77(2-3):209-17.

[55] Cao LH, Lee YJ, Kang DG, Kim JS, Lee HS. Effect of Zanthoxylum schinifolium on TNF-alpha-induced vascular inflammation in human umbilical vein endothelial cells. *Vascul Pharmacol.* 2009 May-Jun;50(5-6):200-7.

[56] Riera CE, Menozzi-Smarrito C, Affolter M, Michlig S, Munari C, Robert F, et al. Compounds from Sichuan and Melegueta peppers activate, covalently and non-covalently, TRPA1 and TRPV1 channels. *Br J Pharmacol.* 2009 Aug;157(8):1398-409.

[57] De M, De AK, Sen P, Banerjee AB. Antimicrobial properties of star anise (Illicium verum Hook f). *Phytother Res.* 2002 Feb;16(1):94-5.

[58] Wang X, Wang H, Ma J, Xu Y, Guan Y. *[Analysis of volatile oil in Illicium verum fruit by on-line coupled packed capillary liquid chromatography/capillary gas chromatography].* Se Pu. 2004 Mar;22(2):101-5.

[59] Huang Y, Zhao J, Zhou L, Wang J, Gong Y, Chen X, et al. Antifungal activity of the essential oil of Illicium verum fruit and its main component trans-anethole. *Molecules.* 2010;15(11):7558-69.

[60] Yang JF, Yang CH, Chang HW, Yang CS, Wang SM, Hsieh MC, et al. Chemical composition and antibacterial activities of Illicium verum against antibiotic-resistant pathogens. *J Med Food.* 2010 Oct;13(5):1254-62.

[61] Lee SW, Li G, Lee KS, Jung JS, Xu ML, Seo CS, et al. Preventive agents against sepsis and new phenylpropanoid glucosides from the fruits of Illicium verum. *Planta Med.* 2003 Sep;69(9):861-4.

[62] Choi J, Lee KT, Ka H, Jung WT, Jung HJ, Park HJ. Constituents of the essential oil of the Cinnamomum cassia stem bark and the biological properties. *Arch Pharm Res.* 2001 Oct;24(5):418-23.

[63] Lee HS, Ahn YJ. Growth-Inhibiting Effects of Cinnamomum cassia Bark-Derived Materials on Human Intestinal Bacteria. *J Agric Food Chem.* 1998 Jan 19;46(1):8-12.

[64] Giordani R, Regli P, Kaloustian J, Portugal H. Potentiation of antifungal activity of amphotericin B by essential oil from Cinnamomum cassia. *Phytother Res.* 2006 Jan;20(1):58-61.

[65] Ooi LS, Li Y, Kam SL, Wang H, Wong EY, Ooi VE. Antimicrobial activities of cinnamon oil and cinnamaldehyde from the Chinese medicinal herb Cinnamomum cassia Blume. *Am J Chin Med.* 2006;34(3):511-22.

[66] Lin CC, Wu SJ, Chang CH, Ng LT. Antioxidant activity of Cinnamomum cassia. *Phytother Res.* 2003 Aug;17(7):726-30.

[67] Shimada Y, Goto H, Kogure T, Kohta K, Shintani T, Itoh T, et al. Extract prepared from the bark of Cinnamomum cassia Blume prevents glutamate-induced neuronal death in cultured cerebellar granule cells. *Phytother Res.* 2000 Sep;14(6):466-8.

[68] Lee HS, Kim BS, Kim MK. Suppression effect of Cinnamomum cassia bark-derived component on nitric oxide synthase. *J Agric Food Chem.* 2002 Dec 18;50(26):7700-3.

[69] Reddy AM, Seo JH, Ryu SY, Kim YS, Kim YS, Min KR, et al. Cinnamaldehyde and 2-methoxycinnamaldehyde as NF-kappaB inhibitors from Cinnamomum cassia. *Planta Med.* 2004 Sep;70(9):823-7.

[70] Lee SH, Lee SY, Son DJ, Lee H, Yoo HS, Song S, et al. Inhibitory effect of 2'-hydroxycinnamaldehyde on nitric oxide production through inhibition of NF-kappa B activation in RAW 264.7 cells. *Biochem Pharmacol.* 2005 Mar 1;69(5):791-9.

[71] Moon EY, Lee MR, Wang AG, Lee JH, Kim HC, Kim HM, et al. Delayed occurrence of H-ras12V-induced hepatocellular carcinoma with long-term treatment with cinnamaldehydes. *Eur J Pharmacol.* 2006 Jan 20;530(3):270-5.

[72] Lee CW, Lee SH, Lee JW, Ban JO, Lee SY, Yoo HS, et al. 2-hydroxycinnamaldehyde inhibits SW620 colon cancer cell growth through AP-1 inactivation. *J Pharmacol Sci.* 2007 May;104(1):19-28.

[73] Liao BC, Hsieh CW, Liu YC, Tzeng TT, Sun YW, Wung BS. Cinnamaldehyde inhibits the tumor necrosis factor-alpha-induced expression of cell adhesion molecules in endothelial cells by suppressing NF-kappaB activation: effects upon IkappaB and Nrf2. *Toxicol Appl Pharmacol.* 2008 Jun 1;229(2):161-71.

[74] Choi DY, Baek YH, Huh JE, Ko JM, Woo H, Lee JD, et al. Stimulatory effect of Cinnamomum cassia and cinnamic acid on angiogenesis through up-regulation of VEGF and Flk-1/KDR expression. *Int Immunopharmacol.* 2009 Jul;9(7-8):959-67.

[75] Kwon HK, Hwang JS, So JS, Lee CG, Sahoo A, Ryu JH, et al. Cinnamon extract induces tumor cell death through inhibition of NFkappaB and AP1. *BMC Cancer.* 2010;10:392.

[76] Wondrak GT, Villeneuve NF, Lamore SD, Bause AS, Jiang T, Zhang DD. The cinnamon-derived dietary factor cinnamic aldehyde activates the Nrf2-dependent antioxidant response in human epithelial colon cells. *Molecules.* 2010 May;15(5):3338-55.

[77] Verspohl EJ, Bauer K, Neddermann E. Antidiabetic effect of Cinnamomum cassia and Cinnamomum zeylanicum in vivo and in vitro. *Phytother Res.* 2005 Mar;19(3):203-6.

[78] Lakshmi BS, Sujatha S, Anand S, Sangeetha KN, Narayanan RB, Katiyar C, et al. Cinnamic acid, from the bark of Cinnamomum cassia, regulates glucose transport via activation of GLUT4 on L6 myotubes in a phosphatidylinositol 3-kinase-independent manner. *J Diabetes.* 2009 Jun;1(2):99-106.

[79] Kirkham S, Akilen R, Sharma S, Tsiami A. The potential of cinnamon to reduce blood glucose levels in patients with type 2 diabetes and insulin resistance. *Diabetes Obes Metab.* 2009 Dec;11(12):1100-13.

[80] Lee KH, Choi EM. Stimulatory effects of extract prepared from the bark of Cinnamomum cassia blume on the function of osteoblastic MC3T3-E1 cells. *Phytother Res.* 2006 Nov;20(11):952-60.

[81] Yu HS, Lee SY, Jang CG. Involvement of 5-HT1A and GABAA receptors in the anxiolytic-like effects of Cinnamomum cassia in mice. *Pharmacol Biochem Behav.* 2007 May;87(1):164-70.

[82] Kong YH, Jo YO, Cho CW, Son D, Park S, Rho J, et al. Inhibitory effects of cinnamic acid on melanin biosynthesis in skin. *Biol Pharm Bull.* 2008 May;31(5):946-8.

[83] Gurdip S, Marimuthu, P., Catalan, C., Lampasona, M. P. Chemical, antioxidant and antifungal activities of volatile oil of black pepper and its acetone extract. *Journal of the Science of Food and Agriculture.* 2004;84(14):1878-84.

[84] Lin Z, Liao Y, Venkatasamy R, Hider RC, Soumyanath A. Amides from Piper nigrum L. with dissimilar effects on melanocyte proliferation in-vitro. *J Pharm Pharmacol.* 2007 Apr;59(4):529-36.

[85] 85.     Lee SW, Kim YK, Kim K, Lee HS, Choi JH, Lee WS, et al. Alkamides from the fruits of Piper longum and Piper nigrum displaying potent cell adhesion inhibition. *Bioorg Med Chem Lett.* 2008 Aug 15;18(16):4544-6.

[86] Khajuria A, Zutshi U, Bedi KL. Permeability characteristics of piperine on oral absorption--an active alkaloid from peppers and a bioavailability enhancer. *Indian J Exp Biol.* 1998 Jan;36(1):46-50.

[87] Pattanaik S, Hota D, Prabhakar S, Kharbanda P, Pandhi P. Effect of piperine on the steady-state pharmacokinetics of phenytoin in patients with epilepsy. *Phytother Res.* 2006 Aug;20(8):683-6.

[88] Lin Z, Hoult JR, Bennett DC, Raman A. Stimulation of mouse melanocyte proliferation by Piper nigrum fruit extract and its main alkaloid, piperine. *Planta Med.* 1999 Oct;65(7):600-3.

[89]   Pradeep CR, Kuttan G. Effect of piperine on the inhibition of lung metastasis induced B16F-10 melanoma cells in mice. *Clin Exp Metastasis.* 2002;19(8):703-8.

[90]   El Hamss R, Idaomar M, Alonso-Moraga A, Munoz Serrano A. Antimutagenic properties of bell and black peppers. *Food Chem Toxicol.* 2003 Jan;41(1):41-7.

[91]   Vijayakumar RS, Surya D, Nalini N. Antioxidant efficacy of black pepper (Piper nigrum L.) and piperine in rats with high fat diet induced oxidative stress. *Redox Rep.* 2004;9(2):105-10.

[92]   Selvendiran K, Banu SM, Sakthisekaran D. Oral supplementation of piperine leads to altered phase II enzymes and reduced DNA damage and DNA-protein cross links in Benzo(a)pyrene induced experimental lung carcinogenesis. *Mol Cell Biochem.* 2005 Jan;268(1-2):141-7.

[93]   Selvendiran K, Thirunavukkarasu C, Singh JP, Padmavathi R, Sakthisekaran D. Chemopreventive effect of piperine on mitochondrial TCA cycle and phase-I and glutathione-metabolizing enzymes in benzo(a)pyrene induced lung carcinogenesis in Swiss albino mice. *Mol Cell Biochem.* 2005 Mar;271(1-2):101-6.

[94]   Nalini N, Manju V, Menon VP. Effect of spices on lipid metabolism in 1,2-dimethylhydrazine-induced rat colon carcinogenesis. *J Med Food.* 2006 Summer;9(2):237-45.

[95]   Selvendiran K, Prince Vijeya Singh J, Sakthisekaran D. In vivo effect of piperine on serum and tissue glycoprotein levels in benzo(a)pyrene induced lung carcinogenesis in Swiss albino mice. *Pulm Pharmacol Ther.* 2006;19(2):107-11.

[96]   Choi BM, Kim SM, Park TK, Li G, Hong SJ, Park R, et al. Piperine protects cisplatin-induced apoptosis via heme oxygenase-1 induction in auditory cells. *J Nutr Biochem.* 2007 Sep;18(9):615-22.

[97]   Kapoor IP, Singh B, Singh G, De Heluani CS, De Lampasona MP, Catalan CA. Chemistry and in vitro antioxidant activity of volatile oil and oleoresins of black pepper (Piper nigrum). *J Agric Food Chem.* 2009 Jun 24;57(12):5358-64.

[98]   Liu Y, Yadev VR, Aggarwal BB, Nair MG. Inhibitory effects of black pepper (Piper nigrum) extracts and compounds on human tumor cell proliferation, cyclooxygenase enzymes, lipid peroxidation and nuclear transcription factor-kappa-B. *Nat Prod Commun.* 2010 Aug;5(8):1253-7.

[99]   Majdalawieh AF, Carr RI. In vitro investigation of the potential immunomodulatory and anti-cancer activities of black pepper (Piper nigrum) and cardamom (Elettaria cardamomum). *J Med Food.* 2010 Apr;13(2):371-81.

[100] Ingkaninan K, Temkitthawon P, Chuenchom K, Yuyaem T, Thongnoi W. Screening for acetylcholinesterase inhibitory activity in plants used in Thai traditional rejuvenating and neurotonic remedies. *J Ethnopharmacol.* 2003 Dec;89(2-3):261-4.

[101] Wattanathorn J, Chonpathompikunlert P, Muchimapura S, Priprem A, Tankamnerdthai O. Piperine, the potential functional food for mood and cognitive disorders. *Food Chem Toxicol.* 2008 Sep;46(9):3106-10.

[102] Chonpathompikunlert P, Wattanathorn J, Muchimapura S. Piperine, the main alkaloid of Thai black pepper, protects against neurodegeneration and cognitive impairment in animal model of cognitive deficit like condition of Alzheimer's disease. *Food Chem Toxicol.* 2010 Mar;48(3):798-802.

[103] Fu M, Sun ZH, Zuo HC. Neuroprotective effect of piperine on primarily cultured hippocampal neurons. *Biol Pharm Bull.* 2010;33(4):598-603.

[104] Panda S, Kar A. Piperine lowers the serum concentrations of thyroid hormones, glucose and hepatic 5'D activity in adult male mice. *Horm Metab Res.* 2003 Sep;35(9):523-6.

[105] Vijayakumar RS, Nalini N. Efficacy of piperine, an alkaloidal constituent from Piper nigrum on erythrocyte antioxidant status in high fat diet and antithyroid drug induced hyperlipidemic rats. *Cell Biochem Funct.* 2006 Nov-Dec;24(6):491-8.

[106] Vijayakumar RS, Nalini N. Piperine, an active principle from Piper nigrum, modulates hormonal and apo lipoprotein profiles in hyperlipidemic rats. *J Basic Clin Physiol Pharmacol.* 2006;17(2):71-86.

[107] Matsuda D, Ohte S, Ohshiro T, Jiang W, Rudel L, Hong B, et al. Molecular target of piperine in the inhibition of lipid droplet accumulation in macrophages. *Biol Pharm Bull.* 2008 Jun;31(6):1063-6.

[108] Pathak N, Khandelwal S. Cytoprotective and immunomodulating properties of piperine on murine splenocytes: an in vitro study. *Eur J Pharmacol.* 2007 Dec 8;576(1-3):160-70.

[109] Bae GS, Kim MS, Jung WS, Seo SW, Yun SW, Kim SG, et al. Inhibition of lipopolysaccharide-induced inflammatory responses by piperine. *Eur J Pharmacol.* 2010 Sep 10;642(1-3):154-62.

[110] Mehmood MH, Gilani AH. Pharmacological basis for the medicinal use of black pepper and piperine in gastrointestinal disorders. *J Med Food.* 2010 Oct;13(5):1086-96.

[111] Hlavackova L, Urbanova A, Ulicna O, Janega P, Cerna A, Babal P. Piperine, active substance of black pepper, alleviates hypertension induced by NO synthase inhibition. *Bratisl Lek Listy.* 2010;111(8):426-31.

[112] Chun H, Shin DH, Hong BS, Cho WD, Cho HY, Yang HC. Biochemical properties of polysaccharides from black pepper. *Biol Pharm Bull.* 2002 Sep;25(9):1203-8.

[113] Gulcin I. The antioxidant and radical scavenging activities of black pepper (Piper nigrum) seeds. *Int J Food Sci Nutr.* 2005 Nov;56(7):491-9.

[114] Kaleem M, Sheema, Sarmad H, Bano B. Protective effects of Piper nigrum and Vinca rosea in alloxan induced diabetic rats. *Indian J Physiol Pharmacol.* 2005 Jan;49(1):65-71.

[115] Agbor GA, Vinson JA, Oben JE, Ngogang JY. In vitro antioxidant activity of three Piper species. *J Herb Pharmacother.* 2007;7(2):49-64.

[116] Chinese Materia Medica Compiling Committee CSTA, editor. Chinese Materia Medica (Concise edition). *Shanghai: Shanghai Science and Technology Press;* 1998.

[117] Sautour M, Mitaine-Offer AC, Miyamoto T, Wagner H, Lacaille-Dubois MA. A new phenanthrene glycoside and other constituents from Dioscorea opposita. *Chem Pharm Bull* (Tokyo). 2004 Oct;52(10):1235-7.

[118] Yang MH, Yoon KD, Chin YW, Park JH, Kim J. Phenolic compounds with radical scavenging and cyclooxygenase-2 (COX-2) inhibitory activities from Dioscorea opposita. *Bioorg Med Chem.* 2009 Apr 1;17(7):2689-94.

[119] Yang MH, Yoon KD, Chin YW, Park JH, Kim SH, Kim YC, et al. Neuroprotective effects of Dioscorea opposita on scopolamine-induced memory impairment in in vivo behavioral tests and in vitro assays. *J Ethnopharmacol.* 2009 Jan 12;121(1):130-4.

[120] Ma C, Wang W, Chen YY, Liu RN, Wang RF, Du LJ. Neuroprotective and antioxidant activity of compounds from the aerial parts of Dioscorea opposita. *J Nat Prod.* 2005 Aug;68(8):1259-61.

[121] Cals-Grierson MM. Modulation of activity of the adipocyte aquaglyceroporin channel by plant extracts. *Int J Cosmet Sci.* 2007 Feb;29(1):7-14.

[122] Gao X, Li B, Jiang H, Liu F, Xu D, Liu Z. Dioscorea opposita reverses dexamethasone induced insulin resistance. *Fitoterapia.* 2007 Jan;78(1):12-5.

[123] Shujun W, Jinglin Y, Wenyuan G, Hongyan L, Peigen X. New starches from traditional Chinese medicine (TCM)--Chinese yam (Dioscorea opposita Thunb.) cultivars. *Carbohydr Res.* 2006 Feb 6;341(2):289-93.

[124] Xu Q, Xu ZL, Shen ZG, Shi YY. [Research of polysaccharide from Dioscorea opposita Thunb]. *Zhong Yao Cai.* 2006 Sep;29(9):909-12.

[125] Nagai T, Nagashima T. Functional properties of dioscorin, a soluble viscous protein from Japanese yam (Dioscorea opposita thunb.) tuber mucilage Tororo. *Z Naturforsch* [C]. 2006 Nov-Dec;61(11-12):792-8.

[126] Li M, Yang GL, Mi S, Gao XY, Wang Y, Li MR. [Extract process of cyclic adenosinemonophosphate (cAMP) in Ziziphus jujuba]. *Zhong Yao Cai.* 2007 Sep;30(9):1143-5.

[127] Guo S, Duan JA, Tang YP, Yang NY, Qian DW, Su SL, et al. Characterization of triterpenic acids in fruits of ziziphus species by HPLC-ELSD-MS. *J Agric Food Chem.* 2010 May 26;58(10):6285-9.

[128] Guo S, Duan JA, Tang YP, Zhu ZH, Qian YF, Yang NY, et al. Characterization of nucleosides and nucleobases in fruits of Ziziphus jujuba by UPLC-DAD-MS. *J Agric Food Chem.* 2010 Oct 13;58(19):10774-80.

[129] Zhang H, Jiang L, Ye S, Ye Y, Ren F. Systematic evaluation of antioxidant capacities of the ethanolic extract of different tissues of jujube (Ziziphus jujuba Mill.) from China. *Food Chem Toxicol.* 2010 Jun;48(6):1461-5.

[130] Huang YL, Yen GC, Sheu F, Chau CF. Effects of water-soluble carbohydrate concentrate from Chinese jujube on different intestinal and fecal indices. *J Agric Food Chem.* 2008 Mar 12;56(5):1734-9.

[131] Guil-Guerrero JL, Diaz Delgado A, Matallana Gonzalez MC, Torija Isasa ME. Fatty acids and carotenes in some ber (Ziziphus jujuba Mill) varieties. *Plant Foods Hum Nutr.* 2004 Winter;59(1):23-7.

[132] Naftali T, Feingelernt H, Lesin Y, Rauchwarger A, Konikoff FM. Ziziphus jujuba extract for the treatment of chronic idiopathic constipation: a controlled clinical trial. *Digestion.* 2008;78(4):224-8.

[133] Potterat O. Goji (Lycium barbarum and L. chinense): Phytochemistry, pharmacology and safety in the perspective of traditional uses and recent popularity. *Planta Med.* 2010 Jan;76(1):7-19.

[134] Liu XL, Sun JY, Li HY, Zhang L, Qian BC. [Extraction and isolation of active component for inhibiting PC3 cell proliferation in vitro from the fruit of Lycium barbarum L.]. *Zhongguo Zhong Yao Za Zhi.* 2000 Aug;25(8):481-3.

[135] Huang Y, Tan A, Shen Y, Lu J. [Scavenging effect of total flavonoids of lycium barbarum L on active oxygen radicals and inhibitory effects on heat output from L1210 cells]. *Wei Sheng Yan Jiu.* 1998 Mar;27(2):109-11, 15.

[136] Huang Y, Lu J, Shen Y, Lu J. [The protective effects of total flavonoids from Lycium Barbarum L. on lipid peroxidation of liver mitochondria and red blood cell in rats]. *Wei Sheng Yan Jiu.* 1999 Mar 30;28(2):115-6.

[137] Li G, Sepkovic DW, Bradlow HL, Telang NT, Wong GY. Lycium barbarum inhibits growth of estrogen receptor positive human breast cancer cells by favorably altering estradiol metabolism. *Nutr Cancer.* 2009;61(3):408-14.

[138] Reeve VE, Allanson M, Arun SJ, Domanski D, Painter N. Mice drinking goji berry juice (Lycium barbarum) are protected from UV radiation-induced skin damage via antioxidant pathways. *Photochem Photobiol Sci.* 2010 Apr;9(4):601-7.

[139] Feng Z, Jia H, Li X, Bai Z, Liu Z, Sun L, et al. A milk-based wolfberry preparation prevents prenatal stress-induced cognitive impairment of offspring rats, and inhibits oxidative damage and mitochondrial dysfunction in vitro. *Neurochem Res.* 2010 May;35(5):702-11.

[140] Huang L, Lin Y, Tian G, Ji G. [Isolation, purification and physico-chemical properties of immunoactive constituents from the fruit of Lycium barbarum L.]. *Yao Xue Xue Bao.* 1998 Jul;33(7):512-6.

[141] Luo Q, Yan J, Zhang S. [Effects of pure and crude Lycium barbarum polysaccharides on immunopharmacology]. *Zhong Yao Cai.* 1999 May;22(5):246-9.

[142] Gan L, Zhang SH, Liu Q, Xu HB. A polysaccharide-protein complex from Lycium barbarum upregulates cytokine expression in human peripheral blood mononuclear cells. *Eur J Pharmacol.* 2003 Jun 27;471(3):217-22.

[143] Du G, Liu L, Fang J. Experimental study on the enhancement of murine splenic lymphocyte proliferation by Lycium barbarum glycopeptide. *J Huazhong Univ Sci Technolog Med Sci.* 2004;24(5):518-20, 27.

[144] Gan L, Hua Zhang S, Liang Yang X, Bi Xu H. Immunomodulation and antitumor activity by a polysaccharide-protein complex from Lycium barbarum. *Int Immunopharmacol.* 2004 Apr;4(4):563-9.

[145] He YL, Ying Y, Xu YL, Su JF, Luo H, Wang HF. [Effects of Lycium barbarum polysaccharide on tumor microenvironment T-lymphocyte subsets and dendritic cells in H22-bearing mice]. *Zhong Xi Yi Jie He Xue Bao.* 2005 Sep;3(5):374-7.

[146] Zhu J, Zhao LH, Chen Z. [Stimulation by Lycium bararum polysaccharides of the maturation of dendritic cells in murine bone marrow]. *Zhejiang Da Xue Xue Bao Yi Xue Ban.* 2006 Nov;35(6):648-52.

[147] Chen Z, Kwong Huat Tan B, Chan SH. Activation of T lymphocytes by polysaccharide-protein complex from Lycium barbarum L. *Int Immunopharmacol.* 2008 Dec 10;8(12):1663-71.

[148] Chen Z, Lu J, Srinivasan N, Tan BK, Chan SH. Polysaccharide-protein complex from Lycium barbarum L. is a novel stimulus of dendritic cell immunogenicity. *J Immunol.* 2009 Mar 15;182(6):3503-9.

[149] Chen Z, Soo MY, Srinivasan N, Tan BK, Chan SH. Activation of macrophages by polysaccharide-protein complex from Lycium barbarum L. *Phytother Res.* 2009 Aug;23(8):1116-22.

[150] Chiu K, Chan HC, Yeung SC, Yuen WH, Zee SY, Chang RC, et al. Modulation of microglia by Wolfberry on the survival of retinal ganglion cells in a rat ocular hypertension model. *J Ocul Biol Dis Infor.* 2009 Jun;2(2):47-56.

[151] Ling Y, Li S, Yang J, Yuan J, He C. Co-administration of the Polysaccharide of Lycium Barbarum with DNA Vaccine of Chlamydophila abortus Augments Protection. *Immunol Invest.* 2011;40(1):1-13.

[152] Gan L, Wang J, Zhang S. [Inhibition the growth of human leukemia cells by Lycium barbarum polysaccharide]. *Wei Sheng Yan Jiu.* 2001 Nov;30(6):333-5.

[153] Zhang M, Chen H, Huang J, Li Z, Zhu C, Zhang S. Effect of lycium barbarum polysaccharide on human hepatoma QGY7703 cells: inhibition of proliferation and induction of apoptosis. *Life Sci.* 2005 Mar 18;76(18):2115-24.

[154] Luo Q, Li Z, Yan J, Zhu F, Xu RJ, Cai YZ. Lycium barbarum polysaccharides induce apoptosis in human prostate cancer cells and inhibits prostate cancer growth in a xenograft mouse model of human prostate cancer. *J Med Food.* 2009 Aug;12(4):695-703.

[155] Miao Y, Xiao B, Jiang Z, Guo Y, Mao F, Zhao J, et al. Growth inhibition and cell-cycle arrest of human gastric cancer cells by Lycium barbarum polysaccharide. *Med Oncol.* 2010 Sep;27(3):785-90.

[156] Deng HB, Cui DP, Jiang JM, Feng YC, Cai NS, Li DD. Inhibiting effects of Achyranthes bidentata polysaccharide and Lycium barbarum polysaccharide on nonenzyme glycation in D-galactose induced mouse aging model. *Biomed Environ Sci.* 2003 Sep;16(3):267-75.

[157] Yu MS, Leung SK, Lai SW, Che CM, Zee SY, So KF, et al. Neuroprotective effects of anti-aging oriental medicine Lycium barbarum against beta-amyloid peptide neurotoxicity. *Exp Gerontol.* 2005 Aug-Sep;40(8-9):716-27.

[158] Yu MS, Ho YS, So KF, Yuen WH, Chang RC. Cytoprotective effects of Lycium barbarum against reducing stress on endoplasmic reticulum. *Int J Mol Med.* 2006 Jun;17(6):1157-61.

[159] Li XM. Protective effect of Lycium barbarum polysaccharides on streptozotocin-induced oxidative stress in rats. *Int J Biol Macromol.* 2007 Apr 10;40(5):461-5.

[160] Yu MS, Lai CS, Ho YS, Zee SY, So KF, Yuen WH, et al. Characterization of the effects of anti-aging medicine Fructus lycii on beta-amyloid peptide neurotoxicity. *Int J Mol Med.* 2007 Aug;20(2):261-8.

[161] Chang RC, So KF. Use of anti-aging herbal medicine, Lycium barbarum, against aging-associated diseases. What do we know so far? *Cell Mol Neurobiol.* 2008 Aug;28(5):643-52.

[162] Niu AJ, Wu JM, Yu DH, Wang R. Protective effect of Lycium barbarum polysaccharides on oxidative damage in skeletal muscle of exhaustive exercise rats. *Int J Biol Macromol.* 2008 Jun 1;42(5):447-9.

[163] Amagase H, Sun B, Borek C. Lycium barbarum (goji) juice improves in vivo antioxidant biomarkers in serum of healthy adults. *Nutr Res.* 2009 Jan;29(1):19-25.

[164] Lin CL, Wang CC, Chang SC, Inbaraj BS, Chen BH. Antioxidative activity of polysaccharide fractions isolated from Lycium barbarum Linnaeus. *Int J Biol Macromol.* 2009 Aug 1;45(2):146-51.

[165] Wu HT, He XJ, Hong YK, Ma T, Xu YP, Li HH. Chemical characterization of Lycium barbarum polysaccharides and its inhibition against liver oxidative injury of high-fat mice. *Int J Biol Macromol.* 2010 Jun;46(5):540-3.

[166] Chan HC, Chang RC, Koon-Ching Ip A, Chiu K, Yuen WH, Zee SY, et al. Neuroprotective effects of Lycium barbarum Lynn on protecting retinal ganglion cells in an ocular hypertension model of glaucoma. *Exp Neurol.* 2007 Jan;203(1):269-73.

[167] Ho YS, Yu MS, Lai CS, So KF, Yuen WH, Chang RC. Characterizing the neuroprotective effects of alkaline extract of Lycium barbarum on beta-amyloid peptide neurotoxicity. *Brain Res.* 2007 Jul 16;1158:123-34.

[168] Ho YS, Yu MS, Yik SY, So KF, Yuen WH, Chang RC. Polysaccharides from wolfberry antagonizes glutamate excitotoxicity in rat cortical neurons. *Cell Mol Neurobiol.* 2009 Dec;29(8):1233-44.

[169] Chiu K, Zhou Y, Yeung SC, Lok CK, Chan OO, Chang RC, et al. Up-regulation of crystallins is involved in the neuroprotective effect of wolfberry on survival of retinal ganglion cells in rat ocular hypertension model. *J Cell Biochem.* 2010 May 15;110(2):311-20.

[170] Ho YS, Yu MS, Yang XF, So KF, Yuen WH, Chang RC. Neuroprotective effects of polysaccharides from wolfberry, the fruits of Lycium barbarum, against homocysteine-induced toxicity in rat cortical neurons. *J Alzheimers Dis.* 2010;19(3):813-27.

[171] Wen J, Yang BN, Ren D. [Effect of Lycium barbarum polysaccharides on neurogenesis and learning & memory in manganese poisoning mice]. *Zhongguo Zhong Xi Yi Jie He Za Zhi.* 2010 Mar;30(3):295-8.

[172] Huang LJ, Tian GY, Wang ZF, Dong JB, Wu MP. [Studies on the glycoconjugates and glycans from Lycium barbarum L in inhibiting low density lipoprotein (LDL) peroxidation]. *Yao Xue Xue Bao.* 2001 Feb;36(2):108-11.

[173] Luo Q, Cai Y, Yan J, Sun M, Corke H. Hypoglycemic and hypolipidemic effects and antioxidant activity of fruit extracts from Lycium barbarum. *Life Sci.* 2004 Nov 26;76(2):137-49.

[174] Zhao R, Li Q, Xiao B. Effect of Lycium barbarum polysaccharide on the improvement of insulin resistance in NIDDM rats. *Yakugaku Zasshi.* 2005 Dec;125(12):981-8.

[175] Gu S, Wang PL, Jiang R. [A study on the preventive effect of Lycium barbarum polysaccharide on the development of alcoholic fatty liver in rats and its possible mechanisms]. *Zhonghua Gan Zang Bing Za Zhi.* 2007 Mar;15(3):204-8.

[176] Wu H, Guo H, Zhao R. Effect of Lycium barbarum polysaccharide on the improvement of antioxidant ability and DNA damage in NIDDM rats. *Yakugaku Zasshi.* 2006 May;126(5):365-71.

[177] Jing L, Cui G, Feng Q, Xiao Y. Evaluation of hypoglycemic activity of the polysaccharides extracted from Lycium barbarum. *Afr J Tradit Complement Altern Med.* 2009;6(4):579-84.

[178] Zhao R, Li QW, Li J, Zhang T. Protective effect of Lycium barbarum polysaccharide 4 on kidneys in streptozotocin-induced diabetic rats. *Can J Physiol Pharmacol.* 2009 Sep;87(9):711-9.

[179] Lu SP, Zhao PT. Chemical characterization of Lycium barbarum polysaccharides and their reducing myocardial injury in ischemia/reperfusion of rat heart. *Int J Biol Macromol.* 2010 Dec 1;47(5):681-4.

[180] Amagase H, Nance DM. A randomized, double-blind, placebo-controlled, clinical study of the general effects of a standardized Lycium barbarum (Goji) Juice, GoChi. *J Altern Complement Med.* 2008 May;14(4):403-12.

[181] Amagase H, Sun B, Nance DM. Immunomodulatory effects of a standardized Lycium barbarum fruit juice in Chinese older healthy human subjects. *J Med Food.* 2009 Oct;12(5):1159-65.

[182] Liu Z, Saarinen NM, Thompson LU. Sesamin is one of the major precursors of mammalian lignans in sesame seed (Sesamum indicum) as observed in vitro and in rats. *J Nutr.* 2006 Apr;136(4):906-12.

[183] Moazzami AA, Andersson RE, Kamal-Eldin A. HPLC analysis of sesaminol glucosides in sesame seeds. *J Agric Food Chem.* 2006 Feb 8;54(3):633-8.

[184] Kim KS, Park SH. Anthrasesamone F from the seeds of black Sesamum indicum. *Biosci Biotechnol Biochem.* 2008 Jun;72(6):1626-7.

[185] Suja KP, Jayalekshmy A, Arumughan C. Free radical scavenging behavior of antioxidant compounds of sesame (sesamum indicum L.) in DPPH(*) system. *J Agric Food Chem.* 2004 Feb 25;52(4):912-5.

[186] Joshi R, Kumar MS, Satyamoorthy K, Unnikrisnan MK, Mukherjee T. Free radical reactions and antioxidant activities of sesamol: pulse radiolytic and biochemical studies. *J Agric Food Chem.* 2005 Apr 6;53(7):2696-703.

[187] Nahar L, Rokonuzzaman. Investigation of the analgesic and antioxidant activity from an ethanol extract of seeds of Sesamum indicum. *Pak J Biol Sci.* 2009 Apr 1;12(7):595-8.

[188] Visavadiya NP, Soni B, Dalwadi N. Free radical scavenging and antiatherogenic activities of Sesamum indicum seed extracts in chemical and biological model systems. *Food Chem Toxicol.* 2009 Oct;47(10):2507-15.

[189] Hu Q, Xu J, Chen S, Yang F. Antioxidant activity of extracts of black sesame seed (Sesamum indicum L.) by supercritical carbon dioxide extraction. *J Agric Food Chem.* 2004 Feb 25;52(4):943-7.

[190] Kumar P, Kalonia H, Kumar A. Sesamol attenuate 3-nitropropionic acid-induced Huntington-like behavioral, biochemical, and cellular alterations in rats. *J Asian Nat Prod Res.* 2009;11(5):439-50.

[191] Um MY, Ahn JY, Kim S, Kim MK, Ha TY. Sesaminol glucosides protect beta-amyloid peptide-induced cognitive deficits in mice. *Biol Pharm Bull.* 2009 Sep;32(9):1516-20.

[192] Jamarkattel-Pandit N, Pandit NR, Kim MY, Park SH, Kim KS, Choi H, et al. Neuroprotective effect of defatted sesame seeds extract against in vitro and in vivo ischemic neuronal damage. *Planta Med.* 2010 Jan;76(1):20-6.

[193] Kumar P, Kalonia H, Kumar A. Protective effect of sesamol against 3-nitropropionic acid-induced cognitive dysfunction and altered glutathione redox balance in rats. *Basic Clin Pharmacol Toxicol.* 2010 Jul;107(1):577-82.

[194] Sirato-Yasumoto S, Katsuta M, Okuyama Y, Takahashi Y, Ide T. Effect of sesame seeds rich in sesamin and sesamolin on fatty acid oxidation in rat liver. *J Agric Food Chem.* 2001 May;49(5):2647-51.

[195] Takeuchi H, Mooi LY, Inagaki Y, He P. Hypoglycemic effect of a hot-water extract from defatted sesame (Sesamum indicum L.) seed on the blood glucose level in genetically diabetic KK-Ay mice. *Biosci Biotechnol Biochem.* 2001 Oct;65(10):2318-21.

[196] Visavadiya NP, Narasimhacharya AV. Sesame as a hypocholesteraemic and antioxidant dietary component. *Food Chem Toxicol.* 2008 Jun;46(6):1889-95.

[197] Xu H, Yang X, Yang J, Qi W, Liu C, Yang Y. [Antitumor effect of alcohol extract from Sesamum indicum flower on S180 and H22 experimental tumor]. *Zhong Yao Cai.* 2003 Apr;26(4):272-3.

[198] Harikumar KB, Sung B, Tharakan ST, Pandey MK, Joy B, Guha S, et al. Sesamin manifests chemopreventive effects through the suppression of NF-kappa B-regulated cell survival, proliferation, invasion, and angiogenic gene products. *Mol Cancer Res.* 2010 May;8(5):751-61.

[199] Ashamu E, Salawu E, Oyewo O, Alhassan A, Alamu O, Adegoke A. Efficacy of vitamin C and ethanolic extract of Sesamum indicum in promoting fertility in male Wistar rats. *J Hum Reprod Sci.* 2010 Jan;3(1):11-4.

[200] Jan KC, Ku KL, Chu YH, Hwang LS, Ho CT. Tissue distribution and elimination of estrogenic and anti-inflammatory catechol metabolites from sesaminol triglucoside in rats. *J Agric Food Chem.* 2010 Jul 14;58(13):7693-700.

[201] Cui T, Li JZ, Kayahara H, Ma L, Wu LX, Nakamura K. Quantification of the polyphenols and triterpene acids in chinese hawthorn fruit by high-performance liquid chromatography. *J Agric Food Chem.* 2006 Jun 28;54(13):4574-81.

[202] Chu CY, Lee MJ, Liao CL, Lin WL, Yin YF, Tseng TH. Inhibitory effect of hot-water extract from dried fruit of Crataegus pinnatifida on low-density lipoprotein (LDL) oxidation in cell and cell-free systems. *J Agric Food Chem.* 2003 Dec 17;51(26):7583-8.

[203] Kao ES, Wang CJ, Lin WL, Yin YF, Wang CP, Tseng TH. Anti-inflammatory potential of flavonoid contents from dried fruit of Crataegus pinnatifida in vitro and in vivo. *J Agric Food Chem.* 2005 Jan 26;53(2):430-6.

[204] Kao ES, Wang CJ, Lin WL, Chu CY, Tseng TH. Effects of polyphenols derived from fruit of Crataegus pinnatifida on cell transformation, dermal edema and skin tumor formation by phorbol ester application. *Food Chem Toxicol.* 2007 Oct;45(10):1795-804.

[205] Li HB, Fang KY, Lu CT, Li XE. [Study on lipid-regulating function for the extracts and their prescriptions from Semen Cassiae and fructus crataegi]. *Zhong Yao Cai.* 2007 May;30(5):573-5.

[206] Kuo DH, Yeh CH, Shieh PC, Cheng KC, Chen FA, Cheng JT. Effect of shanzha, a Chinese herbal product, on obesity and dyslipidemia in hamsters receiving high-fat diet. *J Ethnopharmacol.* 2009 Jul 30;124(3):544-50.

[207] Ye XL, Huang WW, Chen Z, Li XG, Li P, Lan P, et al. Synergetic effect and structure-activity relationship of 3-hydroxy-3-methylglutaryl coenzyme A reductase inhibitors from Crataegus pinnatifida Bge. *J Agric Food Chem.* 2010 Mar 10;58(5):3132-8.

[208] Min BS, Huong HT, Kim JH, Jun HJ, Na MK, Nam NH, et al. Furo-1,2-naphthoquinones from Crataegus pinnatifida with ICAM-1 expression inhibition activity. *Planta Med.* 2004 Dec;70(12):1166-9.

[209] Ling JH, Wang, J. H., Wang, N., Li, W., Sha, Y., Li, X. Studies on the chemical constituents of Malt. *Journal of Shenyang Pharmaceutical* University. 2005;22(4):267-70.

[210] Ling JH, Wang, N., Ren, Y. Z., Wang, L. H., Wang, J. H., Li, X. Determination of tricin in malt by HPLC. *Chinese Traditional and Herbal Drugs.* 2005;36(11):1632-4.

[211] Liu YT, Hu, Z. F., Zheng, H. B., Cheng, D. Q., Pan, P. L., Zhou, F. M. Effects of fiber extracted from germinated barley on intestinal microflora of rats with UC. *Zhejiang Journal of Integrated Traditional Chinese and Western Medicine.* 2008;18(8):471-2.

[212] Kanauchi O, Mitsuyama K, Andoh A, Iwanaga T. Modulation of intestinal environment by prebiotic germinated barley foodstuff prevents chemo-induced colonic carcinogenesis in rats. *Oncol Rep.* 2008 Oct;20(4):793-801.

[213] Kanauchi O, Oshima T, Andoh A, Shioya M, Mitsuyama K. Germinated barley foodstuff ameliorates inflammation in mice with colitis through modulation of mucosal immune system. *Scand J Gastroenterol.* 2008;43(11):1346-52.

[214] Kanauchi O, Mitsuyama K, Homma T, Takahama K, Fujiyama Y, Andoh A, et al. Treatment of ulcerative colitis patients by long-term administration of germinated barley foodstuff: multi-center open trial. *Int J Mol Med.* 2003 Nov;12(5):701-4.

[215] Fukuda M, Kanauchi O, Araki Y, Andoh A, Mitsuyama K, Takagi K, et al. Prebiotic treatment of experimental colitis with germinated barley foodstuff: a comparison with probiotic or antibiotic treatment. *Int J Mol Med.* 2002 Jan;9(1):65-70.

[216] Kanauchi O, Iwanaga T, Andoh A, Araki Y, Nakamura T, Mitsuyama K, et al. Dietary fiber fraction of germinated barley foodstuff attenuated mucosal damage and diarrhea, and accelerated the repair of the colonic mucosa in an experimental colitis. *J Gastroenterol Hepatol.* 2001 Feb;16(2):160-8.

[217] Kanauchi O, Iwanaga T, Mitsuyama K. Germinated barley foodstuff feeding. A novel neutraceutical therapeutic strategy for ulcerative colitis. *Digestion.* 2001;63 Suppl 1:60-7.

[218] Araki Y, Andoh A, Fujiyama Y, Kanauchi O, Takenaka K, Higuchi A, et al. Germinated barley foodstuff exhibits different adsorption properties for hydrophilic versus hydrophobic bile acids. *Digestion.* 2001;64(4):248-54.

[219] Kanauchi O, Araki Y, Andoh A, Iwanaga T, Maeda N, Mitsuyama K, et al. Effect of germinated barley foodstuff administration on mineral utilization in rodents. *J Gastroenterol.* 2000;35(3):188-94.

[220] Araki Y, Andoh A, Koyama S, Fujiyama Y, Kanauchi O, Bamba T. Effects of germinated barley foodstuff on microflora and short chain fatty acid production in dextran sulfate sodium-induced colitis in rats. *Biosci Biotechnol Biochem.* 2000 Sep;64(9):1794-800.

[221] Kanauchi O, Fujiyama Y, Mitsuyama K, Araki Y, Ishii T, Nakamura T, et al. Increased growth of Bifidobacterium and Eubacterium by germinated barley foodstuff, accompanied by enhanced butyrate production in healthy volunteers. *Int J Mol Med.* 1999 Feb;3(2):175-9.

[222] Kanauchi O, Iwanaga T, Mitsuyama K, Saiki T, Tsuruta O, Noguchi K, et al. Butyrate from bacterial fermentation of germinated barley foodstuff preserves intestinal barrier function in experimental colitis in the rat model. *J Gastroenterol Hepatol.* 1999 Sep;14(9):880-8.

[223] Kanauchi O, Hitomi Y, Agata K, Nakamura T, Fushiki T. Germinated barley foodstuff improves constipation induced by loperamide in rats. *Biosci Biotechnol Biochem.* 1998 Sep;62(9):1788-90.

[224] Kanauchi O, Mitsuyama K, Saiki T, Agata K, Nakamura T, Iwanaga T. Preventive effects of germinated barley foodstuff on methotrexate-induced enteritis in rats. *Int J Mol Med.* 1998 Jun;1(6):961-6.

[225] Kanauchi O, Mitsuyama K, Saiki T, Fushikia T, Iwanaga T. Germinated barley foodstuff increases fecal volume and butyrate production in humans. *Int J Mol Med.* 1998 Jun;1(6):937-41.

[226] Kanauchi O, Mitsuyama K, Saiki T, Nakamura T, Hitomi Y, Bamba T, et al. Germinated barley foodstuff increases fecal volume and butyrate production at relatively low doses and relieves constipation in humans. *Int J Mol Med.* 1998 Oct;2(4):445-50.

[227] Kanauchi O, Nakamura T, Agata K, Fushiki T, Hara H. Effects of germinated barley foodstuff in preventing diarrhea and forming normal feces in ceco-colectomized rats. *Biosci Biotechnol Biochem.* 1998 Feb;62(2):366-8.

[228] Kanauchi O, Nakamura T, Agata K, Mitsuyama K, Iwanaga T. Effects of germinated barley foodstuff on dextran sulfate sodium-induced colitis in rats. *J Gastroenterol.* 1998 Apr;33(2):179-88.

[229] Mitsuyama K, Saiki T, Kanauchi O, Iwanaga T, Tomiyasu N, Nishiyama T, et al. Treatment of ulcerative colitis with germinated barley foodstuff feeding: a pilot study. *Aliment Pharmacol Ther.* 1998 Dec;12(12):1225-30.

[230] Bamba T, Kanauchi O, Andoh A, Fujiyama Y. A new prebiotic from germinated barley for nutraceutical treatment of ulcerative colitis. *J Gastroenterol Hepatol.* 2002 Aug;17(8):818-24.

[231] Kanauchi O, Suga T, Tochihara M, Hibi T, Naganuma M, Homma T, et al. Treatment of ulcerative colitis by feeding with germinated barley foodstuff: first report of a multicenter open control trial. *J Gastroenterol.* 2002 Nov;37 Suppl 14:67-72.

[232] Hanai H, Kanauchi O, Mitsuyama K, Andoh A, Takeuchi K, Takayuki I, et al. Germinated barley foodstuff prolongs remission in patients with ulcerative colitis. *Int J Mol Med.* 2004 May;13(5):643-7.

[233] Zhou W, Zhang, E. J., Gao, T. X. Studies on the effects of malt extract for experimental hyperpro-lactinemia Hubei *Journal of Traditional Chinese Medicine.* 2008;30(10):10-1.

[234] Peng LY, Mei SX, Jiang B, Zhou H, Sun HD. Constituents from Lonicera japonica. *Fitoterapia.* 2000 Dec;71(6):713-5.

[235] Leung HW, Wu CH, Lin CH, Lee HZ. Luteolin induced DNA damage leading to human lung squamous carcinoma CH27 cell apoptosis. *Eur J Pharmacol.* 2005 Jan 31;508(1-3):77-83.

[236] Leung HW, Kuo CL, Yang WH, Lin CH, Lee HZ. Antioxidant enzymes activity involvement in luteolin-induced human lung squamous carcinoma CH27 cell apoptosis. *Eur J Pharmacol.* 2006 Mar 18;534(1-3):12-8.

[237] Son MJ, Moon TC, Lee EK, Son KH, Kim HP, Kang SS, et al. Naturally occurring biflavonoid, ochnaflavone, inhibits cyclooxygenases-2 and 5-lipoxygenase in mouse bone marrow-derived mast cells. *Arch Pharm Res.* 2006 Apr;29(4):282-6.

[238] Suh SJ, Chung TW, Son MJ, Kim SH, Moon TC, Son KH, et al. The naturally occurring biflavonoid, ochnaflavone, inhibits LPS-induced iNOS expression, which is mediated by ERK1/2 via NF-kappaB regulation, in RAW264.7 cells. *Arch Biochem Biophys.* 2006 Mar 15;447(2):136-46.

[239] Lin LM, Zhang XG, Zhu JJ, Gao HM, Wang ZM, Wang WH. Two new triterpenoid saponins from the flowers and buds of Lonicera japonica. *J Asian Nat Prod Res.* 2008 Oct;10(10):925-9.

[240] Song W, Li S, Wang S, Wu Y, Zi J, Gan M, et al. Pyridinium alkaloid-coupled secoiridoids from the flower buds of Lonicera japonica. *J Nat Prod.* 2008 May;71(5):922-5.

[241] Kakuda R, Imai M, Yaoita Y, Machida K, Kikuchi M. Secoiridoid glycosides from the flower buds of Lonicera japonica. *Phytochemistry*. 2000 Dec;55(8):879-81.

[242] Yip EC, Chan AS, Pang H, Tam YK, Wong YH. Protocatechuic acid induces cell death in HepG2 hepatocellular carcinoma cells through a c-Jun N-terminal kinase-dependent mechanism. *Cell Biol Toxicol*. 2006 Jul;22(4):293-302.

[243] Chen CY, Peng WH, Wu LC, Wu CC, Hsu SL. Luteolin ameliorates experimental lung fibrosis both in vivo and in vitro: implications for therapy of lung fibrosis. *J Agric Food Chem*. 2010 Nov 24;58(22):11653-61.

[244] Kang OH, Choi JG, Lee JH, Kwon DY. Luteolin isolated from the flowers of Lonicera japonica suppresses inflammatory mediator release by blocking NF-kappaB and MAPKs activation pathways in HMC-1 cells. *Molecules*. 2010 Jan;15(1):385-98.

[245] Lee JP, Li YC, Chen HY, Lin RH, Huang SS, Chen HL, et al. Protective effects of luteolin against lipopolysaccharide-induced acute lung injury involves inhibition of MEK/ERK and PI3K/Akt pathways in neutrophils. *Acta Pharmacol Sin*. 2010 Jul;31(7):831-8.

[246] Jeong JJ, Ha YM, Jin YC, Lee EJ, Kim JS, Kim HJ, et al. Rutin from Lonicera japonica inhibits myocardial ischemia/reperfusion-induced apoptosis in vivo and protects H9c2 cells against hydrogen peroxide-mediated injury via ERK1/2 and PI3K/Akt signals in vitro. *Food Chem Toxicol*. 2009 Jul;47(7):1569-76.

[247] Lee JH, Ko WS, Kim YH, Kang HS, Kim HD, Choi BT. Anti-inflammatory effect of the aqueous extract from Lonicera japonica flower is related to inhibition of NF-kappaB activation through reducing I-kappaBalpha degradation in rat liver. *Int J Mol Med*. 2001 Jan;7(1):79-83.

[248] Tae J, Han SW, Yoo JY, Kim JA, Kang OH, Baek OS, et al. Anti-inflammatory effect of Lonicera japonica in proteinase-activated receptor 2-mediated paw edema. *Clin Chim Acta*. 2003 Apr;330(1-2):165-71.

[249] Kang OH, Choi YA, Park HJ, Lee JY, Kim DK, Choi SC, et al. Inhibition of trypsin-induced mast cell activation by water fraction of Lonicera japonica. Arch Pharm Res. 2004 Nov;27(11):1141-6.

[250] Choi CW, Jung HA, Kang SS, Choi JS. Antioxidant constituents and a new triterpenoid glycoside from Flos Lonicerae. *Arch Pharm Res*. 2007 Jan;30(1):1-7.

[251] Xu Y, Oliverson BG, Simmons DL. Trifunctional inhibition of COX-2 by extracts of Lonicera japonica: direct inhibition, transcriptional and post-transcriptional down regulation. *J Ethnopharmacol*. 2007 May 22;111(3):667-70.

[252] Leung HW, Hour MJ, Chang WT, Wu YC, Lai MY, Wang MY, et al. P38-associated pathway involvement in apoptosis induced by photodynamic therapy with Lonicera japonica in human lung squamous carcinoma CH27 cells. *Food Chem Toxicol*. 2008 Nov;46(11):3389-400.

[253] Yoo HJ, Kang HJ, Song YS, Park EH, Lim CJ. Anti-angiogenic, antinociceptive and anti-inflammatory activities of Lonicera japonica extract. *J Pharm Pharmacol*. 2008 Jun;60(6):779-86.

[254] Fang XL, Wang XT, Huang SR, Li X. [Effect of Chrysanthemum morifolium Ramat on apoptosis of bovine aortic smooth muscle cells]. *Zhejiang Da Xue Xue Bao Yi Xue Ban*. 2002 Aug;31(5):347-50.

[255] Jiang H, Xia Q, Xu W, Zheng M. Chrysanthemum morifolium attenuated the reduction of contraction of isolated rat heart and cardiomyocytes induced by ischemia/reperfusion. *Pharmazie*. 2004 Jul;59(7):565-7.

[256] Lii CK, Lei YP, Yao HT, Hsieh YS, Tsai CW, Liu KL, et al. Chrysanthemum morifolium Ramat. reduces the oxidized LDL-induced expression of intercellular adhesion molecule-1 and E-selectin in human umbilical vein endothelial cells. *J Ethnopharmacol*. 2010 Mar 2;128(1):213-20.

[257] Lin GH, Lin L, Liang HW, Ma X, Wang JY, Wu LP, et al. Antioxidant action of a Chrysanthemum morifolium extract protects rat brain against ischemia and reperfusion injury. *J Med Food*. 2010 Apr;13(2):306-11.

[258] Kim IS, Koppula S, Park PJ, Kim EH, Kim CG, Choi WS, et al. Chrysanthemum morifolium Ramat (CM) extract protects human neuroblastoma SH-SY5Y cells against MPP+-induced cytotoxicity. *J Ethnopharmacol*. 2009 Dec 10;126(3):447-54.

[259] Ukiya M, Akihisa T, Yasukawa K, Kasahara Y, Kimura Y, Koike K, et al. Constituents of compositae plants. 2. Triterpene diols, triols, and their 3-o-fatty acid esters from edible chrysanthemum flower extract and their anti-inflammatory effects. *J Agric Food Chem*. 2001 Jul;49(7):3187-97.

[260] Ukiya M, Akihisa T, Tokuda H, Suzuki H, Mukainaka T, Ichiishi E, et al. Constituents of Compositae plants III. Anti-tumor promoting effects and cytotoxic activity against human cancer cell lines of triterpene diols and triols from edible chrysanthemum flowers. *Cancer Lett*. 2002 Mar 8;177(1):7-12.

[261] Xie YY, Yuan D, Yang JY, Wang LH, Wu CF. Cytotoxic activity of flavonoids from the flowers of Chrysanthemum morifolium on human colon cancer Colon205 cells. *J Asian Nat Prod Res*. 2009 Sep;11(9):771-8.

[262] Lee JS, Kim HJ, Lee YS. A new anti-HIV flavonoid glucuronide from Chrysanthemum morifolium. *Planta Med*. 2003 Sep;69(9):859-61.

[263] Miyazawa M, Hisama M. Antimutagenic activity of flavonoids from Chrysanthemum morifolium. *Biosci Biotechnol Biochem*. 2003 Oct;67(10):2091-9.

[264] Chen T, Li LP, Lu XY, Jiang HD, Zeng S. Absorption and excretion of luteolin and apigenin in rats after oral administration of Chrysanthemum morifolium extract. *J Agric Food Chem*. 2007 Jan 24;55(2):273-7.

[265] Kim HJ, Lee YS. Identification of new dicaffeoylquinic acids from Chrysanthemum morifolium and their antioxidant activities. *Planta Med*. 2005 Sep;71(9):871-6.

[266] Li L, Gu L, Chen Z, Wang R, Ye J, Jiang H. Toxicity study of ethanolic extract of Chrysanthemum morifolium in rats. *J Food Sci*. 2010 Aug 1;75(6):T105-9.

[267] Chen W, An W, Chu J. [Effect of water extract of Poria on cytosolic free calcium concentration in brain nerve cells of neonatal rats]. *Zhongguo Zhong Xi Yi Jie He Za Zhi*. 1998 May;18(5):293-5.

[268] Jin Y, Zhang L, Zhang M, Chen L, Cheung PC, Oi VE, et al. Antitumor activities of heteropolysaccharides of Poria cocos mycelia from different strains and culture media. *Carbohydr Res*. 2003 Jul 4;338(14):1517-21.

[269] Lee KY, Jeon YJ. Polysaccharide isolated from Poria cocos sclerotium induces NF-kappaB/Rel activation and iNOS expression in murine macrophages. *Int Immunopharmacol*. 2003 Oct;3(10-11):1353-62.

[270] Chen YY, Chang HM. Antiproliferative and differentiating effects of polysaccharide fraction from fu-ling (Poria cocos) on human leukemic U937 and HL-60 cells. *Food Chem Toxicol.* 2004 May;42(5):759-69.

[271] Lee KY, You HJ, Jeong HG, Kang JS, Kim HM, Rhee SD, et al. Polysaccharide isolated from Poria cocos sclerotium induces NF-kappaB/Rel activation and iNOS expression through the activation of p38 kinase in murine macrophages. *Int Immunopharmacol.* 2004 Aug;4(8):1029-38.

[272] Lin Y, Zhang L, Chen L, Jin Y, Zeng F, Jin J, et al. Molecular mass and antitumor activities of sulfated derivatives of alpha-glucan from Poria cocos mycelia. *Int J Biol Macromol.* 2004 Oct;34(5):289-94.

[273] Wang Y, Zhang L, Li Y, Hou X, Zeng F. Correlation of structure to antitumor activities of five derivatives of a beta-glucan from Poria cocos sclerotium. *Carbohydr Res.* 2004 Oct 20;339(15):2567-74.

[274] Zhang L, Chen L, Xu X, Zeng F, Cheung PC. Effect of molecular mass on antitumor activity of heteropolysaccharide from Poria cocos. *Biosci Biotechnol Biochem.* 2005 Mar;69(3):631-4.

[275] Zhang M, Chiu LC, Cheung PC, Ooi VE. Growth-inhibitory effects of a beta-glucan from the mycelium of Poria cocos on human breast carcinoma MCF-7 cells: cell-cycle arrest and apoptosis induction. *Oncol Rep.* 2006 Mar;15(3):637-43.

[276] Chang HH, Yeh CH, Sheu F. A novel immunomodulatory protein from Poria cocos induces Toll-like receptor 4-dependent activation within mouse peritoneal macrophages. *J Agric Food Chem.* 2009 Jul 22;57(14):6129-39.

[277] Yasukawa K, Kaminaga T, Kitanaka S, Tai T, Nunoura Y, Natori S, et al. 3 beta-p-hydroxybenzoyldehydrotumulosic acid from Poria cocos, and its anti-inflammatory effect. *Phytochemistry.* 1998 Aug;48(8):1357-60.

[278] Ukiya M, Akihisa T, Tokuda H, Hirano M, Oshikubo M, Nobukuni Y, et al. Inhibition of tumor-promoting effects by poricoic acids G and H and other lanostane-type triterpenes and cytotoxic activity of poricoic acids A and G from Poria cocos. *J Nat Prod.* 2002 Apr;65(4):462-5.

[279] Akihisa T, Mizushina Y, Ukiya M, Oshikubo M, Kondo S, Kimura Y, et al. Dehydrotrametenonic acid and dehydroeburiconic acid from Poria cocos and their inhibitory effects on eukaryotic DNA polymerase alpha and beta. *Biosci Biotechnol Biochem.* 2004 Feb;68(2):448-50.

[280] Li G, Xu ML, Lee CS, Woo MH, Chang HW, Son JK. Cytotoxicity and DNA topoisomerases inhibitory activity of constituents from the sclerotium of Poria cocos. *Arch Pharm Res.* 2004 Aug;27(8):829-33.

[281] Mizushina Y, Akihisa T, Ukiya M, Murakami C, Kuriyama I, Xu X, et al. A novel DNA topoisomerase inhibitor: dehydroebriconic acid, one of the lanostane-type triterpene acids from Poria cocos. *Cancer Sci.* 2004 Apr;95(4):354-60.

[282] Gapter L, Wang Z, Glinski J, Ng KY. Induction of apoptosis in prostate cancer cells by pachymic acid from Poria cocos. *Biochem Biophys Res Commun.* 2005 Jul 15;332(4):1153-61.

[283] Fuchs SM, Heinemann C, Schliemann-Willers S, Hartl H, Fluhr JW, Elsner P. Assessment of anti-inflammatory activity of Poria cocos in sodium lauryl sulphate-induced irritant contact dermatitis. *Skin Res Technol.* 2006 Nov;12(4):223-7.

[284] Akihisa T, Nakamura Y, Tokuda H, Uchiyama E, Suzuki T, Kimura Y, et al. Triterpene acids from Poria cocos and their anti-tumor-promoting effects. *J Nat Prod.* 2007 Jun;70(6):948-53.

[285] Ling H, Zhou L, Jia X, Gapter LA, Agarwal R, Ng KY. Polyporenic acid C induces caspase-8-mediated apoptosis in human lung cancer A549 cells. *Mol Carcinog.* 2008 Oct 30.

[286] Zhou L, Zhang Y, Gapter LA, Ling H, Agarwal R, Ng KY. Cytotoxic and anti-oxidant activities of lanostane-type triterpenes isolated from Poria cocos. *Chem Pharm Bull* (Tokyo). 2008 Oct;56(10):1459-62.

[287] Akihisa T, Uchiyama E, Kikuchi T, Tokuda H, Suzuki T, Kimura Y. Anti-tumor-promoting effects of 25-methoxyporicoic acid A and other triterpene acids from Poria cocos. *J Nat Prod.* 2009 Oct;72(10):1786-92.

[288] Ling H, Zhou L, Jia X, Gapter LA, Agarwal R, Ng KY. Polyporenic acid C induces caspase-8-mediated apoptosis in human lung cancer A549 cells. *Mol Carcinog.* 2009 Jun;48(6):498-507.

[289] Sato M, Tai T, Nunoura Y, Yajima Y, Kawashima S, Tanaka K. Dehydrotrametenolic acid induces preadipocyte differentiation and sensitizes animal models of noninsulin-dependent diabetes mellitus to insulin. *Biol Pharm Bull.* 2002 Jan;25(1):81-6.

[290] Huang YC, Chang WL, Huang SF, Lin CY, Lin HC, Chang TC. Pachymic acid stimulates glucose uptake through enhanced GLUT4 expression and translocation. *Eur J Pharmacol.* 2010 Dec 1;648(1-3):39-49.

[291] Park YH, Son IH, Kim B, Lyu YS, Moon HI, Kang HW. Poria cocos water extract (PCW) protects PC12 neuronal cells from beta-amyloid-induced cell death through antioxidant and antiapoptotic functions. *Pharmazie.* 2009 Nov;64(11):760-4.

[292] Sohn DH, Kim YC, Oh SH, Park EJ, Li X, Lee BH. Hepatoprotective and free radical scavenging effects of Nelumbo nucifera. *Phytomedicine.* 2003 Mar;10(2-3):165-9.

[293] Ling ZQ, Xie BJ, Yang EL. Isolation, characterization, and determination of antioxidative activity of oligomeric procyanidins from the seedpod of Nelumbo nucifera Gaertn. *J Agric Food Chem.* 2005 Apr 6;53(7):2441-5.

[294] Rai S, Wahile A, Mukherjee K, Saha BP, Mukherjee PK. Antioxidant activity of Nelumbo nucifera (sacred lotus) seeds. *J Ethnopharmacol.* 2006 Apr 6;104(3):322-7.

[295] Xiao JH, Zhang JH, Chen HL, Feng XL, Wang JL. Inhibitory effects of isoliensinine on bleomycin-induced pulmonary fibrosis in mice. *Planta Med.* 2005 Mar;71(3):225-30.

[296] Xiao JH, Zhang YL, Feng XL, Wang JL, Qian JQ. Effects of isoliensinine on angiotensin II-induced proliferation of porcine coronary arterial smooth muscle cells. *J Asian Nat Prod Res.* 2006 Apr-May;8(3):209-16.

[297] Chen J, Liu JH, Wang T, Xiao HJ, Yin CP, Yang J. Effects of plant extract neferine on cyclic adenosine monophosphate and cyclic guanosine monophosphate levels in rabbit corpus cavernosum in vitro. *Asian J Androl.* 2008 Mar;10(2):307-12.

[298] Sugimoto Y, Furutani S, Itoh A, Tanahashi T, Nakajima H, Oshiro H, et al. Effects of extracts and neferine from the embryo of Nelumbo nucifera seeds on the central nervous system. *Phytomedicine.* 2008 Nov 14.

[299] Pan Y, Cai B, Wang K, Wang S, Zhou S, Yu X, et al. Neferine enhances insulin sensitivity in insulin resistant rats. *J Ethnopharmacol.* 2009 Jul 6;124(1):98-102.

[300] Jung HA, Jin SE, Choi RJ, Kim DH, Kim YS, Ryu JH, et al. Anti-amnesic activity of neferine with antioxidant and anti-inflammatory capacities, as well as inhibition of ChEs and BACE1. *Life Sci.* 2010 Sep 25;87(13-14):420-30.

[301] Sugimoto Y, Furutani S, Nishimura K, Itoh A, Tanahashi T, Nakajima H, et al. Antidepressant-like effects of neferine in the forced swimming test involve the serotonin1A (5-HT1A) receptor in mice. *Eur J Pharmacol.* 2010 May 25;634(1-3):62-7.

[302] Jung HA, Jung YJ, Hyun SK, Min BS, Kim DW, Jung JH, et al. Selective cholinesterase inhibitory activities of a new monoterpene diglycoside and other constituents from Nelumbo nucifera stamens. *Biol Pharm Bull.* 2010 Feb;33(2):267-72.

[303] Oh JH, Choi BJ, Chang MS, Park SK. Nelumbo nucifera semen extract improves memory in rats with scopolamine-induced amnesia through the induction of choline acetyltransferase expression. *Neurosci Lett.* 2009 Sep 11;461(1):41-4.

[304] Liu CP, Tsai WJ, Shen CC, Lin YL, Liao JF, Chen CF, et al. Inhibition of (S)-armepavine from Nelumbo nucifera on autoimmune disease of MRL/MpJ-lpr/lpr mice. *Eur J Pharmacol.* 2006 Feb 15;531(1-3):270-9.

[305] Liu CP, Kuo YC, Shen CC, Wu MH, Liao JF, Lin YL, et al. (S)-armepavine inhibits human peripheral blood mononuclear cell activation by regulating Itk and PLCgamma activation in a PI-3K-dependent manner. *J Leukoc Biol.* 2007 May;81(5):1276-86.

[306] Ka SM, Kuo YC, Ho PJ, Tsai PY, Hsu YJ, Tsai WJ, et al. (S)-armepavine from Chinese medicine improves experimental autoimmune crescentic glomerulonephritis. *Rheumatology* (Oxford). 2010 Oct;49(10):1840-51.

[307] Mukherjee D, Khatua TN, Venkatesh P, Saha BP, Mukherjee PK. Immunomodulatory potential of rhizome and seed extracts of Nelumbo nucifera Gaertn. *J Ethnopharmacol.* 2010 Mar 24;128(2):490-4.

[308] Kuo YC, Lin YL, Liu CP, Tsai WJ. Herpes simplex virus type 1 propagation in HeLa cells interrupted by Nelumbo nucifera. *J Biomed Sci.* 2005 Dec;12(6):1021-34.

[309] Arao T, Udayama M, Kinjo J, Nohara T. Preventive effects of saponins from the Pueraria lobata root on in vitro immunological liver injury of rat primary hepatocyte cultures. *Planta Med.* 1998 Jun;64(5):413-6.

[310] Oh SR, Kinjo J, Shii Y, Ikeda T, Nohara T, Ahn KS, et al. Effects of triterpenoids from Pueraria lobata on immunohemolysis: beta-D-glucuronic acid plays an active role in anticomplementary activity in vitro. *Planta Med.* 2000 Aug;66(6):506-10.

[311] Jeon GC, Park MS, Yoon DY, Shin CH, Sin HS, Um SJ. Antitumor activity of spinasterol isolated from Pueraria roots. *Exp Mol Med.* 2005 Apr 30;37(2):111-20.

[312] Zheng G, Zhang X, Meng Q, Gong W, Wen X, Xie H. [Protective effect of total isoflavones from Pueraria lobata on secondary osteoporosis induced by dexamethasone in rats]. *Zhong Yao Cai.* 2002 Sep;25(9):643-6.

[313] Zheng G, Zhang X, Zheng J, Gong W, Zheng X, Chen A. [Hypocholesterolemic effect of total isoflavones from Pueraria lobata in ovariectomized rats]. *Zhong Yao Cai.* 2002 Apr;25(4):273-5.

[314] Choi YH, Hong SS, Shin YS, Hwang BY, Park SY, Lee D. Phenolic compounds from Pueraria lobata protect PC12 cells against Abeta-induced toxicity. *Arch Pharm Res.* 2010 Oct;33(10):1651-4.

[315] Hsu HH, Chang CK, Su HC, Liu IM, Cheng JT. Stimulatory effect of puerarin on alpha1A-adrenoceptor to increase glucose uptake into cultured C2C12 cells of mice. *Planta Med*. 2002 Nov;68(11):999-1003.

[316] Hsu FL, Liu IM, Kuo DH, Chen WC, Su HC, Cheng JT. Antihyperglycemic effect of puerarin in streptozotocin-induced diabetic rats. *J Nat Prod*. 2003 Jun;66(6):788-92.

[317] Xu ME, Xiao SZ, Sun YH, Zheng XX, Ou-Yang Y, Guan C. The study of anti-metabolic syndrome effect of puerarin in vitro. *Life Sci*. 2005 Nov 4;77(25):3183-96.

[318] Xiong FL, Sun XH, Gan L, Yang XL, Xu HB. Puerarin protects rat pancreatic islets from damage by hydrogen peroxide. *Eur J Pharmacol*. 2006 Jan 4;529(1-3):1-7.

[319] Yan LP, Chan SW, Chan AS, Chen SL, Ma XJ, Xu HX. Puerarin decreases serum total cholesterol and enhances thoracic aorta endothelial nitric oxide synthase expression in diet-induced hypercholesterolemic rats. *Life Sci*. 2006 Jun 20;79(4):324-30.

[320] Kim JM, Lee YM, Lee GY, Jang DS, Bae KH, Kim JS. Constituents of the roots of Pueraria lobata inhibit formation of advanced glycation end products (AGEs). *Arch Pharm Res*. 2006 Oct;29(10):821-5.

[321] Kim YS, Kim NH, Jung DH, Jang DS, Lee YM, Kim JM, et al. Genistein inhibits aldose reductase activity and high glucose-induced TGF-beta2 expression in human lens epithelial cells. *Eur J Pharmacol*. 2008 Oct 10;594(1-3):18-25.

[322] Lee OH, Seo DH, Park CS, Kim YC. Puerarin enhances adipocyte differentiation, adiponectin expression, and antioxidant response in 3T3-L1 cells. *Biofactors*. 2010 Nov-Dec;36(6):459-67.

[323] 3Rezvani AH, Overstreet DH, Perfumi M, Massi M. Plant derivatives in the treatment of alcohol dependency. *Pharmacol Biochem Behav*. 2003 Jun;75(3):593-606.

[324] Kwon HJ, Hyun SH, Choung SY. Traditional Chinese Medicine improves dysfunction of peroxisome proliferator-activated receptor alpha and microsomal triglyceride transfer protein on abnormalities in lipid metabolism in ethanol-fed rats. *Biofactors*. 2005;23(3):163-76.

[325] Kwon HJ, Kim YY, Choung SY. Amelioration effects of traditional Chinese medicine on alcohol-induced fatty liver. *World J Gastroenterol*. 2005 Sep 21;11(35):5512-6.

[326] Zhang S, Ji G, Liu J. Reversal of chemical-induced liver fibrosis in Wistar rats by puerarin. *J Nutr Biochem*. 2006 Jul;17(7):485-91.

[327] Hwang YP, Choi CY, Chung YC, Jeon SS, Jeong HG. Protective effects of puerarin on carbon tetrachloride-induced hepatotoxicity. *Arch Pharm Res*. 2007 Oct;30(10):1309-17.

[328] Woo J, Lau E, Ho SC, Cheng F, Chan C, Chan AS, et al. Comparison of Pueraria lobata with hormone replacement therapy in treating the adverse health consequences of menopause. *Menopause*. 2003 Jul-Aug;10(4):352-61.

[329] Bo J, Ming BY, Gang LZ, Lei C, Jia AL. Protection by puerarin against MPP+-induced neurotoxicity in PC12 cells mediated by inhibiting mitochondrial dysfunction and caspase-3-like activation. *Neurosci Res*. 2005 Oct;53(2):183-8.

[330] Xu X, Zhang S, Zhang L, Yan W, Zheng X. The Neuroprotection of puerarin against cerebral ischemia is associated with the prevention of apoptosis in rats. *Planta Med*. 2005 Jul;71(7):585-91.

[331] Xu X, Zhang Z. Effects of puerarin on synaptic structural modification in hippocampus of ovariectomized mice. *Planta Med*. 2007 Aug;73(10):1047-53.

[332] Chen HT, Yao CH, Chao PD, Hou YC, Chiang HM, Hsieh CC, et al. Effect of serum metabolites of Pueraria lobata in rats on peripheral nerve regeneration: in vitro and in vivo studies. *J Biomed Mater Res B Appl Biomater*. 2008 Jan;84(1):256-62.

[333] Zhang HY, Liu YH, Wang HQ, Xu JH, Hu HT. Puerarin protects PC12 cells against beta-amyloid-induced cell injury. *Cell Biol Int*. 2008 Oct;32(10):1230-7.

[334] Gu L, Yang Y, Sun Y, Zheng X. Puerarin inhibits acid-sensing ion channels and protects against neuron death induced by acidosis. *Planta Med*. 2010 Apr;76(6):583-8.

[335] Li J, Wang G, Liu J, Zhou L, Dong M, Wang R, et al. Puerarin attenuates amyloid-beta-induced cognitive impairment through suppression of apoptosis in rat hippocampus in vivo. *Eur J Pharmacol*. 2010 Dec 15;649(1-3):195-201.

[336] Zhou J, Wang H, Xiong Y, Li Z, Feng Y, Chen J. Puerarin attenuates glutamate-induced neurofilament axonal transport impairment. *J Ethnopharmacol*. 2010 Oct 28;132(1):150-6.

[337] Zhu G, Wang X, Chen Y, Yang S, Cheng H, Wang N, et al. Puerarin protects dopaminergic neurons against 6-hydroxydopamine neurotoxicity via inhibiting apoptosis and upregulating glial cell line-derived neurotrophic factor in a rat model of Parkinson's disease. *Planta Med*. 2010 Nov;76(16):1820-6.

[338] Zhang H, Liu Y, Lao M, Ma Z, Yi X. Puerarin protects Alzheimer's disease neuronal cybrids from oxidant-stress induced apoptosis by inhibiting pro-death signaling pathways. *Exp Gerontol*. 2011 Jan;46(1):30-7.

[339] Wong R, Rabie B. Effect of puerarin on bone formation. *Osteoarthritis Cartilage*. 2007 Aug;15(8):894-9.

[340] Zhang Y, Zeng X, Zhang L, Zheng X. Stimulatory effect of puerarin on bone formation through activation of PI3K/Akt pathway in rat calvaria osteoblasts. *Planta Med*. 2007 Apr;73(4):341-7.

[341] Chueh FS, Chang CP, Chio CC, Lin MT. Puerarin acts through brain serotonergic mechanisms to induce thermal effects. *J Pharmacol Sci*. 2004 Dec;96(4):420-7.

[342] Yasuda T, Endo M, Kon-no T, Kato T, Mitsuzuka M, Ohsawa K. Antipyretic, analgesic and muscle relaxant activities of pueraria isoflavonoids and their metabolites from Pueraria lobata Ohwi-a traditional Chinese drug. *Biol Pharm Bull*. 2005 Jul;28(7):1224-8.

[343] Cherdshewasart W, Sutjit W. Correlation of antioxidant activity and major isoflavonoid contents of the phytoestrogen-rich Pueraria mirifica and Pueraria lobata tubers. *Phytomedicine*. 2008 Jan;15(1-2):38-43.

[344] Hwang YP, Jeong HG. Mechanism of phytoestrogen puerarin-mediated cytoprotection following oxidative injury: Estrogen receptor-dependent up-regulation of PI3K/Akt and HO-1. *Toxicol Appl Pharmacol*. 2008 Sep 19.

[345] Sun XH, Ding JP, Li H, Pan N, Gan L, Yang XL, et al. Activation of large-conductance calcium-activated potassium channels by puerarin: the underlying mechanism of puerarin-mediated vasodilation. *J Pharmacol Exp Ther*. 2007 Oct;323(1):391-7.

[346] Hien TT, Kim HG, Han EH, Kang KW, Jeong HG. Molecular mechanism of suppression of MDR1 by puerarin from Pueraria lobata via NF-kappaB pathway and cAMP-responsive element transcriptional activity-dependent up-regulation of AMP-activated protein kinase in breast cancer MCF-7/adr cells. *Mol Nutr Food Res*. 2010 Jul;54(7):918-28.

[347] Jang DS, Kim JM, Lee YM, Kim YS, Kim JH, Kim JS. Puerariafuran, a new inhibitor of advanced glycation end products (AGEs) isolated from the roots of Pueraria lobata. *Chem Pharm Bull* (Tokyo). 2006 Sep;54(9):1315-7.

[348] Kim NH, Kim YS, Lee YM, Jang DS, Kim JS. Inhibition of aldose reductase and xylose-induced lens opacity by puerariafuran from the roots of Pueraria lobata. *Biol Pharm Bull.* 2010;33(9):1605-9.

[349] China State Food and Drug Administration. Regulations on dietary supplements registration and examination and other related regulations *Chinese Journal of Food Hygiene.* 2005;17(4):364-75.

[350] China State Food and Drug Administration. Requirements for healthy food products registration and approval. *Chinese Journal of Food Hygiene.* 2005;17(4):376-83.

[351] China State Food and Drug Administration. *Regulations on dietary supplement registration and examination and other related 7 regulations.* 2005.

[352] China State Food and Drug Administration. *Requirements for healthy food products registration and approval.* 2005.

[353] China Ministry of Health. *Regulation on novel food products.* 2007.

In: Bioactive Molecules in Plant Foods
Editor: Florence Ojiugo Uruakpa

ISBN: 978-1-62081-515-1
© 2012 Nova Science Publishers, Inc.

*Chapter II*

# SEED STORAGE PROTEINS AS SOURCES OF BIOACTIVE PEPTIDES

*P. W. M. L. H. K. Marambe[1] and J. P. D. Wanasundara[2]*
[1]Department of Food and Bioproduct Sciences,
College of Agriculture and Bioresources,
University of Saskatchewan, Saskatoon, SK, Canada
[2]Agriculture and Agri-Food Canada,
Saskatoon Research Centre, Saskatoon, SK, Canada

## ABSTRACT

Of all the food proteins, animal proteins, especially milk proteins, have been well researched in terms of the possibility of releasing bioactive peptides.However, plant proteins, particularly seed storage proteins (SSP) have received less attention compared to animal proteins in this respect. Several studies have identified SSP as sources of bioactive peptides with various bioactivities including antihypertensive, antioxidative, cholesterol lowering, immunomodulating and opioid activities. These peptides are inactive within the sequence of the precursor proteins and can be released due to proteolysis.

Several studies have reported the ability of SSP to release bioactive peptides. Of these the potential of SSP to release ACEI peptides have been extensively studied. According to the amino acid composition of different bioactive peptides from SSP it is evident that certain amino acids are under-represented. SSP of soybeans are the most researched and they have been identified to release bioactive peptides with various physiological functions. However, published studies on bioactive peptides derived from other SSP are limited and the available studies are confined to a single bioactivity. Depending on the initial protein source, the enzyme employed, and processing conditions used, the biological activities of the peptides are different. Hydrolysis of same SSP with different enzymes gives rise to peptides with different bioactivities. The bioactivities of SSP derived peptides have been investigated mainly based on *in vitro* studies and in animal models. Human clinical studies to confirm such findings are very limited, also the understanding of the *in vivo* availability of bioactive peptides from food proteins in human digestive system. It is necessary to examine SSP of widely consumed grains and oilseeds to explore whether they could release bioactive peptides. Most of the identified bioactive peptides are reactive due to its low molecular weight. However, their exact mechanism of activities is not clear. A highly challenging future need is to investigate the exact mechanism of the bioactive peptides on the physiological functions of interest.Findings of such studies will reveal the value of SSP beyond the currently accepted nutritional value. This chapter summarises the research findings on SSP-derived bioactive peptides in preventing lifestyle related diseases.

## INTRODUCTION

The plant seeds are nutrient dense. They are rich in carbohydrates, lipids and proteins and contain less lignin and cellulose than other plant parts. The proteins of the seeds are mainly in the storage form, have no known enzymatic activity, and are biochemically well characterized [1]. Due to the abundance and versatility of seed storage proteins (SSP), scientists have endeavoured to exploit their various properties. Apart from providing amino acid requirement essential for human and animal nutrition, SSP function as a source of numerous bioactive peptides with antihypertensive, antioxidative, immunomodulating, opioid and other activities. Such peptides, which are hidden in the latent state within the SSP primary structure, may be released during *in vivo* digestion or food processing [2]. Many bioactive peptides have common structural properties including a relatively short residue length, hydrophobic amino acid residues, and the presence of Arg, Lys and Pro. It can be predicted that in future specific bioactive peptides will find many applications as functional ingredients in health promoting foods. The majority of the bioactive peptides studied are from animal protein sources including milk and few from plant proteins have been studied [3].This chapter discusses the bioactive peptides identified from SSP and their physiological functions.

## 1. SEED STORAGE PROTEINS - GENERAL DESCRIPTION

Seeds are the major plant tissues harvested by human kind. They act as a major source of dietary proteins with a protein content ranging from 10% (in cereals) to 40% (in certain legumes and oilseeds) of the seed weight [4]. Proteins in seeds are of two categories, namely storage proteins and housekeeping proteins. The storage proteins are in abundance. The housekeeping proteins are responsible for maintaining normal cell metabolism [5]. According to another classification, seed proteins are divided into storage, structural and biologically active proteins [6]. Of these, the structural proteins contribute to the structure (*e.g.,* cell wall) whereas biologically active proteins are part of cellular defence mechanism (*e.g.,* lections, enzymes and enzyme inhibitors). Structural- and biologically active proteins are in minor quantities. The non-enzyme proteins that are present in high amounts serve as a store of amino acids required for germination and seedling growth. These proteins are referred to as SSP [4]. SSP are the most abundantly consumed proteins by humans [7] and the major proteins in grains [8]. In the seed, primarily SSP are found in the protein storage vacuoles (PSV) as protein bodies. Mature seeds contain densely packed SSP deposits that entirely fill the PSV [9].

SSP represent a major fraction of human protein intake, either directly or indirectly. A vast majority of the global population depends on the proteins obtained from edible seeds of cereals, legumes, and nuts to satisfy their dietary protein need and requirement [10].No single seed type contains the complete spectrum of essential amino acid requirement of human or farm animals. For example, cereal proteins are deficient in Lys and Trp and legume proteins are deficient in S-containing amino acids, Met and Cys [8,11].

Because of the abundance and economic importance SSP were among the earliest of all plant proteins to be characterized. Detailed studies on SSP ensued when Osborne [12] classified them into following groups based on their extraction and solubility. They are albumins (water extractable), globulins (extractable in dilute salt solutions), prolamins (extractable in aqueous alcohol) and glutelins (most difficult to solubilise but extractable by weakly acidic or alkaline or dilute sodium dodecyl sulphate solution). Of these, albumins and globulins comprise the storage proteins of dicots (*e.g.*, pulses, Table 1), whereas prolamins and glutelins are the major storage proteins of monocots (*e.g.*, cereals, Table 1) [8]. As SSP, serve as a reserve of nitrogen for the seedling, they are generally rich in Asn, Gln and Arg or Pro. Most of the SSP have high molecular weights and their water solubility is poor. This may play an important role in the deposition and higher order aggregation of storage proteins because of the osmotic conditions that exist in the drying and imbibing seed [13]. However, there are many examples of small water soluble SSP in dicot seeds like alfalfa, *Amaranthus*, castor bean, *Chenopodium*, mung bean, mustard, pea, and many other oil bearing seeds.

With an understanding of the relation between protein structure, genetic encoding and evolution, SSPare classified into families based on their amino acid sequences and elements of 3D structure. Some of these families are further grouped into large superfamilies, which have less similarity in sequence but share common structural features. The two major protein superfamilies identified are cupin and prolamin. The prolamin superfamily was first identified by Kreis and group [14] based on the existence of a conserved skeleton of eight Cys residues. The low molecular mass sulphur rich proteins (*e.g.*, 2S albumins of dicot seeds, inhibitors of α-amylase and trypsin, puroindolines and grain softness proteins of cereals, hydrophobic protein of soybean, and non-specific lipid transfer proteins) and prolamines of SSP are included in the prolamin superfamily[15]. The cupin proteins are characterized by the "β-barrel" or "jelly-roll" like structure of the molecule ("cupa" is the latin term for small barrel). OfSSP, globulins (7S vicillin like globulins and 11S legumin like globulins) belong to the cupin superfamily [16].

## 1.1. Cereals

Cereal grains contain relatively little protein compared tolegume seeds, with an average of 10 to12% on a dry weight basis [17]. In mature cereal grains SSPaccountfor about 50% of the total proteins. They generally lack Lys, Thr and Trp. About 80 to 90% of cereal SSP is consisted of prolamins and glutelins whereas albumins and globulins account for the remainder. Prolamins and glutelins are present in approximately equal amounts in wheat, barley and rye. In sorghum and maize prolamins are in excess compared to glutelins. In oats, glutelins are excessive compared to prolamins. Rice is unique as its protein is largely consisted of glutelin[11]. The cereal prolamins are present as monomers or small aggregates whereas glutelins form large disulphide bonded aggregates.Table 1 provides the trivial names used for cereal proteins based on their latin generic names.

## 1.2. Legumes

Much of the proteins in legume seeds are salt soluble globulins (7S and 11S of cupin superfamily; Table 1). Legume proteins tend to be deficient in sulphur-containing amino acidsCys and Met and also in Trp. They are high inglutamic and aspartic acidamides and Arg.

Legume globulins are named as legumin (11S) and vicillin (7S). Vicillin consists of dicarboxyllic acids and their amides and small amounts of Met, Cys and Trp [8] and has no disulphide bonds.

## 1.3. Brassica and other Oilseeds

The major oilseeds include soybean (*Glycine max* (L.) Merr.), cottonseed (*Gossypium hirstum* L.), rapeseed/canola (*Brassica napus* L. *B. rapa* L. and *B. juncea*), sunflower seed (*Helianthus annus* L. var *marcocarpus* DC), peanut (*Arachis hypogae* L.), linseed or flaxseed (*Linum usitatissimum* L.), safflower (*Carthamus tinctorius*), sesame (*Sesamum indicum* L.) and coconut (*Cocus nucifera*) with protein contents ranging from 20 to 40% [24]. Unlike food legumes, most of the oilseed proteins are destined for animal feed after oil extraction. By far, soybean protein is the major seed protein utilized in foods and is available commercially in a variety of products. Furthermore, soybean protein has attracted more scientific research due to health benefits derived from soy protein consumption. The majority of the oilseeds contain 11S globulin and 2S albumin as the major SSP except for soybean (11S glycinin and 7S β-conglycinin) and flaxseed (12S linin and 2S conlinin) (Table 1).

## 2. BIOACTIVE PEPTIDES

Apart from providing the amino acid requirements, food proteins, including seed proteins have the ability to generate bioactive peptides possessing various physiological and health benefits. These bioactive peptides are defined as specific protein fragments that have a positive impact on body functions or conditions and may ultimately influence health [25]. They are inactive within the sequence of the parent protein, and can be released during gastrointestinal (GI) digestion, hydrolysis by proteolytic microorganisms and through the action of proteolytic enzymes derived from micro organisms or plants [26]. Once liberated, bioactive peptides possess different activities *in vitro* and *in vivo* including antihypertensive, antimicrobial, antioxidative, antithrombotic and immunomodulatory [27]. Therefore, upon oral administration bioactive peptides may affect the major body systems namely the cardiovascular, digestive, immune and nervous systems depending on their amino acid sequence [26].

**Table 1. Predominant storage proteintypes, their common names and storage sites in the seeds of important crops [18-23]**

| Family, species and common name | Predominant storage protein types and their common names | Primary storage site |
|---|---|---|
| **Compositae** | | |
| *Helianthus annus* (Sunflower) | 11S Helianthinin | Cotyledons (embryo) |
| | 2S Albumin | |
| **Cruciferae** | | |
| *Brassica napus* (Canola/Rapeseed) | 11S Globulin (Cruciferin) | Cotyledons (embryo) |
| | 2S Albumin (Napin) | |
| **Graminae** | | |
| *Avena sativa* (Oats) | Prolamin (Avenin), 11S Globulin | Starchy endosperm |
| | 7S Globulin | Embryo/Aleuron layer |
| *Hordeum vulgare* (Barley) | Prolamin (Hordein) | Starchy endosperm |
| | 7S Globulin | Embryo/Aleuron layer |
| *Oryza sativa* (Rice) | 11S Globulin (Glutelin), Prolamin | Starchy endosperm |
| | 7S Globulin | Embryo |
| *Triticum aestivum* (Wheat) | Prolamin (Gliadin+Glutenin) | Starchy endosperm |
| | 7S Globulin | Embryo/Aleuron layer Starchy |
| *Zea mays* (Maize) | Prolamin (Zein) | endosperm |
| | 7S Globulin | Embryo |
| **Leguminoceae** | | |
| *Arachis hypogea* (Peanut) | 11S Arachin, 7S Conarachin | Cotyledons (embryo) |
| *Glycine max* (Soybean) | 11S Glycinin, 7S β-Conglycinin | Cotyledons (embryo) |
| *Phaseolus vulgaris* (French bean) | 2S Albumin | Cotyledons (embryo) |
| *Pisum sativum* (Field pea) | 7S Phaseolin | Cotyledons (embryo) |
| *Vicia faba* (Broad bean) | 11S Legumin, 7S Vicillin & Convicillin, 2S Albumin | Cotyledons (embryo) |
| | 7S Vicillin 11S Legumin | |
| **Linaceae** | | |
| *Linum usitatissimum* (Flaxseed) | 12S Linin, 2S Conlinin | Cotyledons (embryo) |
| **Palmae** | | |
| *Cocos nucifera* (Coconut) | 11S and 7S Globulins, 2S Albumin | Endosperm |
| *Elais guineenis* (Oil palm) | 7S Globulin | Endosperm |
| **Pedialaceae** | | |
| *Sesamum indicum* (Sesame) | 11S α-Globulin, 2S β-Globulin | Cotyledons (embryo) |

Food-derived bioactive peptides commonly contain 2 to 9 amino acids [25], however, this range may be extended to 3 to 20 or more amino acid residues [28]. For example lunasin, a food-derived peptide with proven anticancer activity, contains 43 amino acids with a molecular weight of 5400 Da [29]. In order to perform biological functions, these peptides must cross the intestinal epithelium and enter into the blood circulation, or bind directly to specific epithelial cell surface receptor sites [3].

A significant proportion of dietary nitrogen is absorbed into the body in the form of small peptides. The human GI tract secrets number of peptidases that function synergistically to cleave polypeptide chains into amino acids and small peptides. The small intestine is the primary absorption site of these end products of protein digestion. Small (2 to 3 amino acids) and large (10 to 51 amino acids) peptides generated in the diet can be absorbed intact through the intestine and produce biological effects at the tissue level [30]. The results of electrophysiological studies carried out in 1970s and 1980s have suggested the existence of a peptide transport system in the intestinal epithelium by which peptides would be actively transported through the intestinal membrane under $H^+$ gradient [31]. However, this transport mechanism carries only di- and tri-peptides [32]. Oligopeptides with more than four residues transport through the intestinal epithelium via other routes such as pinocytosis or through para cellular channels [30, 33] depending on the molecular size and hydrophobicity. After absorption, the intestinal tract serum peptidase can further hydrolyse the peptide bonds. Therefore, resistance to peptidase degradation is a prerequisite to sustain the physiological effects of bioactive peptides following oral ingestion or intravenous infusion.

Bioactive peptides have been mainly isolated and studied from animal protein sources including milk. However, there is ample evidence to suggest that SSP are precursors of bioactive peptides of physiological importance. Thishas been confirmed by various *in vitro* and *in vivo* studies, which are discussed further herein.

# 3. PHYSIOLOGICAL FUNCTIONS OF SSP-DERIVED BIOACTIVE PEPTIDES

## 3.1. Antihypertensive Effect and Angiotensin I-Converting Enzyme (ACE) Inhibiting Peptides

Hypertension or high blood pressure is a major health problem all over the world, with 50% of individuals above 55 years in many industrialized countries are suffering. It is a major risk factor for coronary heart disease, congestive heart failure, stroke and renal disease [34]. In humans the systolic blood pressure (SBP) refers to the blood pressure at the active contraction phase of the cardiac cycle whereas diastolic blood pressure (DBP) is the pressure at the relaxation phase of the cardiac cycle [35]. A person is said to be hypertensive when SBP is $\geq$ 140 mmHg or DBP is $\geq$90 mmHg (140/90 mmHg) or taking medications for hypertension [36].

ACE plays a critical role in the regulation of blood pressure. It is a zinc metalloprotease, a component in the rennin-angiotensin system (RAS), and a dipeptidyl carboxypeptidase that catalyses hydrolysis of carboxy terminal dipeptides from oligopeptide substrates (Figure 1). ACE and other components of RAS coexist locally in various tissues including blood vessels, kidney, adrenal glands, heart and brain in addition to circulation. High concentrations of ACE are found on epithelial surfaces such as intestinal, choroids plexus, and placental brush borders influencing the fluid and electrolyte balance at these fluid membrane interfaces [37]. ACE increases the blood pressure by catalysing the conversion of decapeptide angiotensin I into the potent vasoconstricting octapeptide angiotensin II, and also by catalysing the degradation of bradykinin, a blood pressure lowering nonapeptide. Angiotensin II leads to several effects that are central and link to a further increase in blood pressure (Figure 1). Therefore, inhibition of ACE results in an overall antihypertensive effect [38].

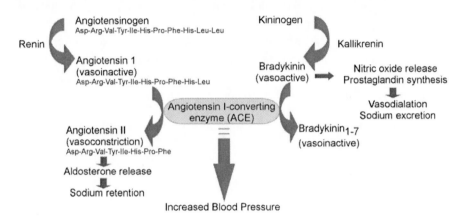

Figure 1. Summary of the effects of ACE on rennin-angiotensin system.

ACE has two domains (N and C), each of which contains an active site with a His-Glu-X-X-His. The His residues are considered to participate in Zn binding. Glu residue is involved in the catalysis by binding the activated water molecule, which initiates a nucleophilic attack on the susceptible peptide bond of the substrate. Of these, the C domain is the dominant angiotensin 1-converting site [39]. The first available competitive inhibitors of ACE were isolated from *Bothrops jararaca* snake venom as naturally occurring pentapeptide Glu-Lys-Trp-Ala-Pro and the nonapeptideGlu-Trp-Pro-Arg-Pro-Gln-Ile-Pro-Pro[40].Structure-activity correlation studies of analogs of these peptides indicated that their carboxy terminal tripeptide residues (Trp-Ala-Pro) play a dominant role in competitive binding to the active site of ACE [41] (Figure 2). Captopril, a highly potent ACE inhibitory (ACEI) drug, was developed based on the antihypertensive mechanism of these peptides. The sulphydryl group of captopril, which is coupled to the dipeptide Ala-Pro, binds strongly with the Zn atom in the active site of ACE and inhibits the enzyme activity (Figure 2). Numerous other ACE inhibitors such as enalapril and lisinopril have also been developed [42]. As stated by Cheung and others [41], Trp, Tyr, Phe, and Pro are the most potent C-terminal amino acids of these peptides that contribute most to substrate binding at the active site and thereby inhibit the activity of ACE.

From a database containing 168 dipeptides and 140 tripeptides Wu and others [44] identified that amino acid residues with bulky or hydrophobic side chains are preferred for ACEI dipeptides (Table 2). For tripeptides, the most favourable residues for the carboxyl terminus are found to be aromatic amino acids, while positively charged amino acids are preferred for the middle position, and hydrophobic amino acids are preferred for the amino terminus. At present, many ACE inhibitors have been discovered from enzyme catalysed hydrolysis of proteins from animal sources including bovine casein, human casein and fish proteins [45] and also from plant sources such as enzymatic digests of SSP.

### Brassica spp.

Seeds of canola/rapeseed (*Brassica napus*) have significant protein content which constitutes 20 to 25% of the dry seed weight whereas the meal that remains after oil extraction consists of approximately 40% protein. Four potent ACEI peptides, Ile-Tyr, Arg-Ile-Tyr, Val-Trp and Val-Trp-Ile-Ser, have been isolated from the Subtilisin® digest of rapeseed protein [46].Among thesepeptides, Arg-Ile-Tyr and Val-Trp-Ile-Ser have exhibited $IC_{50}$ (50% inhibitoryconcentration) values of 28 and 30 μM (0.013 and 0.016 mg/mL), respectively. All these peptides lowered blood pressure of spontaneously hypertensive rats (SHR) following oral administration. However, the Arg-Ile-Tyr peptide has also reduced blood pressure of old rats in which ACE is less effective indicating that the mechanism of blood pressure reduction by Arg-Ile-Tyr may not be via ACE inhibition.

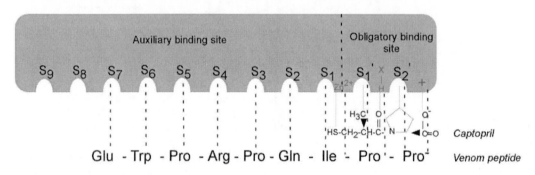

Figure 2. Proposed model for binding of venom nonapeptide and captopril on to the active sites of ACE.

Wu and others [47] have identified ACEI activity in canola protein hydrolysed with Alcalase® with an $IC_{50}$ of 0.19 mg protein/mL. These peptides also exhibited stability against GI protease incubation. The fraction with most potent ACE inhibition ($IC_{50}$ of 0.014 mg protein/mL) had peptides of <870 Da molecular mass as the predominant (87%) molecules. Aromatic amino acids contributed up to 37% of the total amino acids of these peptides. ACEI activity exhibited by Alcalase® hydrolysed rapeseed protein [48] and defatted canola meal [49] showed that SSP in canola protein are good sources of ACEI peptides upon hydrolysis by food grade microbial enzymes. According to Wu and others [49] the $IC_{50}$ for ACEI activity of hydrolysed heat-treated and untreated canola meals were 0.027 to 0.028 mg/mLand 0.035 to 0.044 mg/mL,respectively. Heat denaturation of protein may play a role in generating more ACEI peptides because of the increased susceptibility to hydrolysis. These peptides retained their activity upon *in vitro* GI digestion with pepsin and pancreatin. Two ACEI peptides, Val-Ser-Val ($IC_{50}$: 0.15 μM or $0.05\times10^{-3}$mg/mL) and Phe-Leu ($IC_{50}$:1.33 μM or $0.39\times10^{-3}$mg/mL) were purified from the Alcalase® hydrolysed canola meal with sequence reference to the napin and cruciferin. Interestingly, total protein of canola and isolated napin and cruciferin when hydrolysed with Alcalase® showed $IC_{50}$ of 0.015, 0.035 and 0.029 mg/mL, respectively. However, reliable evidence on the exact canola SSPthat generate ACEI peptides is lacking [50]. Other *Brassica* spp showing ACEI activity upon hydrolysis include

*Brassica carinata* (Ethiopean mustard) which showed ACEI activity upon sequential hydrolysis by trypsin, chymotrypsin and carboxypeptidase A (IC$_{50}$ of 0.338 mg protein/mL) [51].

**Table 2. Prediction and location of ACEI peptides in some seed storage proteins [44]**

| Peptide (known) | Position | Parent protein | Predicted log IC$_{50}$ | Observed log IC$_{50}$ |
|---|---|---|---|---|
| FW | f150-151 | Legumin A2 precursor; garden pea | 0.60 | 0.77 |
| | f149-150 | Legumin A precursor; garden pea | | |
| WW | f150-151 | Glycinin G1 precursor; soybean | 0.52 | 1.91 |
| | f147-148 | Glycinin G2 precursor; soybean | | |
| YW | f219-220 | Legumin J precursor; garden pea | 0.92 | 1.64 |
| | f153-154 | Legumin K; garden pea | | |
| | f3-4 | Conglycinin, chain precursor; soybean | | |
| | f27-28 | Glycinin G3 precursor; soybean | | |
| | f147-148 | Glycinin G4 precursor; soybean | | |
| | f156-157 | Glycinin precursor; soybean | | |
| VRF | f4-6 | Conglycinin, chain precursor; soybean | 0.14 | 1.38 |
| IKP | f265-267 | Glycinin G1 precursor; soybean | 0.37 | 0.44 |
| | f279-281 | Legumin J precursor; garden pea | | |
| | f6-8 | Vicilin 47 kDa protein; garden pea | | |
| LRW | f377-379 | Legumin A2 precursor, garden pea | -0.11 | -0.64 |
| | f374-376 | Legumin A precursor; garden pea | | |

### Buckwheat

Buckwheat (*Fagopyrum esculentum* Moench) is a pseudo cereal and has crude protein content of 12% [52]. The potential health benefits arising from buckwheat include strong hypocholesterolaemic activity [53] and blood pressure-reducing effect [54]. Buckwheat SSP are rich in Asp, Arg and Lysbut lower in Glu and Pro than cereal proteins [55]. The major storage protein of buckwheat seed is a 13S globulin that resembles legumin in structure [56].

Enzymatic hydrolysis of buckwheat globulin with Thermolysin® has shown production of ACE inhibitors with an $IC_{50}$ value of 0.043 mg protein/mL[57]. Li and others [58] showed that *in vitro* digestion of buckwheat flour with GI proteases can enhance the ACEI activity of the digest ($IC_{50}$ of 0.14 mg protein/mL) when compared with intact buckwheat ($IC_{50}$ of 3 mg/mL). When fed to SHR, buckwheat digest was able to lower SBP. The tripeptides Tyr-Gln-Tyr and Pro-Ser-Tyr have been identified as the main ACE inhibitors in the buckwheat digest. Ma and others [59] have isolated and purified an ACEI peptide from buckwheat protein extract without enzymatic digestion. The identified ACE inhibitor was the tripeptide Gly-Pro-Pro that exhibited $IC_{50}$ value of $6.25 \times 10^{-3}$ mg protein/mL. Proline was the C-terminal amino acid of ACEI peptides identified in buckwheat [41, 59].

## Chickpea

The crude protein content of chickpea (*Cicer arietinum* L.) varies from 12.6 to 30.5% [60]. Chickpea is considered as a good source of vegetable proteins because of the well-balanced amino acid composition, high protein bioavailability, and relatively low level of associated antinutritional factors[61]. The main storage protein of chickpea is legumin, which accounts for 64% of the total protein content and 97% of the total globulins in the seed [62]. Pedroche and others [63] reported that the hydrolysate prepared by treating chickpea protein isolate with Alcalase®, possesses ACEI activity. Four ACEI peptides have been purified from the hydrolysate. Two of them were competitive inhibitors of ACE while the other two were uncompetitive inhibitors. Yust and others [27] isolated six ACEI peptides (Met-Asp, Asp-Phe-Leu-Ile, Met-Phe-Asp-Leu, Met-Asp-Leu, Met-Asp-Leu-Ala and amino acid Met) with $IC_{50}$ values ranging from 0.011 to 0.021 mg/mL released due to the Alcalase® treatment of isolated legumin. Methionine was the most abundant amino acid in all these peptides, although hydrophobic amino acids were also in abundance. Among these, Yust and others [27] have identified an ACEI peptide which consists exclusively of Met. ACEI peptides with Met residues were also purified from β-lactoglobulin [64], sardine muscle [65] and human $\alpha_{s1}$ casein [66]. No *in vivo* studies are available on ACEI peptides generated by chickpea proteins.

## Field Pea

The protein content of field pea (*Pisum sativum* L.) varies from 15.6 to 32.5% depending on the cultivar and the conditions prevailing in the growing season [67]. Pea protein is mainly composed of globulins (11S and 7S) and heterogeneous albumins (sulphur-rich PA1 albumin and the larger PA2 albumin) [68]. The globulin fraction consists of about 80% of the total proteins in the mature pea seeds [69]. Several *invitro* studies have shown the possibility of pea proteins to act as a precursor of ACEI peptides. Vermeirssen and others [70] subjected isolated pea protein to simulated GI digestion and investigated theACEI activity of the hydrolysate that exhibited $IC_{50}$ values of 0.076 mg/mL. *In silico* GI digestion of vicilin and albumin PA2 proteins revealed that pea SSP have the ability of releasing a number of potent ACEI peptides [71]. In another study, Vermeirssen and others [72] subjected pea proteins to fermentation with*Lactobacillus helveticus*and *Saccharomyces cerevisiae* and then to simulated GI digestion. When the $IC_{50}$ value of non-fermented and fermented pea proteins were compared at the end of GI digestion the former was found to have the low $IC_{50}$ value suggesting that GI digestion is the predominant factor that controls release of ACEI peptides from pea proteins. Therefore, the hydrolysis of pea proteins by microbial proteases may hinder the action of GI proteases on the pea proteins to release more potent ACEI peptides. Vermeirssen and others [73] have fractionated the GI digest of pea protein isolates using ultrafiltration and reverse phase chromatography to increase the ACEI activity. They found that ACEI activity was increased by four times and all the peptides liberated from pea have similar ACE inhibiting ability. Pea protein isolate digested with GI proteases has exerted a strong hypotensive effect showing a reduction in the mean arterial blood pressure by 44.4 mmHg in SHR after intravenous administration of 50 mg protein/kg body weight. However, only a fraction of ACEIpeptides of the pea protein digest was transported through Caco–2 cells, which are sources of small intestinal peptidases. As the Caco-2 cells are tighter than the intestinal cells of mammals sufficient absorption of these peptides might occur under actual *in vivo* conditions [74].

## Maize

The major proteins of maize (*Zea mays*) seeds are zein and glutelins (Table 1), which represent approximately 60% and 30%, respectively of the total seed proteins [75]. Zein is deficient in Lys and Trp and also to a lesser extent in Arg, His and Met whereas glutelin has a nutritionally balanced amino acid composition [76]. Therefore, the nutritional value of maize protein is said to be poor. There are four main types of zeins ($\alpha,\beta$, $\gamma$ and $\delta$) classified according to their solubility properties. Of these proteins $\alpha$-zein displays more hydrophobic properties [77]. ACEI tripeptides Leu-Arg-Pro, Leu-Ser-Pro and Leu-Gln-Pro, having $IC_{50}$ values of 0.27, 1.7, and 1.9 M (110, 590 and 745 mg/mL), respectively have been isolated from $\alpha$-zeinhydrolysate of Thermolysin® hydrolysis. The hypotensive activity of Leu-Arg-Pro on SHR exhibited a significant decrease in blood pressure (15 mmHg) after a 30 mg/kg intravenous injection [78]. Furthermore, orally administered unpurified Thermolysin® hydrolysate of $\alpha$-zein also reduced the blood pressure level of SHR. Yano and others [79] hydrolysed urea-denatured $\alpha$-zein into small peptides by digestion with Thermolysin®. The ACEI activity ($IC_{50}$) of this Thermolysin® digest of $\alpha$-zein was 24.5 µg/mL (0.024 mg/mL). Thirty-six ACEI peptides, including 5 dipeptides, 14 tripeptides, 9 tetrapeptides, 5 pentapeptides, and 3 hexapeptides, were isolated from this hydrolysate. Although zein is a protein with low nutritional quality, its ability to release ACEI peptides upon enzymatic hydrolysis reveals the value of zein as a source of bioactive peptides.

## Mung Bean

Mung bean (*Phaseolus radiatus* L.) which has a protein content ranging from 20 to 33% has accepted anti-inflammatory, anti-tumor, cholesterol lowering, detoxifying and diuretic properties. The seeds are processed and consumed as cooked whole beans or splits, sprouts, mature seeds and flour [80]. Mung bean protein has been identified as a good source of ACEI peptides when hydrolysed *in vitro* with the protease Alcalase® [81]. An increase of ACEI activity of the mung bean hydrolysates when treated with GI proteases *in vitro* indicated the presence of pro-drug type peptides in the hydrolysate. A significant decrease in SBP has been reported when this hydrolysate was orally administered to SHR [81]. The presence of high levels of hydrophobic amino acids in mung bean protein explains its' potential to generate ACEI peptides. It was confirmed that tripeptides composed of hydrophobic amino acids in the C and N- terminals have potent ACEI activity. Three ACEI peptides have been isolated from mung bean protein hydrolysate treated with Alcalase®; Lys-Asp-Tyr-Arg-Leu, Val-Thr-Pro-Ala-Leu-Arg and Lys-Leu-Pro-Ala-Gly-Thr-Leu-Phe with $IC_{50}$ values of 26.5 μM, 82.4 μM and 13.4 μM (0.02, 0.06, and 0.01 mg/mL), respectively. The presence of hydrophobic amino acids Leu and Phe at the C-terminal position of Lys-Asp-Tyr-Arg-Leu and Lys-Leu-Pro-Ala-Gly-Thr-Leu-Phe, respectively may contribute to the ACEI activity of these peptides. In addition, the peptide Lys-Leu-Pro-Ala-Gly-Thr-Leu-Phe shares the C-terminal dipeptide with α-lactalbumin derived Tyr-Gly-Leu-Phe and β lactoglobulin derived Tyr-Leu-Leu-Phe those possess strong ACEI activity *in vitro* [82]. Meisel [83] suggested that the positive charge on the ε-amino group of Arg and Lys in the C-terminal also contribute to the ACEI potency of peptides; and provides an explanation for the ACEI of Val-Thr-Pro-Ala-Leu-Arg. However, the mung bean SSPthose act as the precursors of ACEI peptides have not been identified.

## Sesame

Sesame (*Sesamum indicum* L.) seeds contain 40 to 50% protein (rich in S-amino acids) on a fat free basis. Sesame is used in confectionery, personal care products and fortification of soft drinks and juices while the protein hydrolysates are found in soups, sauces, gravies, snacks, meat products, and other savory applications [84]. Besides oil and protein, sesame contains characteristic lignans. Ochi and others [85] isolated three peptides with ACEI activity from a Thermolysin® hydrolysate of sesame seed proteins: Met-Leu-Pro-Ala-Tyr, Val-Leu-Tyr-Arg-Asp-Gly and Ileu-Val-Tyr. Each peptide showed antihypertensive effect in SHR when orally administered at the dose of 100 mg/kg. Nakano and others [86] isolated and identified six ACEI peptides from commercially available sesame peptide powder. They are Leu-Val-Tyr, Leu-Gln-Pro, Leu-Lys-Tyr, Leu-Ser-Ala, Ileu-Val-Tyr and Val-Ileu-Tyr. Among these the tripeptides with Tyr and Pro at the C- terminal and Leu at the N-terminal have shown noticeable ACEI activity. These results could be supported by the substrate specificity for ACE as reported by Cheung and others [41]. The peptides derived from sesame peptide powder have also shown to reduce SBP in SHR.

## Soybeans

Soybean (*Glycine max* L. Merr.) proteins are used in a variety of ways and consist mainly of glycinin (11S) and β-conglycinin (7S), but also contain several minor proteins [87].Several peptides derived from soy protein have exhibited ACEI activity in chemical assays and mouse models. Soy peptides with ACEI activity have been reported to contain Gly, nonpolar (Ala or Leu), aromatic (Phe), polar (Asn, Gln or Pro), or negatively charged (Asp or Glu) amino acid residues at the carboxyl terminal and Gly, non-polar (Ile or Val), aromatic (Tyr or Phe), polar (Gln), positively charged (His), or negatively charged (Asp) amino acids at the amino terminal. Val was the most frequently observed residue in ACEI soy peptides, followed by these amino acids in decreasing order of occurrence; Leu, Phe, Asp, Pro, Gln, Gly, Ala, Ile, Asn, Glu, His, Thr, Arg, Met, and Lys [88]. It has been reported that soybean peptide fractions, His-His-Leu (HHL) isolated from fermented soybean paste exerted ACEI activity *in vitro* with an $IC_{50}$ value of 2.2 mg/mL. Moreover, the synthetic tripeptide HHL resulted in a significant decrease of ACE activity in the aorta and led to lower SBP in SHR [89]. ACEI peptides derived from treatment of soy protein with Alcalase® had a significant hypotensive effect on SHR at 100 mg/kg of body weight/day administration level demonstrating its bioactivity *in vivo*. However, the ACEI activity of soy peptide was found to be significantly lower than that of clinical hypotensive drug, captopril [90]. The ACEI peptides Asp-Leu-Pro and Asp-Gly with $IC_{50}$ values of 4.8 μM ($1.82\times10^{-3}$ mg/mL) and 12.3 μM ($2.5\times10^{-3}$ mg/mL), respectively derived from hydrolysis of soy protein by Alcalase®, were stable to GI enzyme digestion *in vitro* [91]. The ACEI peptides generated by peptidic digestion of soy proteins have been characterized and identified as Ile-Ala ($IC_{50}$: 153 μM or 0.03 mg/mL), Tyr-Leu-Ala-Gly-Asn-Gln ($IC_{50}$: 14 μM or 0.01 mg/mL), Phe-Phe-Leu ($IC_{50}$: 37 μM or 0.01 mg/mL), and Ile-Tyr-Leu-Leu ($IC_{50}$: 42 μM or 0.02 mg/mL). These peptides were investigated for reducing blood pressure of SHR when given orally at a dose of 2g/kg body weight [92]. The mean SBP of SHR was reduced to 17.6 mmHg in 2h upon oral administration and this antihypertensive effect was continued for 6h [92]. According to Lo and Chan [88] sequential *in vitro* digestion of soy isolate with pepsin and pancreatin generated peptides with ACEI activity suggesting the potential of soy proteins to release peptides with such activity under the physiological conditions. However, a reduction of ACEI activity of peptides in peptic hydrolysate was reported upon further hydrolysis by pancreatin. Digestion of soy hydrolysate and the fermented products such as *natto* and *tempeh* with a variety of endoproteases (pronase, trypsin, Glu C protease, plasma proteases and kidney membrane proteases) have demonstrated that ACEI peptides were mostly derived from glycinin, the highly expressed soy protein, and were found mainly in the pronase, kidney membrane proteases and plasma proteases digests of the fermented soy products [93]. Among the soy proteins, β-conglycinin was found to be resistant to proteolytic attack even by the multi-enzyme systems, plasma proteases and kidney membrane proteases [94], stable to acid hydrolysis, and resistant to tryptic proteolysis [93]. According to Lo and others [95] isolated soy proteins have the potential to release ACEI peptides under conditions that simulated the upper GI tract. As there could be a reduction of ACEI activity upon pancreatin digestion [88], studies simulating only the upper GI tract are not sufficient to predict the potential of soy proteins as precursors of ACEI peptides. Though soy protein has been extensively studied for production of ACEI peptides further clinical studies are needed to confirm that such peptides are released and active under physiological conditions.

## *Sunflower*

Defatted sunflower (*Helianthus ananus* L.) seed meal contains about 30% proteins, which can be used as a food ingredient. Megias and others [96] have isolated an ACEI peptide from the pepsin and pancreatin digest of sunflower seed protein isolate. The peptide has a sequence of Phe-Val-Asn-Pro-Gln-Ala-Gly-Ser ($IC_{50}$ $5.7\times10^{-3}$ mg/mL) and it corresponded to a fragment of helianthinin (11S globulin, Table 1). Hydrolysis of isolated sunflower protein with Alcalase® followed by Flavourzyme® also has generated ACEIpeptides [97]. The ACEI fractions of the hydrolysates were rich in Asp, Ser, Gly, Thr and Val compared to the original protein hydrolysate whereas some fractions were rich in Ala, Met, Ile, Leu or Phe residues supporting the fact that ACEI peptides are rich in hydrophobic amino acids. The lowest $IC_{50}$value ($0.08\times10^{-3}$ mg/mL) wasresulted in for Flavourzyme®-generated fractions and was much lower than that of ACEI peptides released by *in vitro* GI digestion of sunflower protein as reported by Megias and others [96]. There is no *in vivo* evidence on the ACEI activity of sunflower peptides.

## Wheat

Wheat (*Triticumaestivum* L.) grain has a low protein content, which ranges between 9 to 16% of the dry weight. Wheat grain proteins play a major role in processed food such as bread, biscuits, breakfast cereals and pasta [98]. The major wheat storage proteins are alcohol soluble gliadins and glutelins. Wheat germ (WG), a byproduct of the flour milling industry is an excellent source of vitamins, minerals, dietary fiber, proteins and calories. The defatted wheat germ contains >30% protein that is rich in the essential amino acids, especially Lys, Met, and Thr, which many of the cereal grains are deficient of [99]. Hydrolysate of WG obtained from *Bacillus licheniformis* alkaline protease hydrolysis has demonstrated ACE inhibition *in vitro*. Sixteen peptides having 2 to 7 amino acids with the $IC_{50}$ value less than 20 $\mu M$ have been isolated from the hydrolysate. The major peptide possessing the most powerful ACEI activity ($IC_{50}$ 0.48 $\mu M$ or $0.21 \times 10^{-3}$ mg/mL) was Ile-Val-Tyr [100]. Simulated GI digestion of WG hydrolysate has further increased ACEI ability indicating that there is production of new ACEI peptides due to GI protease activity. Motoi and Kodama [101] isolated ACEI peptide from wheat gliadin hydrolysate prepared with acid proteases. The amino acid sequence of this peptide was identified as Ile-Ala-Pro ($IC_{50}$ 2.7 $\mu M$ or $0.91 \times 10^{-3}$ mg/mL). This peptide inhibited the hypertensive activity of angiotensin II with intravenous injection, and decreased the blood pressure significantly with intraperitoneal administration when tested using SHR.

## Other SSP Derived Peptides with ACEI Activity

There are several other SSP derived peptides with identified ACEI activity. They include protein hydrolysates of peanut [102], kidney bean [103], red bean [104] and Thermolysin® hydrolysed flaxseed meal [105]. The amino acid residues and their sequence arrangement in bioactive peptides determine the bioactivities. Therefore biological activities of peptides can be strengthened by replacing the amino acid residues. Transgenic rice with antihypertensive activity has been developed by introducing antihypertensive ovokinin like peptide structure obtained from egg albumen into the hypervariable regions of glutelin, the major storage protein in rice [106].

## 3.2. Opioid Activity

Human endogenous opioidergic system is consisted of opioid receptors and their ligands, endogenous opioids with alkaloid or peptide structure, which exert their activity upon binding with opioid receptors. Opioid receptors are located in the central and peripheral nervous system, in the immune system and in the endocrine system of mammals [107]. Specific organ tissues that resemble opioid activity include the spinal chord, adrenal gland, digestive tract, pituitary gland and hypothalamus. Of the three types of opioid receptors,μ-, κ- and δ-, the μ-type receptors are responsible for emotional behaviour and suppression of intestinal motility. The δ-type receptor is associated with emotions and reward behaviour whereas the κ-receptors are important for sedation and food intake [3]. The endogenous opioid peptides include enkephalins, endorphin and dynorphins [3]. They possess agonistic as well as antagonistic effects on opioid receptors in the human body and elicit effects in all cells or tissues where opioids are known to be active [3]. Basically the opioid peptides have an effect on the nervous system and GI functions [108]. Also the fixation of opioid peptides to blood vessel opioid receptors is considered as an alternative mechanism of reducing blood pressure by bioactive peptides [109]. There is much evidence on involvement of opioid peptides in food intake regulation and obesity in humans and experimental animals [110]. Agonists to opioid receptors induce a positive energy balance and obesity, whereas antagonists at these receptors reduce food intake andbody weight in rodent obesemodels [111, 112]. Interestingly, the inhibitory effects of opioid receptor antagonistson food intake and body weight appear most pronounced in obeseanimals or when animals were fed a highly palatable diet. Opiates are well recognized to have variety of interactions with the monoamines in the central nervous system, which influences the feeding behaviour. The sensory pleasure response of foods is also largely brought about by the release of the endogenous opioid peptides in the brain. Therefore, blockade of opioid receptors by opioid antagonists could reduce the taste preferences, and diminish consumption of preferred foods. Especially the preferences for sweet taste or dietary fat are under the control of endogenous opioids. Therefore, abnormalities of endogenous opioid system could increase the consumption of sweet and fatty foods that leads to overweight and obesity [113].

Aseries of food protein derived opioid peptides (exogenous opioid peptides), which act as exogenous supplements for the endogenous opiodergic system have been identified [107]. These food derived opioid peptides are found to be important for the human body. One reason is the stability of food-derived opioid towards enzymatic degradation because they are released after intestinal enzymatic action as opposed to the susceptible endogenous opioid peptides. The other is food-derived opioid peptides usually possess weaker activity than endogenous ones, which makes them less likely to cause the adverse side effects often associated with opioids such as dependence, tolerance and addiction [25]. Structurally, both exogenous and endogenous opioid peptides vary in the N-terminal sequence. The endogenous peptides have the same N-terminal sequence of Gly-Gly-Phe whereas several food derived opioid peptides have been found to have a Tyr residue at the amino terminal (e.g., Tyr-X-Phe, Tyr-X1-X2-Phe) [25; 108]. At present several food-derived opioid peptides of animal and plant origin have been identified. Interestingly, opioid peptides derived from animal proteins are mostly μ-receptor selective, while those of plant origin are mostly δ-receptor selective [114]. The bovine β casein fragment was the first food protein that was identified as an opioid receptor ligand, which later led to the identification of several other opioid agonists, and antagonists from milk proteins [107]. Of the plant protein derived opioids, hydrolysates of RuBisCo in spinach leaves [115], alfalfa white protein concentrate [109] and several SSP have been studied for opioid agonist and antagonist activities (Table 3) [107].

Of the SSP-derived opioid peptides the most extensively studied are gluten exorphins (GEs). These are opioid peptides isolated from enzymatic digests of wheat gluten. Digestion of wheat proteins releases peptides that act on opioid receptors in the gut. Zioudrou and others [116] have identified that peptides in the peptic hydrolysate of wheat gluten have morphine like opioid activity in vitro. GEs are classified into three groups according to their structure, namely, GEA, GEB, and GEC. There are two members of GEA: GEA5 (Gly-Tyr-Tyr- Pro-Thr)and GEA4 (Gly-Tyr-Tyr-Pro) and two members of GEB: GEB5 (Tyr-Gly-Gly-Trp-Leu)and GEB4 (Tyr-Gly-Gly-Trp).

**Table 3. SSP studied for opioid activity [107]**

| Seed | Protein | Materials with opioid agonist or antagonist activity | | |
|------|---------|-----------|-------|------------|
| | | **Looked for** | **Found** | **Identified** |
| Barley | Hordein | + | + | - |
| Maize | Zein | + | + | - |
| Oats | Avenin | + | - | - |
| Rice | Albumin | + | + | + |
| Rye | Secalin | + | - | - |
| Soy | α Protein | + | - | - |
| Wheat | Gluten | + | + | - |
| | Gliadin | + | + | - |

Among the gluten derived peptides, GEB5 has the most potent *in vitro* activity as agonist on both μ- and δ- receptors [117] and is also the most potent food-derived δ-opioid peptide that has been reported to date [114]. GEB5 has been identified to be released *in vivo* after gluten ingestion and also crosses the intestinal barrier fully intact. It stimulates prolactin release in rats by acting through opioid receptors in the nerves outside the blood brain barrier [117]. Schusdziarra [118] had administered the digested gluten into the stomach of dogs and noted a more rapid rise in peripheral vein insulin and glucagon levels than when an equivalent amount of undigested protein was administered. Additional studies have suggested that the effect may be related to activation of opiate receptors by exorphins. Fukudome and others [119] reported that GEA5 can stimulate insulin release in rats upon both oral and intravenous administration. Insulin has an appetite suppressing effect in humans. Therefore GEA5, via stimulation of insulin release, may prevent excess energy intake and development of obesity. However, the appetite suppressing effect of insulin is found among lean subjects and not in the obese subjects [120]. No study is available to prove GEs can exert similar opioid activity in human subjects.

The same GEA5 peptide has exhibited the capability of suppressing the endogenous pain inhibitory system, and has facilitated to acquire/consolidation process of learning/memory in mice [121]. GEs have also been studied for GI functions. Hydrolysed gluten has prolonged the intestinal transit time in healthy volunteers, which can be reversed by the administration of the opiate blocker naloxone. The naloxone-reversible increase in plasma somatostatin-like activity may be responsible for the delayed transit time [122]. However, the authors have not found any effect of GEs on appetite regulation of the volunteers.

Cholecystokinin (CCK) is produced in the brain and enteroendocrine cells and is an important physiologic endocrine factor in appetite control. The food intake suppression by CCK is well established [123]. Pupovac and Anderson [124] identified that ingestion of soy hydrolysate by rats lead to satiety as they provided satiety signals through opioid and CCK receptors. Peptic hydrolysate of soyβ-conglycinin is a potent stimulator of CCK release from intestinal mucosal cells and inhibits food intake and gastric emptying through the CCK release [123]. The fragment of β-conglycinin that binds with the rat intestinal membrane to stimulate CCK release has been found to possess the sequence of Gly-Arg-Gly-Arg-Gly-Arg-

Gly. The f51-63 of β-conglycinin was the appetite suppressant and the multiple Arg residues in this fragment may have been involved in manifesting this effect (123).

Oryzatensin (Gly-Tyr-Pro-Met-Tyr-Pro-Leu-Pro-Arg), a bioactive peptide isolated from tryptic digest of rice albumin [124] was able to contract longitudinal muscle strips of the guinea pig ileum. Oryzatensin showed a biphasic ileum contraction, which was characterized by a rapid contraction followed by a slower one. The latter was mediated by the cholinergic nervous system. Although oryzatensin showed weak affinity for μ-opioid receptors, the apparent anti-opioid activity seemed to be associated with the slower contraction. Upon oral administration, the ACEI peptide Arg-Ile-Tyr isolated from rapeseed has also decreased food intake and gastric emptying in mice via stimulating CCK release [125]. This reveals that a peptide with a given sequence of amino acid can perform several bioactivities. Althoughthese studies have encouraging findings on the effect of SSP-derived peptides on opoid activity, long term clinical studies are needed to identify whether such peptides could exert the same effects in humans.

## 3.3. Antioxidant Activity

Free radicals such as superoxide, nitric oxide,and hydroxylandother oxygen-derived species (hydrogen peroxide, and hypochlorous acid) are formed constantly in the human body during metabolism of oxygen. This is in addition to the exposed oxidants such as air pollutants, ozone, oxides of nitrogen, tobacco smoke, and motor vehicle exhaust. These reactive oxygen species (ROS) are highly reactive as they contain an unpaired electron in the outer orbit. Molecules with unpaired electrons such as superoxide are capable of initiating chemical chain reactions through free radical generation [126]. For example superoxide ($O_2^-$) together with $H_2O_2$ can form the reactive hydroxy radical ($OH^-$) via the Haber-Weiss reaction, which proceeds quickly when metal ions such as $Fe^{2+}$ or $Cu^+$ are present (Fenton reaction when iron is the catalyst) [127]. Such chain reactions contribute to lipid peroxidation, DNA damage and protein degredation during oxidatively stressful events [126]. The antioxidant defense systems of the human body consist of a variety of enzymes (catalase, and superoxide dismutase) and antioxidant compounds, to protect against these ROS, but these defenses are not completely efficient [128]. When ROS are generated excessively or the antioxidative defences are depressed, a number of pathological events including aging, cellular injury and DNA degradation take place. Uncontrolled production of free radicals is associated with the onset of many diseases such as cancer, rheumatoid arthritis and atherosclerosis (Figure 3). Therefore antioxidants in the human diet are of great interest as possible protective agents to help the human body to reduce oxidative damages [129]. Antioxidants can prevent or inhibit oxidation by preventing generation of ROS or by inactivating ROS (Table 4).

Several naturally occurring antioxidant peptides such as glutathione (GSH: Glu-Cys-Gly), carnosine (β-Ala-L-His), anserine (β-Ala-3 methyl-L-His), homocarnosine (γ aminobutyryl-L –His), with free radical scavenging activity have been identified in the human body. Of these, GSH scavenge free radicals by donating its H atomand by acting as a co-substrate in reduction of $H_2O_2$ and other hydroperoxides by GSH peroxidase (Figure 4) [130]. Amongst the His containing peptides, carnosine was first identified in 1900 in beef extract [131]. It is one of the most abundant (1-20 mM) nitrogenous compounds present in the nonprotein fraction of vertebrate skeletal muscle and certain other tissues, including olfactory epithelium. In addition to OH· scavenging, carnosine has also been reported to be a scavenger of $O_2$· and a chelator of Cu, which in turn prevent Haber-Weiss reaction [132].

Peptides of antioxidant activities have been also identified from several seed protein hydrolysates. Six antioxidant peptide fragments, which are active against lipid peroxidation, have been isolated from soy β-conglycininenzymatic digest. These peptides are consisted of 5 to 16 amino acid residues including hydrophobic amino acids such as Leu or Valat the N-terminal position and His, Proand Tyr in the sequences [133]. Chen and others [134] have developed 22 synthetic peptides based on the smallest peptide of soy digest, which was Leu-Leu-Pro-His-His, and revealed that the His-containing peptides can act as a metal-ion chelator, an active oxygen quencher, and a OH scavenger. In the peptide sequence, His and Pro played important roles in the antioxidant activity and, among the peptides tested, Pro-His-His had the most antioxidant activity [134]. Oligopeptides isolated from soy hydrolysates, fermented soy and papain hydrolysed soy protein have exhibited antioxidant activity [135]. However, these results are contradictory to those of Pena-Ramos and Xiong [136] who found that papain hydrolysis of soy protein does not generate antioxidant activity indicating that genotype has an effect on the antioxidant peptide release.

Saito and others [138] have constructed peptide libraries using antioxidative tripeptides isolated from soy proteins and have measured the antioxidative activity of the peptides using several *in vitro* methods. Among the antioxidative tripeptides Tyr-His-Tyr showed a strong synergistic effect with phenolic antioxidant inspite of having a marginal reducing activity and a moderate peroxynitrite scavenging activity. Tripeptides with Cys had the strong peroxynitrite scavenging activity whereas tripeptides with Trp or Tyr at the C-terminus had strong radical scavenging activity and weak peroxynitrite scavenging activity [138].

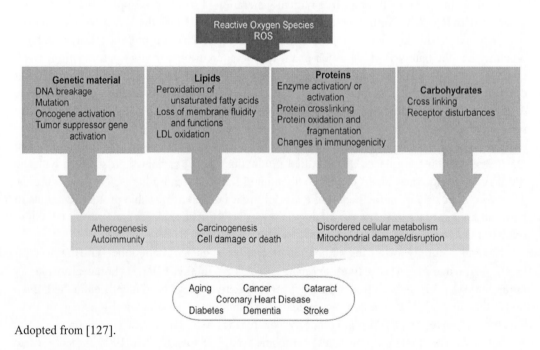

Adopted from [127].

Figure 3. Damage to the biological molecules by reactive oxygen species leading to increased risk of diseases.

**Table 4. Mechanism of action of antioxidants [127]**

|  | Action | Examples |
|---|---|---|
| Prevention | Protein binding/ inactivation of metal ions | Transferrin, Ferritin, Ceruloplasmin, Albumin |
| Enzymatic diversion/neutralization | Specific channelling of ROS into harmless products | Superoxide dismutase, Catalase Glutathione peroxidase |
| Scavenging | Sacrificial interaction with ROS by expandable (replaceable or recyclable) substrates | Ascorbic acid, α-Tcopherol, Uric acid, Bilirubin, Glutathione |
| Quenching | Absorption of electrons and/or energy | α-Tocopherol, β-Carotene |

Wheat germ protein hydrolysates (WGPH) obtained from Alcalase® catalysed hydrolysis had an antioxidant activity close to that of α-tocopherol in a linoleic acid emulsion system [139]. WGPH showed scavenging activity against free radicals such as DPPH, $O_2^{\cdot}$, and OH$^{\cdot}$. Alcalase®-hydrolysed zein has exhibited an antioxidant activity close or comparable to those of butylated hydroxyanisole (BHA), α-tocopherol, and ascorbate by acting as a metal ion chelator or a hydrogen donor, as well as a radical stabilizer to inhibit lipid oxidation [140].

These data suggest the occurrence of antioxidant peptide sequences in SSP, which can be released during enzymatic hydrolysis. The antioxidant mechanism of the released peptides varies with the hydrolysis conditions, structure/amino acid sequence of the peptides, which is determined by the enzyme used to catalyse protein hydrolysis. All these studies show possibility of SSP-derived peptides to act as exogenous antioxidants.

## 3.4. Cholesterol Lowering Ability

Dietary proteins have been known to reduce serum cholesterol. Soy protein, in particular, has been demonstrated to have cholesterol lowering properties in various populations of children [141] and renal patients [142]. However, the mechanism responsible for plasma cholesterol lowering ability of soy protein remained questionable until recently. There is evidence to conclude that the bile acid binding ability of these peptides contributes to blood cholesterol level reduction. Bile acids are acidic steroids synthesized in the liver from cholesterol. They are secreted into the duodenum to participate in the digestion process and are actively reabsorbed from the terminal ileum to undergo enterohepatic circulation [143]. Studies on the hypocholesterolemic effect of soy proteins have resulted in the hypothesis that a peptide with high bile acid binding ability could inhibit the reabsorption of bile acid in the ileum and stimulate cholesterol transformation into bile acids in plasma and liver, ultimately reducing plasma cholesterol level (Figure 5) [144]. Such peptides could also decrease the micellar solubility of cholesterol in the small intestinal epithelial cells and decrease the blood cholesterol level. Soy isoflavones have been considered as the components that contribute to the cholesterol lowering effect of soy protein products. However, Sirtori and others [145] have demonstrated that a marked plasma cholesterol reduction can be obtained using isoflavone–poor soy protein products. Lovati and others [146] have conducted an experiment in which HepG2 cells were exposed to synthetic peptides corresponding to specific sequences of β-conglycinin or to peptides of the *in vitro* digestion of the commercial isoflavone-poor soy protein concentrate. These authors have demonstrated that increased LDL uptake and degradation resulted in after Hep-G2 cell incubation with the synthetic peptide whereas incubation with the digest of soy protein concentrate exhibited a significant up regulation of LDL-receptors. The findings of this study indicated that the low molecular weight peptides released by soy proteins have cholesterol lowering properties. Leu-Pro-Tyr-Pro-Arg, which is a fragment of soybean glycinin, has reduced serum cholesterol in mice after oral administration at a dose of 50 mg/kg for 2 days (25.4% reduction in total cholesterol and 30.6% LDL-cholesterol) [147]. In this study, the excretion of fecal cholesterol and bile acids did not increase indicating that the mechanism responsible for a hypocholesterolemic activity might not be the binding of bile acids. However, there are studies supporting the bile acid binding action of soy glycinin derived peptides. Soy 11S globulin has exhibited higher hypocholesterolemic ability than 7S soy globulin and casein. The peptide Ile-Ala-Val-Pro-Gly-Glu-Val-Ala isolated from the pepsin hydrolysate of 11S globulin was able to bind cholic and deoxycholic acids which lead to hypocholesterolemic effect [144]. Of the five subunits of glycinin (subunit group I: A1aB1b, A1bB2, and A2B1a; subunit group II: A3B4, and A5A4B3), Choi and others [148] have identified a potential bile acid binding peptide sequence (Val-Ala-Trp-Trp-Met-Tyr) in the acidic polypeptide A1a of the A1aB1b subunit. Incorporation of nucleotide sequence encoding this peptide in to the DNA coding of A1a polypeptide exhibited an enhanced bile acid binding ability of glycinin [149].

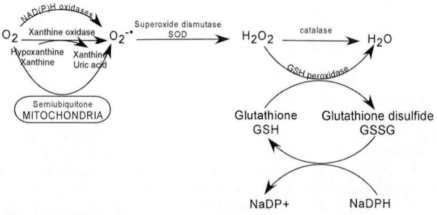

Adopted from Ref. [137].

Figure 4. Pathways of reactive oxygen species (ROS) generation and clearance by the tripeptide glutathione; GSSG.

Soy protein peptic hydrolysate containing phospholipids (SPHP) has shown significantly greater *in vitro* bile acid binding capacity than that of soy protein peptic hydrolysate without phospholipids (SPH) [150]. The cholesterol micelles containing SPHP and SPH significantly suppressed cholesterol uptake by Caco-2 cells compared to cholesterol micelles containing casein tryptic hydrolysate. The *in vivo* rat feeding studies conducted have indicated that the fecal excretion of total steroids was significantly greater in rats fed with SPHP than SPH.

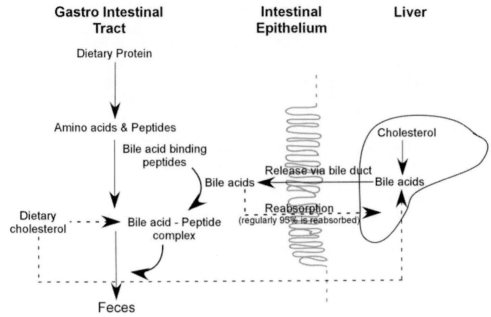

Based on Ref. [144].

Figure 5. Hypocholesterolemic action of bile acid binding peptides. Bile acids are synthesized from cholesterol, conjugated and then excreted into the bile ducts. Released bile acids are reabsorbed via intestinal epithelium facilitating the dietary cholesterol absorption. Dietary protein derived bile acid binding peptides enhance bile acid excretion with feces, reducing the bile acid re-absorption.

## 3.5. Modulation of Immune Function

The function of the immune system is based on the activities of different cell types such as monocytes/macrophage, platelets, erythrocytes, polymorphoneuclear leukocytes (eosinophils, neutrophils, basophils and mast cells), T and B-lymphocytes to protect the body against foreign microbes such as bacteria, viruses and parasites. A number of plant protein derived bioactive peptides, which modulate the immune function have been identified. Among these the major plant protein source is soy. Yoshikawa and others [147] have isolated a peptide soymetide-13 (Met-Ile-Thr-Leu-Ala-Ile-Pro-Val-Asn-Lys-Pro-Gly-Arg) derived from tryptic digest of the alpha subunit of β-conglycinin that stimulates phagocytosis in human polymorphoneuclear leukocytes. Methionine residue of the amino terminus was found to be essential for this activity. The peptide His-Cys-Gln-Arg-Pro-Arg isolated from tryptic digest of soy glycinin was also found to be immuno-stimulating,activating phagocytosis of human neutrophils, and stimulating tumor necrosis factor (TNF) when orally administered to mice [151].

Soymetide is the first food derived peptide agonist of the N-formyl-methionyl-leucyl-phenylalanine (fMLP). fMLP is the synthetic form of N-formylmethionyl peptide that is strongly chemotactic for human neutrophils and macrophages thereby stimulates the immune system. The surface of neutrophils and macrophages carry specific fMLP receptors that mediate the generation of ROS from neutrophils and macrophages as well as the phagocytosis stimulating activity of the neutrophils. These functions lead to a rapid response for bacterial infection as bacterial proteins have an N-formylmethionine residue at their N-termini. Such response leads to bacterial death by phagocytosis and ROS induced bactericidal effects. Soymetides have a weak affinity to the fMLP receptors. Therefore, following ingestion of soy proteins the immune system receives a signal that is similar to what received after a bacterial infection [151]. Soymetide-4 is a tetrapeptide and is the shortest peptide that stimulates phagocytosis. Soymetide–4 did not induce ROS formation by neutrophils *in vitro*, may be due to its lower affinity to fMLP receptors than that of fMLP. Therefore, soymetide-4 could be theoretically safe as an immunostimulating agent without causing any inflammation. Orally administration of soymetide–4 has also prevented hair loss (anti-alopecia mechanism) induced by the anti-cancer agent etoposide [151]. Of the soymetides isolated, the soymetide-4 is more desirable as an immunostimulating peptide due to its short length, which facilitates its absorption in the digestive tract.

Oryzatensin (Gly-Tyr-Pro-Met-Tyr-Pro-Leu-Pro-Arg) obtained from tryptic digestion of rice albumin has also been identified as an immuno-modulatory peptide. Comparatively short C-terminal fragments of oryzatensin demonstrating similar activity were also reported. Oryzatensin also induced phagocytosis and production of superoxide anions in human leukocytes *in vitro* [26]. Horiguchi and others [152] have identified the effect of wheat gluten hydrolysate (hydrolysed with protease and amylase) on the immune system of healthy human volunteers. Intake of 3 g of wheat gluten hydrolysate for 6 days led to a significant increase in natural killer (NK) cell activity of the test group compared to the placebo. NK cells play a critical role in immune surveillance against tumour development and viral infections. Hence NK cell activation is effective in patients with autoimmune disease or cancer and in elderly people who usually have low levels of NK cell activity [152]. The immuno-enhancing activity of wheat gluten hydrolysate might be caused by immuno-stimulating peptides present in the hydrolysate. According to Clare and others [153] ACEI peptides can stimulate the immune system via inactivation of bradykinin. Bradykinin stimulates macrophages to enhance lymphocyte migration and to increase secretion of lymphokines.

## 3.6. Calmodulin Binding Activity

Calmodulin (CaM) is an important soluble protein in humans that bind with $Ca^{2+}$ and regulates the activity of many cellular enzymes [154], including adenylyl cyclase, cyclic neucleotide phosphodiesterase, $Ca^{2+}$-$Mg^{2+}$ ATPase, calcinurin, nitric oxide synthase, andseveral protein kinases. By regulating these enzymes CaM acts as a $Ca^{2+}$ dependent regulator ofcyclic nucleotide metabolism, $Ca^{2+}$ transport, protein phosphorylation-dephosphorylation cascades, ion transport, cytoskeletal function and cell proliferation [155]. Excessive activity of CaM dependent enzymes such as protein kinase II leads to increased phosphorylation of various cellular proteins related to pathogenic chronic diseases. Therefore, any compound capable of reducing the activity of CaM can inhibit these reactions and suppress disease progression.Since CaM is negatively charged with an exposed hydrophobic surface in its active site, peptides having basic amino acids that give net positive charge or peptides with hydrophobic surfaces have the potential to inhibit CaM [156]. A number of peptides in insect venom with these properties have been reported to bind with CaM and inhibit CaM activated phosphodiesterase. The most potent of these peptides also found to have an alpha helical structure [157]. Peptides with CaM binding activity have been identified in the protein hydrolysates of several SSP.

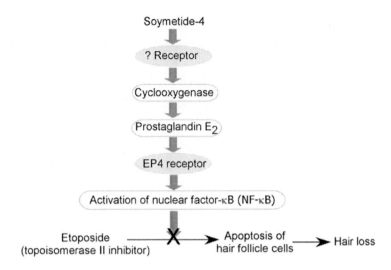

Adapted from Ref. [151].

Figure 6. Hypothetical mechanism of anti-alopecia effect of orally administered soymetide-4: Activation of cycloxygenase by soymetide-4 releases PGE2 which then activates nuclear factor-κB (NF-κB) and suppress apoptosis of hair follicle cells and etoposide induced alopecia.

Pea proteins hydrolysate of Alcalase®-catalysis that was rich in positively charged amino acids such as Lys and Arg and contained short peptides that bind CaM and reduced the activity of CaM dependent protein kinase II *in vitro* [156]. Hydrolysis of flaxseed protein isolate by the same enzyme has yielded peptides that can bind to CaM and inhibit CaM dependent neuronal and endothelial nitric oxide synthase [158]. No research evidence is available for the possibility of other SSP generating CaM binding peptides or the action of such peptides *in vivo*.

## 3.7. Anticancer Activity

Peptides isolated from hydrolysed SSP have demonstrated cancer preventive properties both *in vitro* and *in vivo*. Xiao and group [159] have reported that diets containing soy protein isolate inhibit tumourgenesis in rats by enhancing somatostatin, which is a known antiproliferative agent for colon cancer cells. Part of this anticancer activity may be attributed to the bioactive peptides generated during soy protein digestion. Peptides obtained by Thermolase® hydrolysis of defatted soy protein showed *in vitro* cytotoxicity (IC$_{50}$ value of 0.16 mg/mL) in mouse monocyte macrophage cell line. Further purification of this hydrolysate yielded a nonapeptide, X-Met-Leu-Pro-Ser-Tyr-Ser-Pro-Tyr [160]. Lunasin, a chemopreventive bioactive peptide from 2S albumin of soybean, can reduce carcinogen induced cell transformation in mice [161], and skin tumour incidences [162]. Exogenous application of the lunasin peptide inhibited carcinogen-induced transformation of murine fibroblast cells to cancerous foci *in vitro*. Lunasin is a unique, naturally occurring peptide of 43-amino acids and contains nine Asp residues at its carboxyl end preceded by Arg-Gly-Asp, the cell adhesion motif. It acts as a chemopreventive agent that functions possibly via binding with chromatin. Lunasin has been able to inhibit core histone acetylation by binding to nonacetylated H3 and H4 histones. This mechanism is believed to be responsible for the anticancer property of this chromatin binding peptide [162]. Lunasin has also been isolated from barley (*Hordeum vulgare* L), wheat [161] and amaranth (*Amaranthus hypochondriacus*) [163] seed proteins. The crude and partially purified lunasin from barley has suppressed colony formation in stably *ras*-transfected mouse fibroblast cells. These fractions also inhibited histone acetylation in mouse fibroblast and human breast cells in the presence of the histone deacetylase inhibitor sodium butyrate [30]. According to Jeong and others [159], the bioactive lunasin could be extracted from liver of rats fed with a diet rich in lunasin of wheat. This indicates that lunasin remains intact and biologically active upon GI digestion. In amaranth seeds, the highest concentration of lunasin was observed in the glutelin fraction (3.0 µg/g). Lunasin was also found in albumin, prolamin and globulin fractions and even in popped amaranth seeds [163].

## 4. PREDICTION OF BIOACTIVITIES OF SSP DERIVED PEPTIDES USING PEPTIDE DATABASES

SSP are encoded by families of polymorphic genes by a regulated process. For example, in maize 30 to 100 genes are involved in encoding zein. According to research findings the amino acid composition and sequence in bioactive peptides are the major factors that determine their bioactivities. For example most of the opioid peptides contain Tyr and Phe residues [164]whereas the majority of the ACEI peptides contain Pro residues at the C-terminus [45]. Therefore the primary structure of precursor proteins is a major determinant of the capability of a protein to generate bioactive peptides.

Computer assisted databases are available for predicting bioactivities of peptides located within the parent protein and also to obtain information on isolated bioactive peptides. These peptide libraries include information on peptides constructed via chemical synthesis or genetic engineering. Peptide databases allow comparison of experimental peptide mass and amino acid sequence against the molecular mass and amino acid sequence of peptides in the database and enable the users to find details on the peptide of interest. At present several databases are available (Table 5) to predict the precursor protein of a bioactive peptide with a known amino acid sequence. Such databases also provide information on genes responsible for coding a specific peptide. BIOPEP [165] is a database, which classifies food proteins as potential sources of bioactive peptides. As the database indicates, antihypertensive peptide fragments commonly occur in most of the food proteins [166,167]. This database identifies bovine β-casein and rice prolamin as the best precursors of antihypertensive peptides. Bioactive fragments as well as their surroundings are also found to be hydrophilic and mostly localized at random coil structures of the proteins [167]. According to a database search performed using BIOPEP by Wang and Mejia [168], soy proteins have sequences with antiamnestic, antihypertensive, antioxidative, antithrombotic, dipeptidyl peptidase IV inhibitory, immunostimulating and opioid activities. The 7S and 11S soy proteins were the sources of bioactive peptides while 2S protein has also exhibited some potential. Several opioid peptide sequences in soyproteins, which have not been previously reported, were revealed due to this matching.

**Table 5. Databases available to search for peptides with bioactivities**

| Database | Accessible website | Information available |
|---|---|---|
| UniProt KB/SwissProt | http://www.expasy.org/sprot/ | Protein sequence and function, Post-translational modification(s). Domains and sites, Similarities to other proteins, Disease(s) associated with deficiencies in the protein, Sequence conflicts, and variants |
| BioPep | http://www.uwm.edu.pl/biochemia | Potential prediction of bioactive peptides released from proteins |
| Bioactive polypeptide database (BioPD) | http://biopd.bjmu.edu.cn/help.asp | Basic information and structure of peptide, related gene information, Interactions between the peptide and other proteins, Information about diseases and the peptide if available |
| Antimicrobial peptide database (APD) | http://aps.unmc.edu/AP/main.php | Information on antifungal, antiviral and anticancer peptides. Statistical information on peptide sequence, structure and function to use in novel peptide design. |
| SwePep | http://www.swepep.org | Information on endogenous bioactive peptides, Molecular mass, modifications, Precursor information, and organism affiliation of neuropeptides, Hormones, Characterized and uncharacterized bioactive peptides and potential bioactive peptides |
| *ANTIMIC: a database of antimicrobial sequences* | http://research.i2r.a-star.edu.sg/Templar/DB/ANTIMIC/ | Comprehensive information on natural antimicrobial peptides (AMPs), both known and putative, Facilitates efficient extraction of data and its analysis at molecular level, and search for new AMPs. |
| *JenPep: Peptide binding database* | http://www.jenner.ac.uk/Jenpep/ | Quantitative binding data for immunological protein-peptide interactions |

Dziuba and others [169] carried out abioinformatic-aided analysis of the biologically active fragments and the bonds of food proteins that are susceptible to the action of endopeptidases of known specificity.According to this analysis, wheat gliadins were the mostsusceptible for bioactive peptides release. These peptides showed antihypertensive, dipeptidylpeptidase inhibitory, opioid and antioxidative effect, and were released due to activity of chymotrypsin, elastase, ficin or pepsin. Wu and others [44] have constructed a database of di- and tripeptides having ACEI activity based on the published literature and have predicted the $IC_{50}$ value of ACEI peptides from SSP (of pea and soybean) (Table 2). The other important online databases of bioactive peptides are BioPD [170]and SwePep. In addition to these the antimicrobial peptide database (APD) provides information on antibacterial, antifungal and antiviral peptides.

# REFERENCES

[1]   Habben, J.E., and Larkins, B.A. 1995, *Curr. Opin. Biotech.*, 6, 171-174.

[2]   Smacchi, E., and Gobbetti, M. 2000, *Food Microbiol.*, 17, 129-141.

[3]   Pihlanto, A., and Korhonen, H. 2003, Advances in Food and Nutrition Research; Volume 47, S. L. Taylor (Ed.), Elsevier Academic Press, USA, 175-249.

[4]   Shewry, P.R., Napier, J.A., and Tatham, A.S. 1995, *Plant Cell,* 7, 945-956.

[5]   Mandal, S., and Mandal, R.K. 2000, *Curr. Sci.*, 79, 576-589.

[6]   Fukushima, D. 1991, *Food Rev. Int.*, 7, 323-351.

[7]   Fujiwara, T., Nambara, E., Yamagishi, K., Goto, D.B., and Naito, S. 2002, Storage Proteins *In* The Arabidopsis Book, *The American Society of Plant Biologists*,1-12.

[8]   Derbyshire, E., Wright, D.J., and Boulter, D. 1976, *Phytochem.,* 15, 3-24.

[9]   Herman, E.M., and Larkins, B.A. 1999, *Plant Cell*, 11, 601-614.

[10]  Sathe, S.K. 2004, Proc. 2004 IFT Annual Meeting, July 12-16, Las-Vegas, NV, 60-1.

[11]  Silano, M., and De Vincenzi, M. 1999, *Nahrung/Food*, 43, 175-184.

[12]  Osborne, T.B. 1924, The Vegetable Proteins. Longmans Green & Co., London.

[13]  Higgins, T.J.V. 1984, *Ann. Rev. Plant Physio.*, 35, 191-221.

[14]  Kreis, M., Forde, B.G., Rahman, S., Miflin, B. J., and Shewry, P. R. 1985, *J. Mol. Biol.*, 183, 499-502.

[15]  Shewry, P.R., Beaudoin, F., Jenkins, J., Griffiths-Jones, S., and Mills, E.N.C. 2002, *Biochem. Soc. Trans.*, 30, 906-910.

[16]  Mills, E.N.C., Jenkins, J., Marigheto, N., Belton, P.S., Gunning, A.P., and Morris, V.J. 2002, *Biochem. Soc. Trans.*, 30, 925-929.

[17]  Shewry, P.R., and Halford, N.G. 2002, *J. Exp. Bot.*, 53, 947-958.

[18]  Hoglund, A.S., Rodin, J., Larsson, E., and Rask. L. 1992, *Plant Physiol.*, 98, 509-515.

[19]  Hsiao, E.S.L., Lin, L.J., Li, F.Y., Wang, M.M.C., Liao, M.Y., and Tzen, J.T.C. 2006, *J. Agric. Food Chem.*, 54, 9544-9550.

[20]  Shewry, P.R. 2000, Seed Technology and Its Biological Basis, M. Black, and J.D. Bewley (Eds.), CRC Press, Boca Raton, 42.

[21]  Mouécoucou, J., Villaume, C., Sanchez, C., and Mejean, L. 2004, *Food Res. Int.*, 37, 777-783.

[22]  Madhusudhan, K.T., and Singh, N. 1985, *Phytochem.*, 24, 2507-2509.

[23] Mazhar, H., Quayle, R., Fido, R.J., Stobart, A.K., Napier, J.A., and Shewry, P.R. 1998, *Phytochem.*, 48, 429-432.

[24] Mckevith, B. 2005, *Nutr. Bull.*, 30, 13-26.

[25] Kitts, D.D., and Weiller, K. 2003, *Curr. Pharm. Des.*, 9, 1309-1323.

[26] Korhonen, H., and Pihlanto, A. 2006, *Int. Dairy J.*, 16, 945-960.

[27] Yust, M.M., Pedroche, J., Giron-Calle, J., Alaiz, M., Millan, F., and Vioque, J. 2003, *Food Chem.*, 81, 363-369.

[28] Korhonen, H., and Philanto, A. 2003, *Curr. Pharm. Des.*, 9, 1297-1308.

[29] Jeong, H.J., Lam, Y., and de Lumen, B.O. 2002, *J. Agric. Food Chem.*, 50, 5903 –5908.

[30] Roberts, P.R., Burney, J.D., Black, K.W., and Zaloga, G.P. 1999, *Int. J. Gastroenterol.*, 60, 332-337.

[31] Ganapathy, V., and Leibach, F.H. 1985, *Am. J. Physiol.*, 249, G153-G160.

[32] Daniel, H., Morse, E.L., and Adibi, S.A. 1992, *J. Biol. Chem.*, 267, 9565-9573.

[33] Burton, P.S., Conradi, R.A., Ho, N.F.H., Hilgers, A.R., and Borchardt, R.T. 1996, *J. Pharm. Sci.*, 85, 1336-1340.

[34] Hermansen, K. 2000, *Brit. J. Nutr.*, 83, suppl. 1, s113-s119.

[35] Dodek, P.M., Sackett, D. L., and Schechter, M. T. 1999, *Can. Med. Assoc. J.*, 160, 1475-1477.

[36] Wolz, M., Cutler, J., Roccella, E.J., Rohde, F., Thom, T., and Burt V. 2000, *Am. J. Hypertens.*, 13, 103-104.

[37] Ehlers, M.R.W., and Riordan, J.F. 1989, *Biochemsitry*, 28, 5311-5318.

[38] Vermeirssen, V., Camp, J.V., and Verstraete, W. 2002, *J. Biochem. Bioph. Meth.*, 51,75–87.

[39] Natesh, R., Schwager, S.L.U., Sturrock, E.D., and Acharya, K.R. 2003, *Nature*, 421, 551-554.

[40] Ferreira, S.H., Bartelt, D.C., and Greene, L.J. 1970, *Biochemistry*, 9, 2583-2593.

[41] Cheung, H.S., Wang, F.L., Ondetti, M.A., Sabo, E.F., and Cushman, D.W. 1980, *J. Biol. Chem.*, 255,401-407.

[42] Wei, L., Clauser, E., Alhenc-Gelas, F., and Corvol, P. 1992, *J. Biol. Chem.*, 267, 13398-13405.

[43] Cushman, D.W., Cheung, H.S., Sabo, E.F., and Ondetti, M.A. 1981, Angiotensin Converting Enzyme Inhibitors; Mechanism of Action and Clinical Implications, Z.P. Horovitz (Ed.), Urban and Schwerzenberg Inc., Baltimore, Maryland, 3-25.

[44] Wu, J., Aluko, R.E., and Nakai, S. 2006, *J. Agric. Food Chem.*, 54,732-738.

[45] Yamamoto, N. 1997, *Biopolymers*, 43, 129-134.

[46] Marczak, E.D., Usui, H., Fujita, H., Yang, Y.J., Yokoo, M., Lipkowski, A.W., and Yoshikawa, M. 2003, *Peptides*, **24**, 791–798

[47] Wu, J., Muir, A., and Aluko, R. 2002, Nutraceuticals and Functional Foods II, IFT Annual Meeting and Food Expo, Anaheim, California, 61D-1.

[48] Pedroche, J., Yust, M.M., Megias, C., Lqari, H., Alaiz, M., Giron-Calle, J., Millan, F., and Vioque. J. 2004, *Grasas Aceites*, 55, 354-358.

[49] Wu, J., Aluko, R.E., and Muir, A.D. 2008, *Food Chem.*, 111, 942-950.

[50] Wu, J., and Muir, A.D. 2008, *J. Food Sci.*, 73, C210-C216.

[51] Pedroche, J., Yust, M.M., Lqari, H., Megias, C., Giron Calle, J., Alaiz, M., Vioque, J., and Millan, F. 2007, *Food Res. Int.*, 40, 931-938.

[52] Eggum, B.O, Kreft, I., and Javornik, B. 1980, *Plant Food. Human Nutr.*, 30, 175-179.

[53] Kayashita, J., Shimaoka, I., Nakajoh, M., Yamazaki, M., and Kato, N. 1997, *J. Nutr.*, 127, 1395-1400.

[54] He, J., Klag, M. J., Whelton, P. K., Mo, J. P., Chen, J. Y., Qian, M. C., Mo, P. S., and He, G. Q. 1995, *Am. J. Clin. Nutr.*, 61, 366-372.

[55] Eggum, B.O., and Beames, R.M. 1983, Seed Proteins: Biochemistry, Genetics and Nutritive Value. Advances in Agricultural Biotechnology, W. Gottshalk and E. P. Muller (Ed.), M. Nijhoff and W. Junk, The Hague, Netherlands, 499.

[56] Radovic, S.R., Maksimovic, V.R., and Varkonji-Gasic, E.I. 1996, *J. Agric. Food Chem.*, 44, 972-974.

[57] Kawakami, A., Inbe, T. H., Kayahara, I.T., and Horii, A. 1995, *Curr. Adv. Buckwheat Res.*, 1, 927-934.

[58] Li, C., Matsui, T., Matsumoto, K., Yamasaki, R., and Kawasaki, T. 2002, *J. Pept.* Sci., 8, 267-274.

[59] Ma, M.S., Bae, I.Y., Lee, H.G., and Yang, C. B. 2006, *Food Chem.*, 96, 36-42.

[60] Singh, U. 1985, *Plant Food. Hum. Nutr.*, 35, 339-351.

[61] Friedman, M. 1996, *J. Agric. Food Chem.*, 44, 6-29.

[62] Sánchez-Vioque, R., Clemente, A., Vioque, J., Bautista, J., and Millán, F. 1999, *Food Chem.*, 64, 237-243.

[63] Pedroche, J., Yust, M.M.,Giron-Calle, J., Alaiz, M.., Millan, F., and Vioque. J. 2002, *J. Sci. Food Agric.*, 82, 960-965.

[64] Mullally, M.M., Meisel, H., and FitzGerald, R.J. 1997, *FEBS Letters*, 402, 99-101.

[65] Matsufuji, H., Matsui, T., Seki, E., Osajima, K., Nakashima, M., and Osajima, Y. 1994, *Biosci. Biotech. Biochem.*, 58, 2244-2245.

[66] Kim, Y. K., Yoon, S., Yu, D. Y., Lonnerdal, B., and Chung, B. H. 1999, *J. Dairy Res.*, 66, 431-439.

[67] Castell, A.G., Guenter, W., and Igbasan, F.A. 1996, *Anim. Feed Sci. Tech.*, 60, 209-227.

[68] David, P., and Gerard, D. U. C. 1999, Peas, a promising source of protein, *Oleagineux,Crops Gras, Lipides*, 6, 518-523.

[69] Higgins, T. J. V., and Spencer, D. 1977, *Plant Physiol.*, 60, 655-661.

[70] Vermeirseen, V., Camp, J.V., Devos, L., and Verstraete, W. 2003, *J. Agric. Food Chem.*, 51, 5680-5687.

[71] Vermeirseen, V., Bent, A., Camp, J.V., Amerongen, A.V., and Verstraete, W. 2004, *Biochimie*, 86, 231-239.

[72] Vermeirseen, V., Camp, J.V., Decroos, K., Wijmelbeke, L.V., and Verstraete,W. 2003, *J. Dairy Sci.*, 86, 429-438.

[73] Vermeirseen, V., Camp, J.V., and Verstraete, W. 2005, *J. Sci. Food Agric.*, 85, 399-405.

[74] Vermeirseen, V., Augustijns, P., Morel, N., Van Camp, J., Opsomer, A., and Verstraete, W. 2005, *Int. J. Food Sci. Nutr.*, 56, 415-430.

[75] Lee, K.H., Jones, R.A., Dalby, A., and Tsai, C.Y. 1976, *Biochem. Genet.*, 14, 641-650.

[76] Harvey, B.M.R., and Oaks, A. 1974, *Plant Physiol.*, 53, 453-457.

[77] Momany, F.A., Sessa, D.J., Lawton, J.W., Selling, G.W., Hamaker, S.A.H., and Willet, J.L. 2006, *J. Agric. Food Chem.*, 54, 543 –547.

[78] Miyoshi, S., Ishikawa, H., Kaneko, T., Fukui, F., Tanaka, H., and Maruyama, S. 1991, *Agric. Biol. Chem.*, 55, 1313-1318.

[79] Yano, S., Suzuki, K., and Funatsu, G. 1996, *Biosci. Biotech. Biochem.*, 60, 661-663.

[80] Li, G.H., Le, G.W., Liu, H., and Shi, Y.H. 2005, *Food Sci. Tech. Int.*, 11, 281-287.

[81] Li, G.H., Shi, Y.H., Liu, H., and Le, G.W. 2006, *Eur. Food Res. Technol.*, 222, 733-736.

[82] Li, G., Wan, J., Le, G., and Shi, Y. 2006, *J. Pept. Sci.*, 12, 509-514.

[83] Meisel, H. 1993, Food Protein–Structure and Functionality. K. D. Schwenke and R. Mothes (Ed.), VCH; Weinheim, New York, 61-75.

[84] Bandyopadhyay, K, and Ghosh, S. 2002, *J. Agric. Food Chem.,* 50, 6854-6857.

[85] Ochi, S., Mori, T., Horikawa, M., Mikami, H., and Sato, M. 1995, *Nihon Nogeikagakkai Taikai Koen Yoshi-shu* (In Japanese), 142.

[86] Nakano, D., Ogura, K., Miyakoshi, M., Ishii, F., Kawanishi, H., Kurumazuka, D., Kwak, C., Ikemura, K., Takaoka, M., Moriguchi, S., Iino, T., Kusumoto, A., Asami, S., Shibata, H., Kiso, Y., and Matsumara, Y. 2006, *Biosci. Biotech. Biochem.,* 70, 1118-1126.

[87] Gibbs, B.F,, Zougman, A.., Masse, R., and Mulligan, C. 2004, *Food Res.* Int., 37,123-131.

[88] Lo, W.M.Y., and Li-Chan, E.C.Y. 2005, *J. Agric. Food Chem.,* 53, 3369-3376.

[89] Shin, Z., Yu, R., Park, S., Chung, D.K, Ahn, C., Nam, H., Kim, K., and Lee, H.J. 2001, *J. Agric. Food Chem.*49, 3004–3009.

[90] Wu, J., and Ding, X. 2001, *J. Agric. Food Chem.* 49, 501-506.

[91] Wu, J., and Ding, X. 2002, *Food Res. Int.*, 35, 367-375.

[92] Chen, J., Okada, T., Muramoto, K., Suetsuna, K., and Yang, S. 2003, *J. Food Biochem.*, 26, 543-554.

[93] Deshpande, S.S., and Nielsen, S.S. 1987, *J. Food Sci.*, 52, 1326-1329.

[94] Astwood, J.D., Leach, J.N., and Fuchs, R.L. 1996, *Nat. Biotechnol.*, 14, 1269–1273.

[95] Lo, W.M.Y., Farnworth, E.R., and Li-Chan, E.C.Y. 2006, *J. Food Sci.*, 71, S231-S237.

[96] Megias, C., Yust, M.M., Pedroche, J., Lquari, H., Giron-Calle, J., Alaiz, M., Millan, F., and Vioque, J. 2004, *J. Agric. Food Chem.*, 52, 1928-1932.

[97] Megias, C., Pedroche, J., Yust, M.M., Alaiz, M., Giron-Calle, J., Millan, F., and Vioque, J. 2009, *LWT Food Sci. Technol.*, 42, 228-232.

[98] Payne, P.I., Holt, L.M., Jackson, E.A., and Law, C.N. 1984, *Philos. Trans.Royal Soc. B*, 304, 359-371.

[99] Ge, Y., Sun, A., Ni, Y., and Cai, T. 2000, *J. Agric. Food Chem.*, 48, 6215–6218.

[100] Matsui, T., Li, C.H., and Osajima, Y. 1999, *J. Pept. Sci.*, 5, 289-297.

[101] Motoi, H., and Kodama, T. 2003, *Nahrung*, 47, 354-358.

[102] Huan, L., Guan-Hong, L., and Yong-Hui, S. 2005, *J. Peanut Sci.*, 34, 8-14.

[103] Lee, J. R., Kwon, D.Y., Shin, H.K., and Yang, C.B. 1999, *Food Sci. Biotech.*, **8,** 172–178.

[104] Kwon, Y. S., Lee, H. G., Shin, H. K., and Yang, C. B. 2000, *Food Sci. Biotech.*, 9, 292-296.

[105] Wu J, Muir A.D, and Aluko R.E. 2004, ACE inhibitory peptides from plant materials. U.S. Patent Application 2006217318.

[106] Takaiwa, F. 2004, Rice is life: scientific perspectives for the 21st century-Proc of the World Rice Research Conference, K. Tariyama, K. L. Heong, and B. Hardy (Ed.), *IRRI*, 102-104.

[107] Teschemacher, H. 2003, *Curr. Pharm. Des.*, 9, 1331-1344.

[108] Arihara, K. 2006, *Meat Sci.*, 74, 219-229.

[109] Kapel, R., Chabeau, A., Lesage, J., Riviere, G., Ravallec-Ple, R., Lecouturier, D., Wartelle, M., Guillochon, D., and Dhulster, P. 2006, *Food Chem.*, 98, 120-126.

[110] Cozzolino, D., Sessa, G., Salvatore, T., Sasso, F.C., Giugliano, D., Lefebvre, P.J., and Torella, R. 1996, *J. Clin. Endocrinol. Metabol.*, 81, 713-718.

[111] Margules, D.L., Moisset, B., Lewis, M.J., Shibuya, H., and Pert, C.B. 1978, *Science*, 202, 988-991.

[112] Levine, A.S., Grace, M., Billington, C.J., and Zimmerman, D.M. 1991, *Brain Res.*, 566, 193-197.

[113] Drewnowski, A. 1992, *Trends Food Sci. Tech.*, 31, 97-99.

[114] Yoshikawa, M., Takahashi, M., and Yang, S. 2003, *Curr. Pharm. Des.*, 9, 1325-1330.

[115] Yang, S., Yunden, J., Sonoda, S., Doyama, N., Lipkowski, A.W., Kawamura, Y., and Yoshikawa, M. 2001, *FEBS Lett.*, 509, 213-217.

[116] Zioudrou, C., Streaty, R.A., and Klee, W.A. 1979, *J. Biol. Chem.*, 254, 2446-2449.

[117] Fanciulli, G., Dettori, A., Demontis, M.P., Tomasi, P.A., Anania, V., and Delitala, G. 2005, *Life Sci.*, 76, 1713-1719.

[118] Schusdziarra, V., Henrichs, I., Holland, A., Klier, M., and Pfeiffer, E.F. 1981,*Diabetes, 30, 362-364.*

[119] Fukudome, S., Shimatsu, A., Suganuma, H., and Yoshikawa, M. 1995, *Life Sci.*, 57, 729-734.

[120] Graaf, C., Blom, W.A.M., Smeets, P.A.M., Stafleu, A., and Hendricks, H.F.J. 2004, *Am. J. Clin. Nutr.*, 79, 946-961.

[121] Takahashi, M., Fukunaga, H., Kaneto, H., Fukudome, S., and Yoshikawa, M. 2000, *Jpn. J. Pharmacol.*, 84, 259-265.

[122] Morley, J.E., Levine, A.S., Yamada, T., Gebhard, R.L., Prigge, W.F., Shafer, R.B., Goetz, F.C., and Silvis, S.E. 1983, *Gastroenterology*, 84, 1517-1523.

[123] Nishi, T., Hara, H., and Tomita, F. 2003, *J. Nutr.*, 133, 352-357.

[124] Pupovac, J., and Anderson, H. (2002), *J. Nutr.*, 132, 2775-2780.

[125] Takahashi, M., Moriguchi, S., Yoshikawa, M., and Sasaki, R. 1994, *Biochem. Mol. Biol. Int.*, 33, 1151-1158.

[126] Marczak, E.D., Ohinata, K., Lipkowski, A.W., and Yoshikawa, M. 2006, *Peptides*, 27, 2065-2068.

[127] Benzie, I.F.F. 2000, *Eur. J. Nutr.*, 39, 53-61.

[128] Jacob, R. A., and Burri, B.J. 1996, *Am. J. Clin. Nutr.*, 63, 985S-990S.

[129] Wu, H., Pan, B.S., Chang, C., and Shiau, C. 2005, *J. Food Drug Anal.* 13, 176-183.

[130] Kelly, F.J. 1999, *Food Chem. Toxicol.*, 37, 963-966.

[131] Babizhayev, M. A., Seguin, M. C., Gueyne, J., Evistigneeva, P., Ageyeva, E. A., and Zheltukhina, G. A. 1994, *Biochem. J.*, 304, 509-516.

[132] Gariballa, S.E., and Sinclair, A. 2000, *Age Ageing*, 29, 207-210.

[133] Chen, H.M., Muramoto, K., and Yamauchi, F. 1995, *J. Agric. Food Chem.*, 43, 574-578.

[134] Chen, H.M., Muramoto, K., Yamauchi, F., Fujimoto, K., and Nokihara, K. 1998, *J. Agric. Food Chem.*, 46, 49 –53.

**[135]** Khalil, A.A., Mohamed, S.S., Taha, F.S., and Karlsson, E.N. 2006, *Afr. J. Biotech.*, 5, **907-916.**

[136] Pena-Ramos, E.A., and Xiong, Y.L. 2002, *J. Food Sci.*, 67, 2952-2956.

[137] Droge, W. 2002, *Physiol Rev.*, 82, 47-95.

[138] Saito. K., Jin. D.H., Ogawa, T., Muramoto, K., Hatakeyama, E., Yasuhara, T., and Nokihara, K. 2003, *J. Agric. Food. Chem.,* 51, 3668-3674.

[139] Zhu, K.K., Zhou, H. M., and Qian, H. F. 2006, *Cereal Chem.,* 83, 69-75.

[140] Kong, B., and Xiong, Y.L. 2006, *J. Agric. Food Chem.*, 54, 6059-6068.

[141] Laurin, D., Jacques, H., Moorjani, S., Steinke, F.H., Gagne, C., Brun, D., and Lupien, P.J. 1991,*Am. J. Clin. Nutr.*, 54, 98-103.

[142] D'Amico, G., Gentile, M.G., Manna, G., Fellin, G., Ciceri, R., Cofano, F., Petrini, C., Lavarda, F., Perolini, S., and Porrini, M. 1992, *Lancet*, 339, 1131-1134.

[143] Kahlon, T.S., and Shao, Q. 2004, *Food Chem.*, 86,435-440.

[144] Pak, V.V., Koo, M.S., Kasymova, T.D., and Kwon, D.Y. 2005, *Chem. Nat. Compd.*, 41, 710-714.

[145] Sirtori, C.R., Gianazza, E., Manzoni, C., Lovat,i M.R., and Murphy, P.A., 1997,*Am. J. Clin. Nutr.*, 65, 166-167.

[146] Lovati, M.R., Manzoni, C., Gianazza, E., Arnoldi, A., Kurowska, E., Carroll, K.K., and Sirtori, C.R. 2000, *J. Nutr.*, 130, 2543-2549.

[147] Yoshikawa, M., Fujita, H., Matoba, N., Takenaka, Y., Yamamoto, T., Yamauchi, R., Tsuruki, H., and Takahata, K. 2000, *BioFactors*, 12, 143-146.

[148] Choi, S.K., Adachi, M.A., and Utsumi, S. 2002, *Biosci. Biotech. Bioch.*, 66, 2395-2401.

[149] Choi, S.K., Adachi, M., and Utsumi, S. 2004, *Biosci. Biotech. Bioch.*, 68, 1980-1983.

[150] Nagaoka, S., Miwa, K., Eto, M., Kuzuya, Y., Hori, G., and Yamamoto, K. 1999, *J. Nutr.,* 129, 1725-1730.

[151] Tsuruki, T., Takahata, K., and Yoshikawa, M. 2005, *Peptides*, 26, 707-711.

[152] Horiguchi, N., Horiguchi, H., and Suzuki, Y. 2005, *Biosci. Biotech. Bioch.*, 69, 2445-2449.

[153] Clare, D. A., Catignani, G. L., and Swaisgood, H. E. 2003, *Curr. Pharma.Des.*, 9, 1239-1255.

[154] Cheung, W.Y. 1984, *Fed. Proc.*, 43, 2995-2999.

[155] Gnegy, M.E. 1993, *Annu. Rev. Pharmacol.*, 33, 45-70.

[156] Li, H., and Aluko, R.E. 2005, *J. Nutr. Biochem.*, 16, 656-662.

[157] Barnette, M.S., Daly, R., and Weiss, B. 1983, *Biochem. Pharma.*, 32, 2929-2933.

[158] Omoni, A.O., and Aluko, R.E. 2006, *J. Am. Oil Chem. Soc.*, 83, 335-340.

[159] Xiao, R., Badger, T.M., and Simmen, F.A. 2005, Mol. Cancer, 4,1-14

[160] Kim, S.E., Kim, H.H., Kim, J.Y., Kang, Y.I., Woo, H.J., and Lee, H.J. 2000, *BioFactors*, 12, 151-155.

[161] Jeong, H. J., Jeong, J. B., Kim, D. S., Park, J. H., Lee, J. B., Kweon, D. H., Chung, G. Y., Seo, E. W., and De Lumen, B. O., 2007, *Cancer Lett.*, 255, 42-48.

[162] Galvez, A.F., Chen, N., Macasieb, J., and De Lumen, B.O. 2001,*Cancer Res.*, 61, 7473-7478.

[163] Silva-Sanchez, C., Barba De La Rosa, A. P., Leon-Galvan, M. F., De Lumen, B. O., De Leon-Rodriguez, A., and Gonzalez De Mejia, E. 2008, *J. Agric. Food Chem.*, 56, 1233-1240.

[164] Pihlanto-Leppala, A. 2000, *Trends Food Sci. Technol.*, 11, 347-356.

[165] http://www.uwm.edu.pl/biochemia (Accessed July 2008)

[166] Iwaniak, A., Dziuba, J., and Niklewicz, M. 2005, *Acta Aliment.*, 34, 417-425.

[167] Dziuba, J., Iwaniak, A., and Minkiewicz, P. 2003,*Polimery*, 48, 50-53.

[168] Wang, W., and Gonzalez de Mejia, E. 2004, Neutraceuticals & Functional Foods: Processing and physical properties, 2004, IFT Annual Meeting, July 12-16, Las Vegas, NV, 114F-27.

[169] Dziuba, J., Nicklewicz, M., Iwaniak, A., Darewicz, M., and Minkiewicz, P. 2004, *Acta Aliment.*, 33, 227-235.

[170] http://biopd.bjmu.edu.cn (Accessed May 2008).

In: Bioactive Molecules in Plant Foods
Editor: Florence Ojiugo Uruakpa

ISBN: 978-1-62081-515-1
© 2012 Nova Science Publishers, Inc.

*Chapter III*

# BIOACTIVITY OF FLAXSEED LIGNANS

## *Farah S. Hosseinian[1,*], Ed S. Krol[2] and B. Dave Oomah[3]*

[1]Food Science and Nutrition, Department of Chemistry
Carleton University, Ottawa, ON, Canada
[2]College of Pharmacy & Nutrition
University of Saskatchewan, Saskatoon, SK, Canada
[3]National Bioproducts and Bioprocesses Program,
Pacific Agri-Food Research Centre, Agriculture and Agri-Food Canada, Summerland,
BC, Canada

## ABSTRACT

The lignans derived from flaxseed possess a number of pharmacological properties, both *in vitro* and *in vivo*. The ability of these lignans to reduce oxidative stress likely contributes to many of these biological properties. However, it is likely that flaxseed-derived lignans also provide pharmacological activity as a result of their interactions with specific receptors and enzymes within these biological systems. In order to better understand the therapeutic role that flaxseed and flaxseed lignans may play, further studies into the mechanisms of action is warranted. A better understanding of the pharmacology of flaxseed lignans will ultimately lead to appropriate recommendations for their therapeutic use, either as stand-alone therapies or as adjuvants with other pharmaceutical or natural products.

## ABREVIATIONS

| | |
|---|---|
| AAPH | 2,2'-azobis (2-amidinopropane) dihydrochloride |
| ABC | Three spin-coupled systems |
| ACN | Acetonitrile |
| ADP-ribosylation | Polyadenosine diphosphate ribose synthesis |

* Corresponding author Telephone (613) 520-2600 ext. 2048; fax (613) 520-3749. E-mail: farah_hosseinian@carleton.ca.

| | |
|---|---|
| ALA (18:3, ω-3) | α-Linolenic acid |
| AMVN | 2, 2'-azobis (2, 4-dimethylvaleronitrile) |
| AOM | Active oxygen method |
| AP radical | Carbon-centre free radical of AAPH |
| Apo B | Apolipoprotein B |
| BHA | Butylated hydroxy anisole |
| BHT | Butylated hydroxy toluene |
| CHD | Coronary heart diseases |
| CL | Chemiluminescence |
| COX-1, COX-2 | Cyclooxygenases |
| CVD | Cardiovascular disease |
| CYP450 | Cytochrome P-450 |
| DEPT | Distortionless Enhancement by Polarization Transfer |
| DHA | Docosahexaenoic acid |
| DLPC | 1, 2-Dilinoleoyl-sn-Glycero-3-phosphocholine |
| 2D-NMR | 2-Dimensional-NMR |
| EC | (-)-Epicatechin |
| ECG | (-)-Epicatechin-3-gallate |
| EGC | (-)-Epigallocatechin |
| EGCG | (-)-Epigallocatechin-3-gallate |
| END | Enterodiol |
| ENL | Enterolactone |
| EPA | Eicosapentaenoic acid |
| ES-MS | Electrospray-mass-spectrometry |
| GC-MS | Gas chromatography-mass spectrometry |
| GI | Gastrointestinal |
| GRAS | Generally Recognized as Safe |
| GPx | Glutathione peroxidase |
| GSH | Glutathione |
| GSTs | Glutathione S-transferases |
| $H_2O_2$ | Hydrogen peroxide |
| HDL-C | High-density lipoprotein-cholesterol |
| Hep-G2 cells | Human hepatocarcinoma cells |
| HMBC | Heteronuclear Multiple Bond Correlation |
| HMGA | 3-hydroxy-3-methylglutaric acid |
| HMG-CoAreductase | Hydroxy-methylglutaric CoA reductase |
| HPLC | High performance liquid chromatography |
| IGF-I | Insulin-like growth factor I |
| IT | Induction time |
| L$^{\bullet}$ | Lipid radical |
| LC-MS | Liquid chromatography-mass spectrometry |
| LDL-C | Low-density lipoprotein-cholesterol |
| LOXs | Lipoxygenases |
| MAT | Matairesinol |

| MRFIT | Multiple Risk Factor Intervention Trial |
| MW | Molecular weight |
| NMR | Nuclear magnetic resonance |
| $NO^{\bullet}$ | Nitric oxide |
| $NO_2^{\bullet}$ | Nitric dioxide |
| NZ | New Zealand |
| $^1O_2$ | Singlet oxygen |
| $O_2^{\bullet -}$ | Superoxide anion |
| $OCl^-$ | Hypochlorite |
| $OH^{\bullet}$ | Hydroxyl radical |
| $OONO^-$ | Peroxynitrite |
| GSSG | Oxidized glutathione |
| PAF | Platelet-activating factor |
| PDA | Photodiode array |
| PLR | Pinoresinol lariciresinol reductase |
| PMNL | Polymorphonuclear leukocytes |
| PUFA | Polyunsaturated fatty acids |
| $R^{\bullet}$ | Alkyl radicals |
| $RO^{\bullet}$ | Alkoxyl radical |
| $ROO^{\bullet}$ | Peroxyl radical |
| ROOH | Alkyl peroxides |
| ROS | Reactive oxygen species |
| RP | Reverse phase |
| SDG | Secoisolariciresinol diglycoside |
| SECO | Secoisolariciresinol |
| SHBG | Sex hormone binding globulin |
| SOD | Superoxide dismutase |
| TAM | Tamoxifen |
| TEAC | Trolox equivalent antioxidant capacity |
| TFA | Trifluoroacetic acid |
| UGTs | UDP-glucuronosyltransferases |
| VLDL | Very-low-density lipoproteins |
| ZDF | Zucker diabetic fatty |
| $\omega$-3 | Omega-3 |
| $\omega$-6 | Omega-6 |

## INTRODUCTION

Lignans are diphenolic compounds of higher plants formed by the coupling of two coniferyl alcohol residues present in the plant cell wall [1,2]. Lignans are phytoestrogens with estrogenic or anti-estrogenic activities in addition to their antioxidant activities [3-7]. For example, plant lignan consumption has been associated with numerous health benefits including decreased risk of breast, prostate and colon cancer, reduction of LDL cholesterol levels, and the inhibition of type II diabetes [8-12]. Secoisolariciresinol diglucoside (SDG) is the major lignan in flaxseed, while other lignans including matairesinol, pinoresinol, pinoresinol diglucoside, isolariciresinol are also common.

SDG and its aglycone secoisolariciresinol (SECO) are metabolized by intestinal bacteria to the mammalian lignans enterodiol (END) and enterolactone (ENL) [13]. Enterodiol and enterolactone may also be important contributors to chemoprevention as they display antioxidant properties and inhibit the growth of tumor cells [9]. Studies have shown that SDG and SECO have non-hormonal (e.g. antioxidant activity) and hormonal (e.g. weak esterogenic) activities making them strong candidates for a role as natural cancer protective compounds. Until recently, only secoisolariciresinol and matairesinol were considered enterolignan precursors, but now several new precursors have been identified, of which lariciresinol and pinoresinol have a high degree of conversion. Previously, the richest source of lignans was reported flaxseed (300 to 400 mg/100 g), which contained mainly secoisolariciresinol [14-16]. Later, the total plant lignan concentration in sesame seed (405 to 1178 mg/100 g) was reported to be higher than that in flaxseed [14,17]. For grain products, which are also known to be important sources of lignan, lignan concentrations ranged from 0.007 to 0.764 mg/100 g. However, many vegetables and fruits had similar concentrations, because of the contribution of lariciresinol and pinoresinol. *Brassica* vegetables contained unexpectedly high levels of lignans (0.1 to 0.2 mg/100 g), mainly pinoresinol and lariciresinol [14].

This chapter reviews the chemistry and bioactivity of flaxseed lignans and the mechanisms derived from *in vitro* and *in vivo* studies that provide protection against oxidative stress.

# 1. Lignan-General Description

Lignans are diphenolic compounds of higher plants formed by the coupling of two coniferyl alcohol residues that are present in the plant cell wall [2, 13, 16, 18, 19]. In 1956 Bakke and Klosterman [20] isolated SDG 1 (Figure 1) that was very soluble in water and alcohol from a fat free extract of linseed meal with a 3% yield. The same group isolated SECO 2 [2,3-di-(methoxy-4-hydroxybenzyl) butane-1,4-diol] (Figure 1) by acid hydrolysis of SDG 1. SECO 2 is the aglycone (non-sugar) portion of SDG 1. Both SDG 1 and SECO 2 have UV absorption maximum at 280 nm characteristic for lignans.

Early studies demonstrated that SDG 1 was part of a larger complex [20] consisting of an oligomeric chain 3 (molecular weight of approx. 4000 Da) (Figure 2) of SDG 1 (molecular weight of approx. 4000 Da), comprisedof SDG 1 that is ester-linked via 3-hydroxy-3-methylglutaric acid (HMGA) 4 [22, 23]. Hydrolysis of the SDG oligomer/polymer releases the hydroxycinnamic acid glucosides (*p*-coumaric acid glucoside and ferulic acid glucoside) [24]. Recently, the hydroxycinnamic acid glucosides and the flavonoid herbacetin diglucoside (HDG) were identified as integral components of the phenolic complex [4, 25].

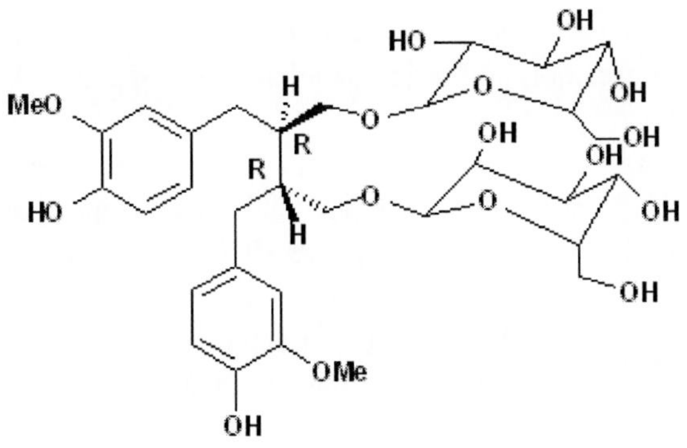

C$_{32}$H$_{46}$O$_{16}$
*MW=686.3
(SDG) **1**

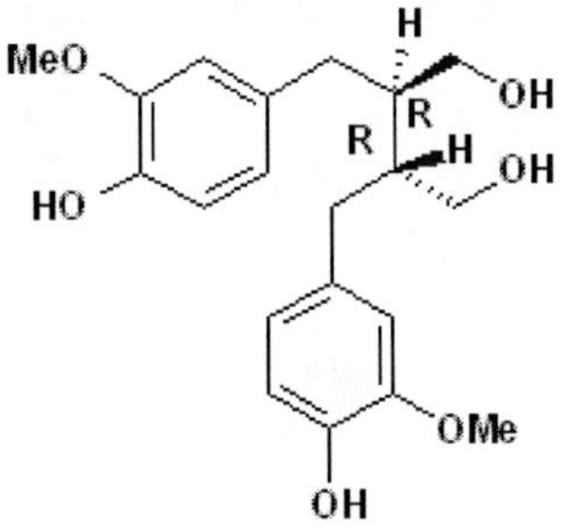

C$_{20}$H$_{26}$O$_{6}$
*MW=362.3
(SECO) **2**

*Molecular weight

Figure 1. Structure of SDG 1 and SECO 2. [21].

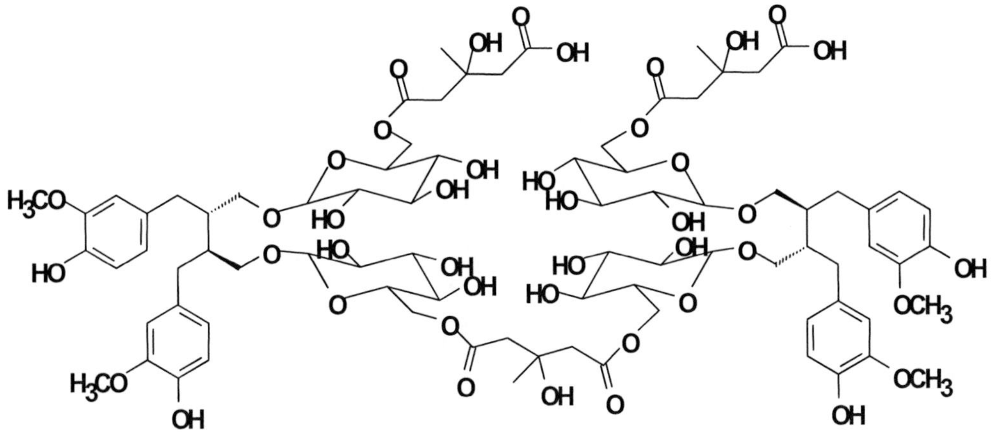

SDG oligomer **3**

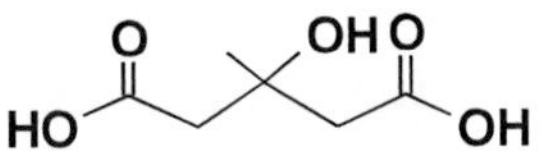

HMGA **4**

Figure 2. Structure of SDG oligomer 3 containing secoisolariciresinol diglycoside 1 and 3 hydroxy-3-methyl-glutaric acid units (HMGA) 4 [7,16].

## 1.1. Food Sources

Flax seed and sesame seed are among the highest known sources of lignans (Table 1) [14,15]. The principal lignan precursor found in flaxseed is secoisolariciresinol (SECO) and its diglucoside SDG. Flaxseed also contains minor amounts of matairesinol, pinoresinol, and lariciresinol [14,15] (Table 1). Sesame seed contains sesamin, sesamolin, and sesaminol as its major lignans and SECO, matairesinol, pinoresinol, and lariciresinol as minor lignans (Table 1) [17].

Sesame seed (*Sesamum indicum*), contains large amounts of the plant lignans sesamin, sesamolin, and sesaminol glucosides [17] [17,26]. The total plant lignan concentration in sesame seed (2180 micromol/100 g) is higher than that in flaxseed (820 micromol/100 g). Other sources of lignans include cereals (rye, wheat, oat, barley - rye being the richest source), pumpkin seeds, soybeans, broccoli, beans, and numerous berries [26]. Secoisolariciresinol and matairesinol were the first plant lignans identified in foods. Pinoresinol and lariciresinol are more recently identified plant lignans that contribute to the total dietary lignan intakes [14,26]. Typically, lariciresinol and pinoresinol contribute about 75% to the total lignan intake whereas secoisolariciresinol and matairesinol contribute only about 25%.

**Table1. Major food sources and their lignans as aglycones (μg / 100 g) [26]**

| Foodstuff | Pino-resinol | Syring-aresinol | Sesamin | Lari-ciresinol | Secoisola-riciresinol | Mataire-sinol | Hydroxy-matair-esinol |
|---|---|---|---|---|---|---|---|
| Flaxseed | 871 | 48 | ND | 1780 | 165759 | 529 | 35 |
| Sesame seed | 47136 | 205 | 62724 | 13060 | 240 | 1137 | 7209 |
| Rye bran | 1547 | 3540 | ND | 1503 | 462 | 729 | 1017 |
| Wheat bran | 138 | 882 | ND | 672 | 868 | 410 | 2787 |
| Oat bran | 567 | 297 | ND | 766 | 90 | 440 | 712 |
| Barley bran | 71 | 140 | ND | 133 | 42 | 42 | |

# 2. MAMMALIAN LIGNANS

## 2.1. Conversion of Plant to Mammalian Lignans

Flaxseed feeding studies with rats, monkeys, or humans showed that a correlation between flaxseed consumption and urinary excretion of the lignans enterodiol (END) 12 and enterolactone (ENL) 13 increases significantly in urine [27-34]. Excretion of END and ENL increased 3-to 285-times after flaxseed consumption (5-10 g daily for six weeks) in the urine of 18 healthy young women, 31 healthy postmenopausal women and six healthy young men [35-37].

The first mammalian lignans, primarily END 12 (MW = 302) and ENL 13 (MW = 298) were identified in humans and animals in 1980 [13]. Mammalian lignans in the human body are formed in the gastrointestinal (GI) tract where bacteria hydrolyze the sugar moiety of SDG 1 to release SECO 2 [38-42]. This is followed by dehydroxylation and demethylation by colonic microflora to give the mammalian lignan END 12 (Figure 3). The GI microbial flora presumably oxidizes END 12 to ENL 13. The latter may also be formed directly from matairesinol 14, although this is likely a minor metabolic route [13, 15, 34, 42-44]. The mammalian lignans differ from plant lignans in the position of the hydroxyl groups at the 3', while plant lignans have their oxygenated substituents at the 3' and 4' positions [39, 45, 46]. Concentrations of mammalian lignans in urine are typically greater than in plasma, thus most analytical methods target the measurement of urinary lignan levels [46].

## 2.2. Role of Gut Flora in the Oxidation of Plant Lignans to Mammalian Lignans

Incubation of flaxseed in faecal samples containing bacteria at concentrations of $10^3$-$10^4$ bacteria/g of stool resulted in the formation of END 12 and ENL 13 [43], demonstratingthat plant lignans are converted irreversibly into END 12 and ENL 13. Conversely, incubation of flaxseed with sterile human faecal cultures was unable to convert END 12 to ENL 13. Together these results suggest that human gut floras are responsible for the conversion of plant lignans to mammalian lignans [13]. A time course study of the metabolism of SDG 1 by human faecal cultures shows initial demethylation, occurs prior (20-30h) to dehydroxylation (48h) [47]. Urinary excretion of END 12 and ENL 13 has been used as an index of plant lignan intake [48].

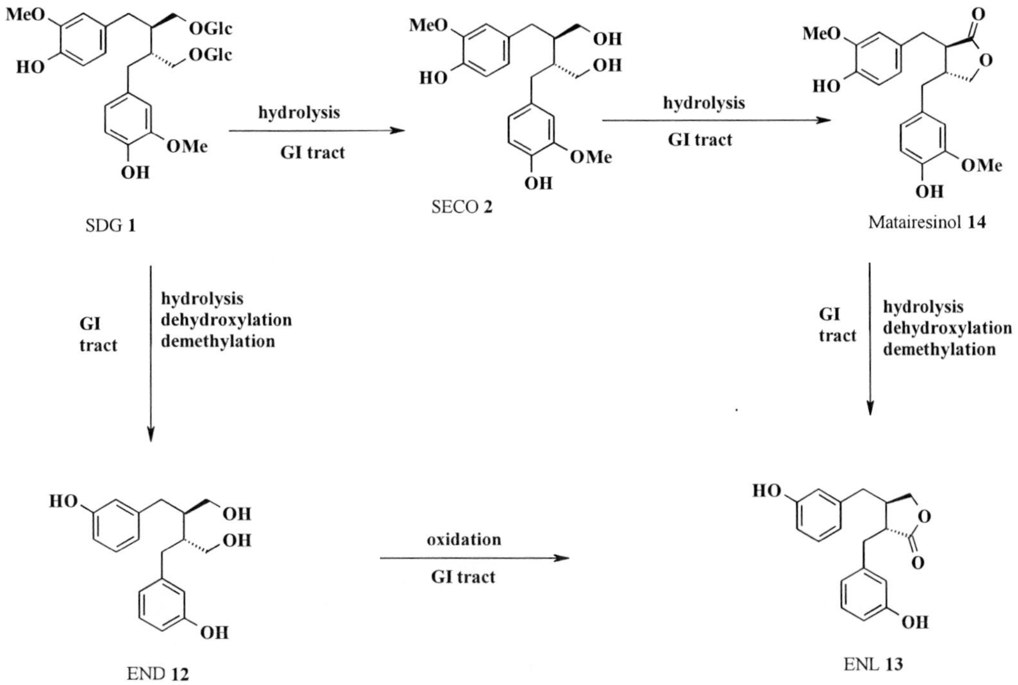

Adapted from Ford *et al.,* 2001) [49].

Figure 3. Biosynthesis pathway of flaxseed lignans SDG 1, SECO 2, and their corresponding mammalian lignans END 12 and ENL 13.

## 2.3. Hepatic Metabolism of Mammalian Lignans

### 2.3.1. Phase I Metabolism

Studies of the hepatic metabolism of the mammalian lignans END 12 and ENL 13 in rat, pig, and human liver microsomes found a series of mono-hydroxylated derivatives of END 12 and ENL 13 [50]. These metabolites have also been found in the bile and urine of rats receiving oral doses of END 12, ENL 13 or flaxseed [46]. A total of six aromatic mono-hydroxylated metabolites of ENL 13 and three corresponding metabolites of END 12 were detected (Figures 4 and 5) with hydroxylation occurring either ortho or para to the aromatic hydroxyl groups [50,51]. A series of aliphatic mono-hydroxylated metabolites were also detected. Only the aromatic hydroxylated metabolites were found in human (female and male) urine after 5 days of flaxseed (25 g/day) consumption [52].

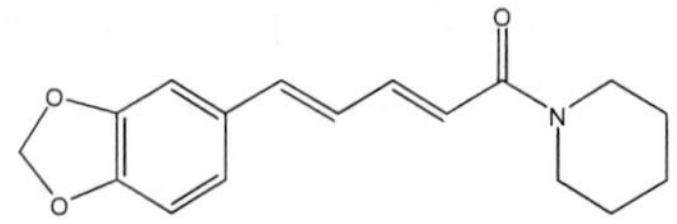

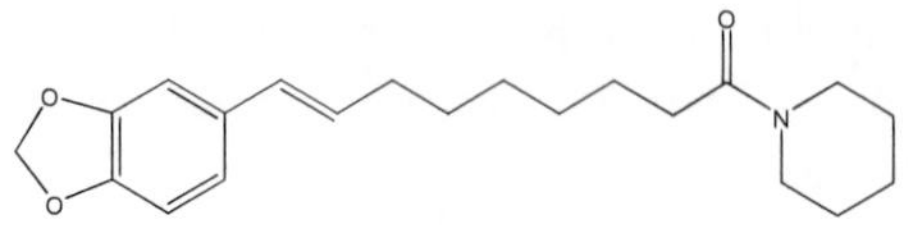

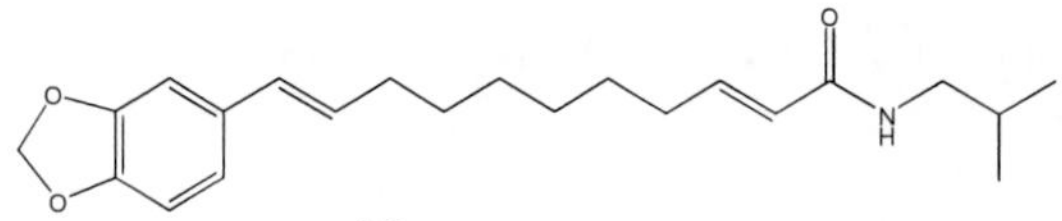

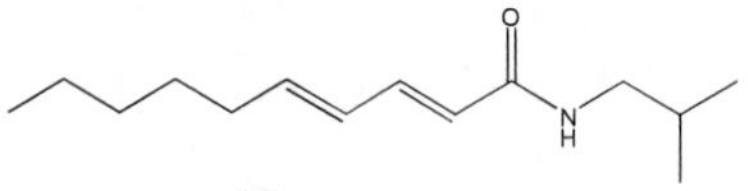

Figure 4. Oxidation metabolites of ENL 13 [46, 56].

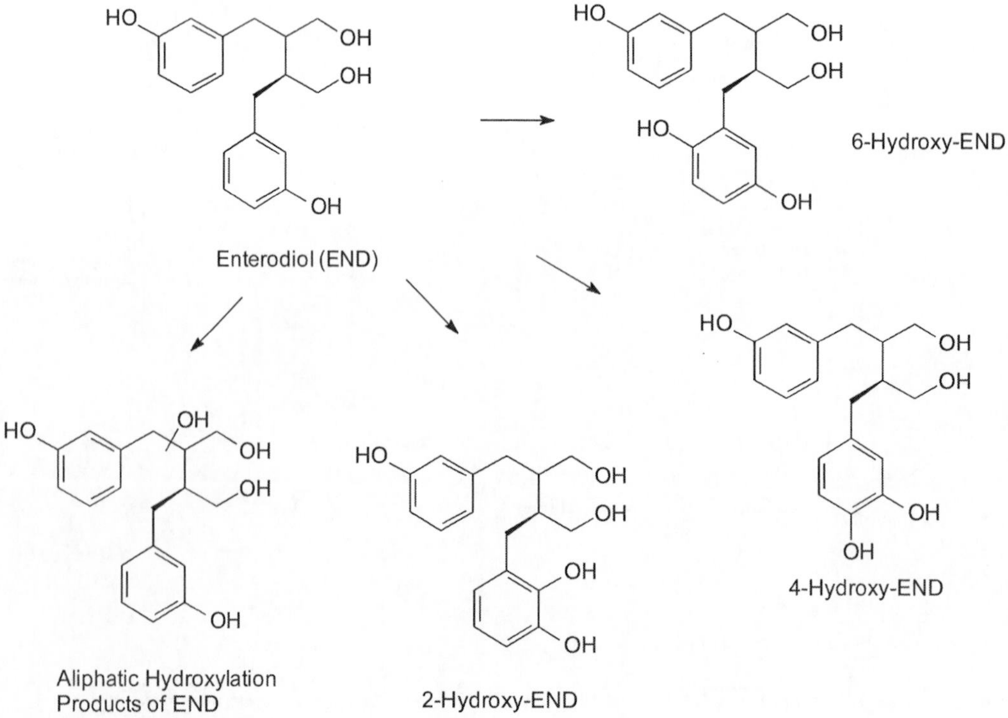

Figure 5. Oxidation metabolites of END 12 [46].

## 2.3.2. Phase 2 Metabolism

All lignans, both mammalian and plant, are found mainly as conjugates of hydrophilic components. Mammalian lignans are found in urine as the glucuronide and sulfate conjugates, whereas plant lignans are linked to various carbohydrates of differing chain length [53]. Once generated in the colon, END 12 and ENL 13 are absorbed and transported to the liver where they conjugate mainly with glucuronic acid or sulfate [19,38,48,53-55].

The conjugated lignans are excreted back into the digestive tract via the bile where a portion reaches the kidney and eventually is excreted in the urine as conjugates [48]. Conjugated lignans are reabsorbed from the intestine and those escaping reabsorption deconjugate during passage through the intestine by bacterial β-glucuronidase and excreted in the faeces in the unconjugated form [49,53]. Therefore, lignans extracted in bile and urine are mainly conjugated glucuronides [53,57] whereas the faeces contain the unconjugated forms of the lignans [58]. This process of circulation pathway of plant lignans is outlined schematically in Figure 6.

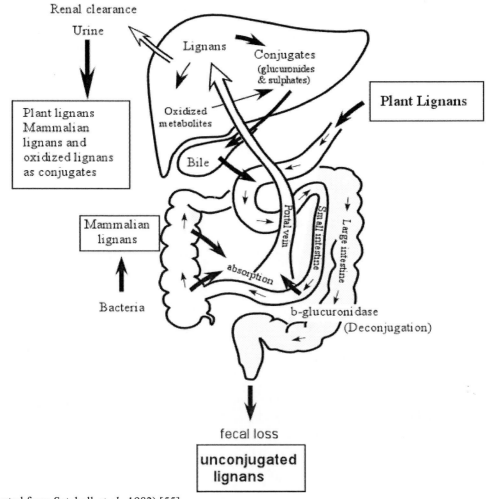

Adapted from Setchell *et al.,* 1982) [55].

Figure 6. The enterohepatic circulation of plant lignans, their colonic and liver metabolites in man.

## 2.4. Flaxseed Lignan Uptake and Urinary Levels

Urinary END 12 and ENL 13 are present in relatively large amounts (10-1000 times more than endogenous estrogens) in humans [59-61]. Mammalian lignan production, based on urinary lignan excretion is linear up to a diet of 5-10% defatted flaxseed or 4.4 μmol SDG 1/day intake in rats, and up to 25 g/day flaxseed intake in humans [28]. One human study showed a linear relationship between the amount of SECO 2 administered and ENL 13 excreted when flaxseed supplementation ranged from 5 to 25 g per day [29]. When the amount of flaxseed exceeded 5%, the excretion of SECO 2 also achieved a plateau, indicating a threshold response [28]. The majority of mammalian lignans are excreted via the faecal route, while concentrations of plant lignans in faeces and in urine are usually insignificant [59,62,63]. Urinary excretion of ENL 13 generally ranges from 1.1 to 4.2 μmol/24 h [59-61, 63-65], while those of END 12 approximates 10 % of the excretion of ENL 13 [60,61]. Rats treated with radiolabelled SDG 1 ($^3$H-SDG 1), excreted most of the radioactivity by 48 h (feces = 60%, urine = 28-30%) [48].

In human urine, ENL 13, END 12, and matairesinol 14 were mainly excreted as mono-glucuronides (73-94%), with lesser amounts of monosulfates, sulfoglucuronides, diglucuronides and disulfates [53]. The first method to study the conjugation patterns of the lignans was based on the modification of an isotope dilution, gas chromatography-mass spectrometry (GC-MS) method for measuring urinary estrogens [53]. However, only the isotopically labelled compounds are detectable by this method. In addition, derivatization is necessary to make compounds volatile enough for GC and GC-MS analysis [46]. Soft ionization techniques such as liquid chromatography-mass spectrometry (LC-MS) and LC-MS/MS are now more commonly used methods for analysis of both glycosides and conjugated lignans [41,46].

## 2.5. Flaxseed Lignan Uptake and Plasma Levels

Studies in human fed 1.5 mg/day SDG 1 resulted in lignan plasma levels of approximately 1 μmol/L [66]. Diets supplemented with 5, 15, or 25 g raw or 25 g processed flaxseed (in muffins or bread) for 8 days, showed that the concentrations of END 12 in nine healthy young women was double that of ENL 13 (6 and 12 nmol/L, respectively) [29]. The conversion rate of END 12 to ENL 13 was very similar at the beginning and end of the study, indicating that microflora were able to metabolize only a certain amount of plant lignans to ENL 13 [29]. Another study determined the plasma concentrations of END 12 in pre- and postmenopausal women including omnivores, vegetarians, a vegan and two lactovegetarians [62,67]. Concentrations of END 12 mainly ranged from 0 to 10 nmol/L with the highest END 12 concentration at 140 nmol/L, while the highest ENL 13 concentrations (1078 nmol/L) was from the plasma of a vegan [62,67].

**Table 2. Chemopreventive effects of flaxseed and its lignans**

| Reference | Experimental Design | Outcome | Material | Concentration |
|---|---|---|---|---|
| Hirano et al (1990) | ZR-75-1 breast cancer cells | Cell proliferation of ZR-71-1 breast cancer cell line | ED and EL | 30 μM |
| Serraino and Thompson (1992)a | Male Sprague-Dawley rats | Cell proliferation in all groups except 5% defatted flaxseed | Full-fat and defatted flaxseed | 5% – 10% of tested materials in diet |
| Serraino and Thompson (1992)b | Female Sprague-Dawley rats; DMBA (5 mg/rat) | Tumor incidence and number of tumors at initiation stage; Tumor size and tendency for tumor multiplicity during promotion stage | Flaxseed exposure during initiation stage of carcinogenesis | 5% of tested Materials in diet |
| Wang and Kurzer (1998) | MCF-7 human breast cancer cells | DNA synthesis in the presence of 0.01 nM estradiol | EL | 10 μM |
| Thompson et al (1996)a | Female Sprague-Dawley rats; DMBA (5 mg/rat) | Established tumor volume | Flaxseed, flaxseed oil and SDG | 2.5% or 5% flaxseed, 1.82% flaxseed oil, 1.5 mg/day SDG |
| Thompson et al (1996)b | Female Sprague-Dawley rats; DMBA (5 mg/rat) | Number of tumors and tumor multiplicity with SDG | SDG | 1.5 mg |
| Saarinen, et al (2007) | DMBA-induced Sprague-Dawley rats | Growth of new and established tumors | ENL | 1 or 10 mg/kg b.w./day |
| Power et al, et al (2006) | Ovariectomized athymic Balb/c nu/nu mice bearing orthotopic MCF-7 tumors | Tumor size similar to negative control | END and ENL | 10 mg/kg b.w./day |
| Saarinen, et al (2000) | DMBA-induced SD rats | Tumor volume and growth, no effect on multiplicity | 7-Hydroxymatairesinol | 15 mg/kg b.w./day |
| Mousavi and Adlercreutz (1992) | MCF-7 human breast cancer cells | Cell proliferation; Cell proliferation | EL; EL | 0.5-10 μM; >10 μM |
| Tou and Thompson (1999) | Female Sprague-Dawley rats during pregnancy and lactation | Number of mammary gland terminal end buds with flaxseed and SDG | flaxseed, flaxseed oil, SDG | 5% or 10% flaxseed, 1.82% flaxseed oil, 1.5 mg SDG |

Abbreviations: DMBA = dimethylbenz(a)anthracene, ED = enterodiol, EL = enterolactone, END = enterodiol, ENL = enterolactone, SDG = secoisolariciresinol diglycoside.
Adapted from Thompson, 1999; Rickard, 2003) [39,73].

**Table 3. Hormonal and non-hormonal properties of flaxseed and its corresponding mammalian lignans**

| Reference | Study | Biological effect | Sample | Concentration |
|---|---|---|---|---|
| Adlercreutz (1993)a | *In-vitro* | Inhibit aromatase in placental microsome | EL | 1-100 μM |
| Adlercreutz et al (1992) | *In-vitro* | Stimulate SHBG synthesis in human HepG2 liver cells | EL | 5-10 μM |
| Adlercreutz et al (1993)b | *In-vitro* | Decrease estrone production via aromatase inhibition in JEG-3 human carcinoma cells | EL | 1-100 μM |
| Martin et al (1995) | *In-vitro* | Inhibition of estradiol and testosterone binding to SHBG | EL | 10 μM |
| Hutchins et al (1999) | *In-vivo* | Decrease estradiol in postmenopausal women | Flaxseed | 5-10 g/day |
| Waters and Knowler (1982) | *In-vivo* | Depress stimulation of uterine RNA synthesis by estradiol in rats | EL | 0.3, 3.0, or 30 μg |
| Phipps et al (1993) | *In-vivo* | Lengthen luteal phase of menstrual cycle in women; increase luteal phase progesterone to oestradiol ratio | Flaxseed | 10 g/day |
| Hosseinian (2006) | *In-vitro* | Antioxidant activity in pure oil system | SDG and SECO | 0.04, 0.06 and 0.08 mM/100 g oil |
| Hosseinian (2006) | *In-vivo* | AAPH-mediated antioxidant reactions of SECO and SDG in a liposomal system | SDG and SECO | 0.01 M/L |
| Prasad (2008) | *In-vivo* | reduces the progression of atherosclerosis by 24%-45% | SDG | SDG 20mg/kg body wt/day |
| Kitts et al (1999) | *In-vitro* | Hydroxy radical scavenging activity; inhibition of DNA scission | ED, EL, and SDG | 10-100 μM |
| Yuan et al (1999) | | Reduction in hepatic glutathione reductase activity | Flaxseed and SDG | 10% and 3 mg/day |
| Mousavi and Adlercreutz (1992) | *In-vitro* | Stimulate growth of MCF-7 human breast cancer cells; Inhibit cell proliferation in the presence of oestradiol | ED and EL | 0.5-10 μM 1μM |

| Reference | Study | Biological effect | Sample | Concentration |
|---|---|---|---|---|
| Cho et al (2007) | *In-vitro* | antifungal activity; suppresses development of rice blast and wheat leaf rust. | *Myristica fragrans Houttyn* (nutmeg) seeds; erythro-austrobailignan-6 (EA6), meso-dihydroguaiaretic acid (MDA) and nectandrin-B (NB) | 125-500 mg/L |
| Qu et al (2005) | *In-vivo* | Increase cell apoptosis in Colon Cancer cells (SW480 Cells) in mice | SDG, END, or both from wheat bran | 82.9 µg/g 40 µmol/L ENL |
| McIntosh et al (2003) | *In-vivo* | 28 subjects (men, 40–65 years old) increase plasma ENL (47% and 71%); decrease plasma insulin by 46-49% | whole-grain rye flour or whole-grain wheat flour | 90 g |

Abbreviations: ED = enterodiol, EL = enterolactone, SDG = secoisolariciresinol diglycoside, SHBG = sex hormone binding globulin.
Adapted from Thompson, 1999; Rickard, 2003) [39,73].

## 3. Lignans – Health Benefits

Lignans SDG 1 and SECO 2 have the potential to prevent hormone sensitive cancers (e.g. breast, prostate and colon cancer), hypercholesterolemic atherosclerosis and diabetes [19,38,54,68-75]. SECO 2 and SDG 1 may possess chemopreventive properties in animals and humans [13,16,34,39,40,58,64,68-71,76-86]. That potential chemopreventive properties of lignans originated from In an early study of urinary lignan excretion, ENL 13 and END 12 were used as an indicator of dietary lignan intake and were found to be 50% lower in women with breast cancer [60]. This observation led to a series of *in vitro*, animal and human experiments to obtain a better understanding of the role of lignans on different types of cancer [19,38,54,68-72]. Most studies have used whole defatted flaxseed or SDG 1 to assess the role of mammalian lignans because flaxseed lignans are the richest precursors for the mammalian lignans END 12 and ENL 13. Table 2, shows the chemopreventive effects of flaxseed and its lignans. Table 3, shows some hormonal and non-hormonal properties of flaxseed and its corresponding mammalian lignans.

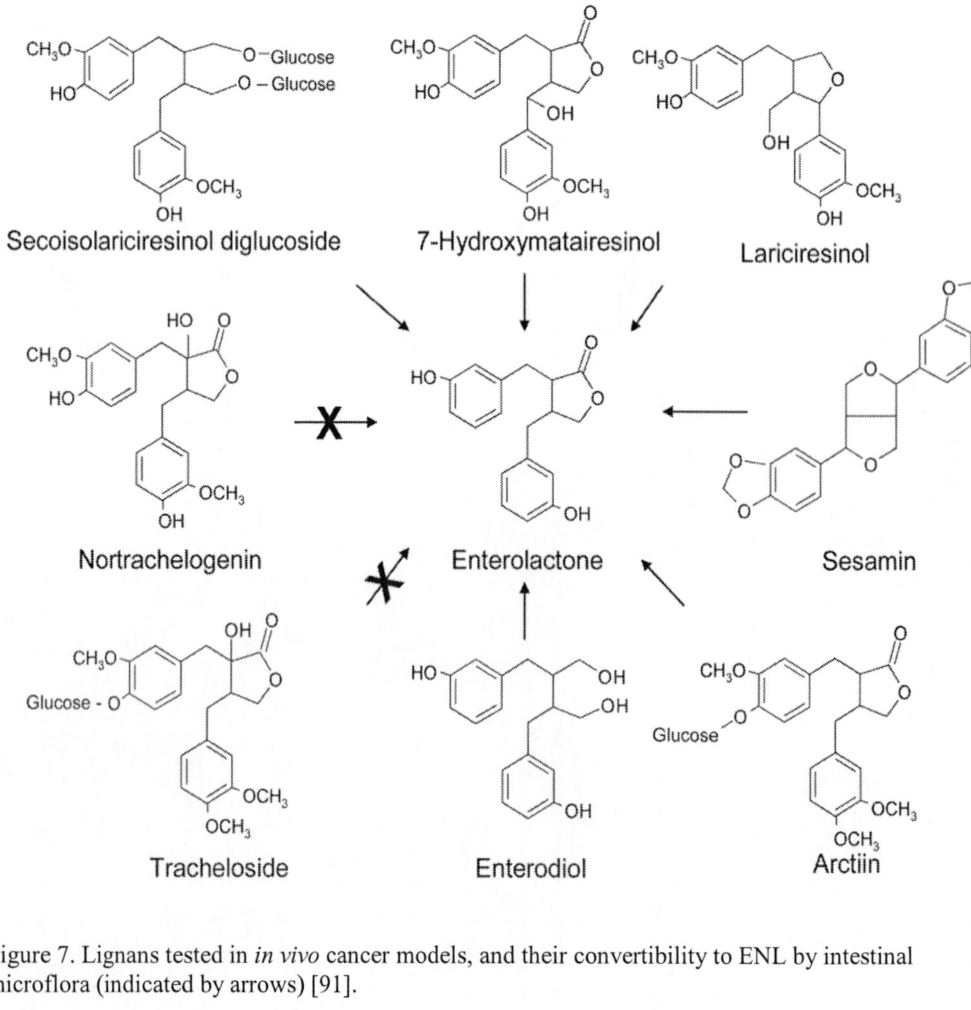

Figure 7. Lignans tested in *in vivo* cancer models, and their convertibility to ENL by intestinal microflora (indicated by arrows) [91].

Several plant lignans, as well as their mammalian metabolites END and ENL, have been tested in experimental mammary cancer models *in vivo* [87-89]. Consequently, lariciresinol and its further metabolites SECO, END and ENL were found in serum of both rats and athymic mice confirming a similar lignan metabolism pattern as in humans [90]. These findings indicate conceivable importance of dietary lignan lariciresinol in inhibition of breast cancer development [90].

The most widely studied lignan so far is SDG which has been tested in 7,12-dimethylbenz[a]anthracene (DMBA) and methylnitrosourea (MNU)-induced, estrogen responsive mammary cancer in rats, and in orthotopic, nonestrogen-responsive MDA-MB-435 xenografts in athymic mice [91]. Thompson and coworkers [76] were the first to demonstrate that administration of rats with SDG at a dose of 1.5 mg/rat (equal to a 5% flaxseed diet) starting 1 wk after the DMBA induction, inhibited both the size and the number of tumors. Similar anticarcinogenic effects were seen when SDG was administered starting 13 wk after the DMBA induction in late promotion stage, and continued for 7 wk [92], These results suggested that SDG can at least partially mediate the anticarcinogenic action of flaxseed. So far, several other plant lignans including arctiin, 7-hydroxymatairesinol (HMR), LAR, and sesamin have also been demonstrated to inhibit mammary tumorigenesis (Figure 7). Administration of arctiin or sesamin to rats both during and post carcinogen induction reduced the mammary tumor multiplicity and numbers [90,93] while administration of HMR to rats during or post DMBA-induction reduced the tumor growth in size but did not significantly alter the multiplicity of the tumors [91]. Accordingly, in MCF-7 tumor bearing mice, dietary LAR (20 or 100 ppm) decreased the estradiol triggered tumor growth (volume and weight) by increasing the cell apoptosis [91].

A lignan-rich diet has been linked with reduced breast cancer risk [88,91]. However, it has not been clear if these compounds are accessible in the mammary tumor tissue *in vivo*. The accessibility and accumulation of lignans in breast cancer tissue was determined after oral administration of tritium labeled dietary lignan secoisolariciresinol diglucoside (3H-SDG) to athymic mice bearing MCF-7 tumors [88]. Dietary lariciresinol showed a reduction in mammary tumor growth and reduced blood vessel density in human MCF-7 breast cancer xenografts and carcinogen-induced mammary tumors in rats [90]. The effect of HMR and its mammalian metabolite ENL showed to inhibit the proliferation and invasion of AH109A hepatoma cells (breast cancer cells) in vitro [94]. ENL suppressed hepatoma cell proliferation by accumulating cells in G1 phase and elongating doubling time of these cells, and by increasing the rate of apoptosis. Subsequently, both of these compounds reduced the growth and metastasis of solid AH109A hepatomas in rats in vivo [94]. These in vitro and in vivo findings suggested that HMR has inhibitory activities on tumor growth and metastasis in the hepatoma-bearing rats, and that this anti-tumor effect is mediated at least partially by ENL, a metabolite of HMR. The effect of a plant lignan HMR (0.15% or 0.30%) on LNCaP human prostate cancer xenografts in athymic mice showed a reduction the growth of LNCaP tumors compared with controls [95]. Mice treated with HMR had smaller tumor volume, lower tumor take rate, increased proportion of nongrowing tumors, and higher tumor cell apoptotic index compared with controls. Furthermore, the cell proliferation index was reduced in mice receiving the 0.30% HMR diet compared with mice receiving the control diet. This study suggested that dietary HMR started at the early phase of the tumor development inhibits the growth of the LNCaP human prostate cancer xenografts in athymic male mice [95]. Cell culture studies using human MCF-7 estrogen-dependent breast cancer cells showed that low concentrations (0.1-10 μM) of ENL induced DNA synthesis (as a marker of cell growth) by 150-235% [96]. On the other hand, ENL 13 at high concentrations (20-90 μM) resulted in a 50% inhibition of DNA synthesis [96]. END 12 and ENL 13 suppress Hep-G2 proliferation in addition to significantly stimulating sex hormone binding globulin (SHBG) production by Hep-G2 cells (human hepatocarcinoma cells) in culture [96,97]. Flaxseed has been shown to decrease some early markers of colon cancer risk partly because of its lignans [19,48,68,98]. The activitiy of β-glucuronidase in the cecum of rats fed 0.75, 1.5, or 3.0 mg of SDG daily by oral gavage increased significantly; the urinary mammalian lignan excretion also increased [19,68]. Because flaxseed and lignans are colon cancer protective, it was suggested that, β-glucuronidase activity may play a beneficial role in their presence by increasing mammalian lignan absorption and enterohepatic circulation [19,68]. The effect of ENL and END alone and in combination with the isoflavone genistein (GEN) on the growth of MCF-7 tumors in ovariectomized nude mice showed that GEN alone promoted the growth of MCF-7 human breast cancer while the mammalian lignans ENL and END did not [89]. When these phytoestrogens were given in combination, no tumor growth-promoting effects were observed [89].

## 3.1. Animal Studies

The beneficial effects of plant lignans supplements in breast cancer [80,99,100] colon cancer, [68,80] skin cancer [101] and lupus nephritis [102] have been demonstrated in mice [102]. The number and size of mammary tumors and risk of colon cancer is significantly reduced by feeding Sprague-Dawley rats with 1.5 mg/day of SDG 1 [68,76]. Other studies have shown that the plasma level of END 12 and ENL 13 in rats fed 1.5 mg/day SDG 1 was estimated to be about 1 μM [103]. Feeding *Inbred* mice with 5% flaxseed flour supplement in a high-fat diet at the promotional stage of (7,12-dimethylbenz[a]anthracene-mediated) tumorigenesis, produced a 66% reduction in tumour size [80,104]. The number and size of mammary tumours significantly decreased compared with the control in *Inbred* mice fed for two weeks with SDG 1 at 73, 147 or 293 μmol/kg (equivalent to SDG 1 provided in the 2.5, 5 or 10% flaxseed diet) [105].

In a study of colon cancer, Sprague-Dawley rats treated with 5% or 10% full fat or defatted flaxseed supplement for four weeks [68,106] reduced tumour number by 50% and significantly increased urinary lignan excretion and cecal β-glucuronidase activity [68,106]. Because both the defatted and full fat flaxseed groups had similar effects in animals, this study suggested that the lignans are responsible for tumor reduction. Higher doses of flaxseed (10%) has no supplementary benefits compared to lower doses (5%), suggesting that even lower doses of flaxseed could be preventative [73]. Mouse studies comparing the effects of defatted flaxseed diets (2.5, 5, 10%) vs. SDG 1 administered at 73, 147 and 293 μM SDG 1/kg diet showed similar results on lung metastasis of melanoma cells [104]. The number of lung tumors was 32, 54 and 63% lower than controls at the above concentrations [68]. This was the first study demonstrating *in-vivo* inhibition of cancer cell metastasis by flaxseed lignans.

Studies in Sprague-Dawley rats suggest that pure SDG 1 has an inhibitory effect on the early stages of tumor development in mammary tissue, whereas flax oil and ground flax primarily affect established mammary tumors at a late stage of tumor development [76,80,92,106].

A diet supplemented with 5% flaxseed inhibits the growth and development of prostate cancer in the transgenic adenocarcinoma mouse prostate (TRAMP) model [107]. SDG 1 reduced serum cholesterol and hypercholesterolemic atherosclerosis in rabbits [11,108]. Rabbits fed a diet containing SDG 1 (15 mg/kg body weight, orally) for eight weeks, showed a slowed development of hypercholesterolemic atherosclerosis, 35% reduction in LDL, and 64% reduction in LDL/HDL [108]. Furthermore, dietary flaxseed (7.5 g/kg daily, orally) containing very little α-linolenic acid (2-3% of the total oil) reduced hypercholesterolemic arteriosclerosis in rabbits by 46% [109] suggesting that the reduction in arteriosclerosis was not due to ALA but probably to the lignan component of the flaxseed [109]. Flaxseed oil may protect against some of the major risks of heart attack (e.g. platelet aggregation). Meanwhile, flaxseed low in ALA not only has protection against the same risks, but also helps in the reduction of serum LDL cholesterol. This suggests that other compounds such as lignans may be responsible for the additional health benefits of flaxseed [108,110,111].

SDG 1 (22 mg/kg body weight, orally in drinking water) in diabetic prone BioBreeding rats, a model of human type 1 diabetes, prevented the development of type 1 diabetes in rats by approximately 71% [74]. Previous studies demonstrated that oral administration of SDG 1 (40 mg/kg body weight, daily, orally in drinking water) caused a 75% reduction in type 2 diabetes in Zucker diabetic fatty (ZDF) female rats, a model of human type 2 diabetes [112]. Plasma insulin-like growth factor I (IGF-I) levels in rats are reduced by dietary supplementation of flaxseed (5%) or SDG 1 (1.5 mg/day) in breast cancer rats [82]. Increased plasma IGF-I concentrations are associated with increased breast cancer risk [82] and reduced plasma IGF-I levels are inversely related to urinary lignan excretion.

## 3.2. Human Studies

A study in postmenopausal women showed that the excretion of the mammalian lignans increased 3 to 285 times after flaxseed consumption (5.0-25.0 g/day) [36]. In humans, a preliminary study suggested a benefit of flax for women with breast cancer [113]. In most studies whole or milled flaxseed has been incorporated into baked products such as breads, muffins, cookies, or breakfast cereals. For example, in one study 39 women with newly diagnosed breast tumors were randomized to eat a muffin containing 25 g (about 3 tbsp) of ground flax daily for 6 weeks experienced significant reductions in cell proliferation and tumor growth of breast cancer compared to the control whole-wheat muffins, and this result correlated to downregulation of insulin-like growth factor I and epidermal growth factor receptor expression [113].

Consumption of 5 or 10 grams of ground flaxseed by post-menopausal women significantly increased urinary excretion of END by 1,009 and 2,867 nmol/day, respectively, ENL by 21,242 and 52,826 nmol/day, and total lignans (END + ENL + MAT) by 24,333 and 60,640 nmol/day, respectively [37]. Flaxseed consumption did not alter MAT excretion significantly. The relative concentration of plasma lignans were 10,000 times higher than endogenous estradiol [73].

A single dose of purified SDG (1.31 micromol/kg body wt) in healthy volunteers showed that enterolignans appeared in plasma 8-10 h after ingestion of SDG. END and ENL reached their maximum plasma concentrations 14.8±5.1 h and 19.7±6.2 h, respectively [66]. Foods (90 g) containing whole-grain rye flour and whole-grain wheat flour were compared with low-fiber refined-cereal foods for their effects on markers of bowel health and the metabolic markers of insulin and glucose [114]. Fecal samples (48-h) and fasting and postprandial blood samples collected from 28 overweight men aged 40-65 y with no history of bowel disease for four weeks were analyzed. Both high-fiber rye and wheat foods increased fecal output by 33-36% (P = 0.004) and reduced fecal beta-glucuronidase activity by 29% (P = 0.027). Postprandial plasma insulin decreased by 46-49% (P = 0.0001) and glucose by 16-19% (P = 0.0005). Rye foods were associated with significant (P = 0.0001) increase in plasma enterolactone (47% and 71%) and fecal butyrate (26% and 36%), relative to wheat and low-fiber options, respectively [114]. This study concluded that the high-fiber rye and wheat food consumption improved several markers of bowel and metabolic health relative to that of low-fiber food. Fiber from rye appears more effective than that from wheat in overall improvement of biomarkers of bowel health [114].

Several studies examined the effects of flaxseed consumption on urinary estrogen metabolite excretion in postmenopausal women [36,97,115]. Ground flaxseed (0, 5, or 10 g/day) consumption significantly increased the ratio of urinary concentrations of 2-hydroxyestrone (estrogen estradiol metabolites) and the 2/16 α-hydroxyestrone in postmenopausal women as compared with the control group [36]. Unlike 2 –hydroxyestrone, the 16 α-hydroxyestrone metabolite of estradiol 15 induces genotoxic DNA damage and aberrant hyperproliferation similar to that produced by chemical carcinogens [97]. One study examined the effects of consuming equal amounts of flaxseed (25 g ground flaxseed) or soy (25 g soy flour) on estrogen metabolism in postmenopausal women for 16 weeks [115]. Urinary concentrations of 2-hydroxyestrone, and the 2/16 -hydroxyestrone ratio increased in the flaxseed group more than those in soy group [115].

## 3.4. Correlation between *In Vitro* Production and *In Vivo* Excretion of Lignans

A study evaluated the performance of SDG 1 in the production of flaxseed lignan and the relationship between *in vitro* production and *in vivo* urinary excretion [28]. Lignan production in rats fed a high fat diet with or without ground flaxseed (2.5, 5 or 10 g/100 g) or SDG 1 (1.1, 2.2 or 4.4 µM /day; equivalent to levels in the respective flaxseed diets) for 4 weeks was dose-related [28]. Urinary lignan excretion increased linearly with doses from 0-5 g/100 g flaxseed and 0.0-2.2 µM SDG. The *in vitro* trend (using human faecal inoculums) for SDG 1 was similar, confirming the high correlation between *in vitro* production and *in vivo* excretion of lignans suggesting the predictability of *in vivo* response based on *in vitro* results [28]. Theoretical urinary END 12 and ENL 13 from the SDG 1 in flaxseed correlated with the actual excretion in flaxseed-fed animals. However, urinary END 12 and ENL 13 of SDG 1-fed rats was only 20% of levels of flaxseed-fed rats, indicating the presence of other precursors or incomplete conversion of SDG 1 to END 12 and ENL 13 [28].

In a preliminary clinical study, 25 men with prostate cancer consumed ground flaxseed (30 g/d) for 4 weeks as part of a low-fat diet [116]. Prostate cancer cell proliferation decreased and apoptosis of cancer cells increased in patients using ground flaxseed compared to the control group. The mammalian lignans END 12 and ENL 13 may be partly responsible for this effect [116,117]. An *in vitro* study also showed that END 12 and ENL 13 significantly inhibited the growth of three human prostate cancer cell lines [117].

# 4. LIGNAN- ANTIOXIDANT ACTIVITY

## 4.1. Antioxidant Activity

Natural antioxidants can be classified as primary (chain-breaking) antioxidants, which can react directly with lipid radicals converting them into stable products, or as secondary (preventive) antioxidants, that can reduce oxidation by different mechanisms [118]. Primary antioxidants often act by donating a hydrogen atom, while secondary antioxidants bind metal ions that catalyze oxidative processes by scavenging oxygen, absorbing UV radiation, inhibiting enzymes or decomposing hydroperoxides [119]. Natural phenolic compounds function as both primary and secondary antioxidants by different mechanisms. Monitoring of either the decrease of the radical or the antioxidant, or the formation of products can be used to evaluate antioxidant activity [118].

The antioxidant activities based on hydroxyl and peroxyl radical scavenging activity in a lipid emulsion system and inhibition of deoxyribose by SDG were lower than END and ENL in both lipid and aqueous *in vitro* model systems [120]. The antioxidant activity of 15 major lignans found in knotwood extracts including hydroxymatairesinol, secoisolariciresinol, nortrachelogenin, pinoresinol, and lariciresinol has been evaluated [121]. The radical scavenging capacity measured by 2,2-diphenyl-1-picrylhydrazyl (DPPH) and 2,2-azobis (2-methylpropionamidine dihydrochloride (ABAP) demonstrated that the reactions with DPPH resulted in more unidentified polymeric material than the corresponding reactions with ABAP. The formation of adducts was a predominant reaction in the experiments with ABAP. Instead, polymerisation seems to be the dominating termination reaction with DPPH. Lignans with catechol (3,4-dihydroxyphenyl) moieties (e.g. dimethyl matairesinol) exhibited the highest radical scavenging capacity, while the corresponding guaiacyl (3-methoxy-4-hydroxyphenyl) lignans (e.g SECO 2) showed a slightly weaker scavenging capacity [121]. In addition, the butanediol structure enhanced the activity, whereas a higher degree of oxidation at the benzylic positions decreased the activity. Additionally, the readily available lignans (−)-secoisolariciresinol, a mixture of hydroxymatairesinol epimers and (−)-matairesinol were studied in more detail, including kinetic measurements and identification of oxidation products in the reactions with DPPH and ABAP. Table 4, shows the radical scavenging capacity ($EC_{50}$) of lignans and reference compounds.

SDG (0.01 M) has been oxidized using 2,2′-azobis-(2-amidopropane) (AAPH, 0.1 M), an *in-vitro* peroxidation model, and the major oxidation products and their formation over time evaluated to better understand the antioxidant properties of plant lignans (Figure 8) [7]. SDG converts to four major products as a result of phenol oxidation [7] ; two highly polar (SDG peroxide and SDG 4-*O*-(1-amidinopropyl) adduct) and two less polar (SDG C-5a dimer and SDG 4-OH-dienone adduct) than SDG.

**Table 4. Radical scavenging capacity (EC$_{50}$) of lignans and reference compounds, in order of radical scavenging capacity. DPPH/AH = stoichiometric factor at EC$_{50}$ [121]**

| Compound | DPPH/AH |
|---|---|
| Matairesinol | 2.9 |
| Hydroxymatairesinol | 2.6 |
| Secoisolariciresinol | 4.5 |
| 7-OH-Secoisolariciresinol | 3.1 |
| Nortrachelogenin | 2.3 |
| Pinoresinol | 2.3 |
| Lariciresinol | 2.3 |

Other plant derived lignan compounds such as sesamin and sesamolin (the major sesame seed lignans) and a series of related dibenzocyclooctene lignans from the fruit of *Schisandra chinensis* including schisandrin B, exhibit antioxidant activity both *in vitro* and *in vivo*. For example, sesame lignans can enhance the antioxidant activity of vitamin E in a lipid peroxidation system [122]. Sesamol, which contains a free phenolic group, inhibited lipid peroxidation in both systems whereas sesamin and sesamolin, which possess methylenedioxy groups, were effective only in the microsomal system [122]. Since detoxifying enzymes are localized in microsomes, the inhibitory effects of sesamin and sesamolin observed in the microsomal system may be attributed to their metabolites. The inhibitory effects of lignans in this study were lower than tocopherols and BHT [122].

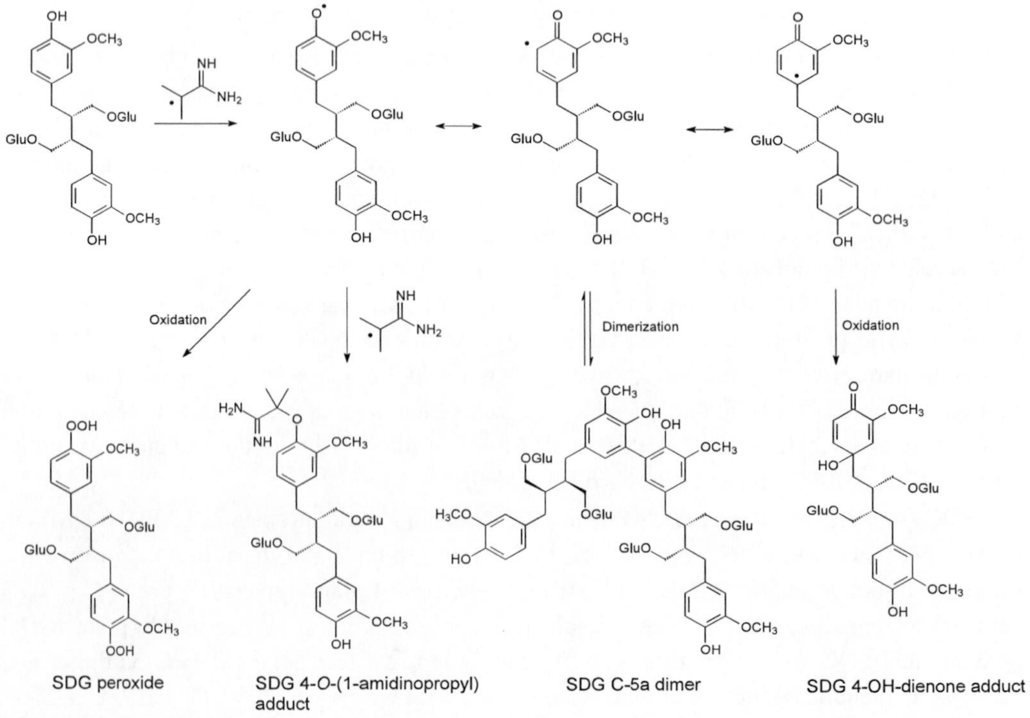

Figure 8. Proposed pathway for the formation of AAPH-mediated SDG oxidation products [7].

# REFERENCES

[1]   Oomah, B.D. and Mazza, G. 1999, Health benefits of pytochemicals from selected Canadian crops. *Trends in Food Science and Technology.* 10: 193-198.

[2]   Mazza, G. and Oomah, B.D., Flaxseed, Dietary Fiber, and Cyanogens. In *Flaxseed in Human Nutrition*, S.C. Cunnane and L.U. Thompson, Eds. AOCS Press: Champaign, IL, 1995; pp 56-81.

[3]   Jin, J.S., Zhao, Y.F., Nakamura, N., Akao, T., Kakiuchi, N., Min, B.S., and Hattori, M. 2007, Enantioselective dehydroxylation of enterodiol and enterolactone precursors by human intestinal bacteria. *Biol Pharm Bull.* 30: 2113-2119.

[4]   Eeckhaut, E., Struijs, K., Possemiers, S., Vincken, J.P., Keukeleire, D.D., and Verstraete, W. 2008, Metabolism of the lignan macromolecule into enterolignans in the gastrointestinal lumen as determined in the simulator of the human intestinal microbial ecosystem. *J Agric Food Chem.* 56: 4806-4812.

[5]   Prasad, K. Antioxidant activity in SDG metabolites. 6,486,126, Nov 26, 2002, 2002.

[6]   Hu, C., Yuan, Y.V., and Kitts, D.D. 2007, Antioxidant activities of the flaxseed lignan secoisolariciresinol diglucoside, its aglycone secoisolariciresinol and the mammalian lignans enterodiol and enterolactone in vitro. *Food and Chemical Toxicology.* 45: 2219-2227.

[7]   Hosseinian, F.S., Muir, A.D., Westcott, N.D., and Krol, E.S. 2007, AAPH-mediated antioxidant reactions of secoisolariciresinol and SDG. *Org Biomol Chem.* 5: 644-654.

[8]   Penumathsa, S.V., Koneru, S., Zhan, L., John, S., Menon, V.P., Prasad, K., and Maulik, N. 2008, Secoisolariciresinol diglucoside induces neovascularization-mediated cardioprotection against ischemia-reperfusion injury in hypercholesterolemic myocardium. *Journal of Molecular and Cellular Cardiology.* 44: 170-179.

[9]   Dodin, S., Cunnane, S.C., Masse, B., Lemay, A., Jacques, H., Asselin, G., Tremblay-Mercier, J., Marc, I., Lamarche, B., Legare, F., and Forest, J.C. 2008, Flaxseed on cardiovascular disease markers in healthy menopausal women: a randomized, double-blind, placebo-controlled trial. *Nutrition.* 24: 23-30.

[10]  Jeng, K.C., Hou, R.C., Wang, J.C., and Ping, L.I. 2005, Sesamin inhibits lipopolysaccharide-induced cytokine production by suppression of p38 mitogen-activated protein kinase and nuclear factor-kappaB. *Immunology Letters.* 97: 101-106.

[11]  Prasad, K. 2008, Regression of hypercholesterolemic atherosclerosis in rabbits by secoisolariciresinol diglucoside isolated from flaxseed. *Atherosclerosis.* 197: 34-42.

[12]  Zhang, W., Wang, X., Liu, Y., Tian, H., Flickinger, B., Empie, M.W., and Sun, S.Z. 2008, Dietary flaxseed lignan extract lowers plasma cholesterol and glucose concentrations in hypercholesterolaemic subjects. *British Journal of Nutrition.* 99: 1301-1309.

[13]  Setchell, K.D., Lawson, A.M., Mitchell, F.L., Adlercreutz, H., Kirk, D.N., and Axelson, M. 1980, Lignans in man and in animal species. *Nature.* 287: 740-742.

[14]  Milder, I.E., Arts, I.C., van de Putte, B., Venema, D.P., and Hollman, P.C. 2005, Lignan contents of Dutch plant foods: a database including lariciresinol, pinoresinol, secoisolariciresinol and matairesinol. *British Journal of Nutrition.* 93: 393-402.

[15]  Muir, A.D. and Westcott, N.D. 2000, Quantitation of the lignan secoisolariciresinol diglucoside in baked goods containing flax seed or flax meal. *Journal of Agricultural and Food Chemistry*. 48: 4048-4052.

[16]  Westcott, N.D. and Muir, A.D., Chemical studies on the constituents of *Linuum* spp. In *Flax, The genus Linum*, A.D. Muir and N.D. Westcott, Eds. Taylor & Francis: London, 2003; pp 55-73.

[17]  Liu, Z., Saarinen, N.M., and Thompson, L.U. 2006, Sesamin is one of the major precursors of mammalian lignans in sesame seed (Sesamum indicum) as observed in vitro and in rats. *Journal of Nutrition*. 136: 906-912.

[18]  Hearon, W.M. and MacGregor, W.S. 1955, The Naturally occurring Lignans. *Chemical Reviews*. 55: 957-1069.

[19]  Jenab, M., Rickard, S.E., Orcheson, L.J., and Thompson, L.U. 1999, Flaxseed and lignans increase cecal beta-glucuronidase activity in rats. *Nutrition and cancer*. 33: 154-158.

[20]  Bakke, J.E. and Klosterman, H.J. 1956, A new diglucoside from flaxseed. *Proceedings of the North Dakota Academy of Science*. 10: 18-22.

[21]  Hosseinian, F.-S., Muir, A.-D., Westcott, N.-D., and Krol, E.-S. 2006, Antioxidant capacity of flaxseed lignans in two model systems. *Journal of the American Oil Chemists' Society*. 83: 835-840.

[22]  Westcott, N.D. and Paton, D. Complex containing lignan, phenolic and aliphatic substances from flax process for preparing. 6,264,853, 2001.

[23]  Kamal-Eldin, A., Peerlkamp, N., Johnsson, P., Andersson, R., Andersson, R.E., Lundgren, L.N., and Aman, P. 2001, An oligomer from flaxseed composed of secoisolariciresinoldiglucoside and 3-hydroxy-3-methyl glutaric acid residues. *Phytochemistry*. 58: 587-590.

[24]  Johnsson, P., Phenolic compounds in flaxseed, chromatographic and spectroscopic analyses of glucosidic conjugates. In *A PhD. thesis from Dept. Food Science*, Swedish University of Agricultural Sciences Uppsala, 2004; pp 1-36.

[25]  Struijs, K., Vincken, J.P., Verhoef, R., van Oostveen-van Casteren, W.H., Voragen, A.G., and Gruppen, H. 2007, The flavonoid herbacetin diglucoside as a constituent of the lignan macromolecule from flaxseed hulls. *Phytochemistry*. 68: 1227-1235.

[26]  Smeds, A.I., Eklund, P.C., Sjoholm, R.E., Willfor, S.M., Nishibe, S., Deyama, T., and Holmbom, B.R. 2007, Quantification of a broad spectrum of lignans in cereals, oilseeds, and nuts. *J Agric Food Chem*. 55: 1337-1346.

[27]  Axelson, M., Sjovall, J., Gustafsson, B.E., and Setchell, K.D. 1982, Origin of lignans in mammals and identification of a precursor from plants. *Nature*. 298: 659-660.

[28]  Rickard, S.E., Orcheson, L.J., Seidl, M.M., Luyengi, L., Fong, H.H., and Thompson, L.U. 1996, Dose-dependent production of mammalian lignans in rats and in vitro from the purified precursor secoisolariciresinol diglycoside in flaxseed. *Journal of Nutrition*. 126: 2012-2019.

[29]  Nesbitt, P.D., Lam, Y., and Thompson, L.U. 1999, Human metabolism of mammalian lignan precursors in raw and processed flaxseed. *American Journal of Clinical Nutrition*. 69: 549-555.

[30]  Nesbitt, P.D. and Thompson, L.U. 1997, Lignans in homemade and commercial products containing flaxseed. *Nutrition and cancer*. 29: 222-227.

[31]  Setchell, K.D.R. and Adlercreutz, H., Mammalian Lignans and Phytoestrogens, recent studies on their formation, metabolism and biological role in health and disease. In *Role of the Gut Flora in Toxicity and Cancer*, I.R. Rowland, Ed. Academic Press: New York, 1988; pp 315-345.

[32]  Westcott, N.D. and Muir, A.D. Process for extraction and purifying lignans and cinnamic acid derivatives from flaxseed. PCT/CA96/00192, 1996.

[33]  Westcott, N.D. and Muir, A.D., Ag Canada study compares lignan levels in flaxseed meal. In *LinolaLink*, 1996; Vol. April 1996, p 3.

[34]  Westcott, N.D. and Muir, A.D. In *Medicinal lignan from Flaxseed*, Prairie Medicinal and Aromatic Plants Conference, Brandon, Manitoba, 1997; Brandon, Manitoba, 1997; pp 71-76.

[35]  Lampe, J.W., Martini, M.C., Kurzer, M.S., Adlercreutz, H., and Slavin, J.L. 1994, Urinary lignan and isoflavonoid excretion in premenopausal women consuming flaxseed powder. *American Journal of Clinical Nutrition*. 60: 122-128.

[36]  Haggans, C.J., Hutchins, A.M., Olson, B.A., Thomas, W., Martini, M.C., and Slavin, J.L. 1999, Effect of flaxseed consumption on urinary estrogen metabolites in postmenopausal women. *Nutrition and cancer*. 33: 188-195.

[37]  Hutchins, A.M., Martini, M.C., Olson, B.A., Thomas, W., and Slavin, J.L. 2000, Flaxseed influences urinary lignan excretion in a dose-dependent manner in postmenopausal women. *Cancer. Epidemiol. Biomarkers. Prev.* 9: 1113-1118.

[38]  Ford, J.D., Davin, L.B., and Lewis, N.G. 1999, Plant lignans and health: cancer chemoprevention and biotechnological opportunities. *Basic Life Sciences*. 66: 675-694.

[39]  Thompson, L.U.1999, *Role of lignans in carcinogeneis, in Phytochemicals in Human Health Protection, Nutrition, and Plant defense*. Kluwer Academic/plenum publishers: New York, Vol. 33, p 51-65.

[40]  Muir, A.D., Westcott, N.D., and Prasad, K. In *Extraction, purification and animal model testing of an anti-atherosclerotic lignan secoisolariciresinol diglucoside from flaxseed (Linum usitatissimum)*. Second World Congress on Medicinal and Aromatic Plants (WOCMAP II), Mendoza, Argentina, 1997; Acta Horticulturae: Mendoza, Argentina, 1997; pp 245-248.

[41]  Muir, A.D., Westcott, N.D., Ballantyne, K., and Northrup, S., Flax Lignans - Recent developments in the analysis of lignans in plant and animal tissues. In *Proc. Flax Institue of the USA*, Flax Institute of the USA: Fargo, ND, 2000; Vol. 58, pp 23-32.

[42]  Muir, A.D., Westcott, N.D., and Aubin, A.A. In *Detection of lignans in α-Linolenic acid enriched Eggs*, 11th Ann. meeting Canadian Section. Amer. Oil Chem. Soc., Saskatoon, 29-30 Sept. 1996, 1996; AOCS: Saskatoon, 1996; p 25.

[43]  Borriello, S.P., Setchell, K.D., Axelson, M., and Lawson, A.M. 1985, Production and metabolism of lignans by the human faecal flora. *Journal of Bacteriology*. 58: 37-43.

[44]  Muir, A.D., Ballantyne, K., Aubin, A.J., and Yurach, D.C. In *LC-MS/MS analysis of lignans in plasma and urine - problems and solutions*, Biomedical Uses of Flax Conference, Winnipeg, Dec 3-5, 1998, 2000; Winnipeg, 2000.

[45]  Axelson, M. and Setchell, K.D. 1981, The excretion of lignans in rats -- evidence for an intestinal bacterial source for this new group of compounds. *FEBS Letters*. 123: 337-342.

[46] Muir, A.D. and Westcott, N.D., Mammalian metabolism of flax lignans. In *Flax, The genus Linum*, A.D. Muir and N.D. Westcott, Eds. Taylor & Francis: London, 2003; pp 230-242.

[47] Wang, L.Q., Meselhy, M.R., Li, Y., Qin, G.W., and Hattori, M. 2000, Human intestinal bacteria capable of transforming secoisolariciresinol diglucoside to mammalian lignans, enterodiol and enterolactone. *Chem Pharm Bull (Tokyo)*. 48: 1606-1610.

[48] Thompson, L.U. 1998, Experimental studies on lignans and cancer. *Baillieres Clinical Endocrinology and Metabolism*. 12: 691-705.

[49] Ford, J.D., Huang, K.S., Wang, H.B., Davin, L.B., and Lewis, N.G. 2001, Biosynthetic pathway to the cancer chemopreventive secoisolariciresinol diglucoside-hydroxymethyl glutaryl ester-linked lignan oligomers in flax (Linum usitatissimum) seed. *Journal of Natural Products*. 64: 1388-1397.

[50] Jacobs, E. and Metzler, M. 1999, Oxidative metabolism of the mammalian lignans enterolactone and enterodiol by rat, pig, and human liver microsomes. *Journal of Agricultural and Food Chemistry*. 47: 1071-1077.

[51] Niemeyer, H.B., Honig, D., Lange-Bohmer, A., Jacobs, E., Kulling, S.E., and Metzler, M. 2000, Oxidative metabolites of the mammalian lignans enterodiol and enterolactone in rat bile and urine. *Journal of Agricultural and Food Chemistry*. 48: 2910-2919.

[52] Jacobs, E., Kulling, S.E., and Metzler, M. 1999, Novel metabolites of the mammalian lignans enterolactone and enterodiol in human urine. *Journal of Steroid Biochemistry and Molecular Biology*. 68: 211-218.

[53] Axelson, M. and Setchell, K.D. 1980, Conjugation of lignans in human urine. *FEBS Letters*. 122: 49-53.

[54] Adlercreutz, C.H.T., Goldin, B.R., Gorbach, S.L., Höckerstedt, K.A.V., Watanabe, S., Hämäläinen, E.K., Markkanen, M.H., Mäkelä, T.H., Wähälä, K.T., Hase, T.A., and Fotsis, T. 1995, Soybean phytoestrogen intake and cancer risk. *Journal of Nutrition*. 125: 757s-770s.

[55] Setchell, K.D.R., Lawson, A.M., Borriello, S.P., Adlercreutz, H., and Axelson, M., Formation of lignans by intestinal microflora. In *Falk Symposium 31, Colonic Carcinogenesis.*, R.A. Malt and R.C.N. Williamson, Eds. MTP Press Ltd.: Lancaster, 1982; pp 93-97.

[56] Dean, B., Chang, S., Doss, G.A., King, C., and Thomas, P.E. 2004, Glucuronidation, oxidative metabolism, and bioactivation of enterolactone in rhesus monkeys. *Archives of Biochemistry and Biophysics*. 429: 244-251.

[57] Adlercreutz, H., van der Widlt, J., Kinzel, J., Attalla, H., Wähälä, K., Mäkelä, T., Hase, T., and Fotsis, T. 1995, Lignan and isoflavonoid conjugates in human urine. *Journal of Steroid Biochemistry and Molecular Biology*. 52: 97-103.

[58] Setchell, K.D., Lawson, A.M., Borriello, S.P., Harkness, R., Gordon, H., Morgan, D.M., Kirk, D.N., Adlercreatz, H., Anderson, L.C., and Axelson, M. 1981, Lignan formation in man--microbial involvement and possible roles in relation to cancer. *Lancet*. 2: 4-7.

[59] Adlercreutz, H., Fotsis, T., Bannwart, C., Wähälä, K., Mäkelä, T., Brunow, G., and Hase, T. 1986, Determination of urinary lignans and phytoestrogens metabolites, potential antiestrogens and anticarcinogens, in urine of women on various habitual diets. *Journal of Biological Chemistry*. 25: 791-797.

[60] Adlercreutz, H., Fotsis, T., Heikkinen, R., Dwyer, J.T., Woods, M., Goldin, B.R., and Gorbach, S.L. 1982, Excretion of the lignans enterolactone and enterodiol and of equol in omnivorous and vegetarian postmenopausal women and in women with breast cancer. *Lancet.* ii: 1295-1299.

[61] Adlercreutz, H., Fotsis, T., Heikkinen, R., Dwyer, J.T., Goldin, B.R., Gorbach, S.L., Lawson, A.M., and Setchell, K.D. 1981, Diet and urinary excretion of lignans in female subjects. *Med. Biol.* 59: 259-261.

[62] Adlercreutz, H., Fotsis, T., Lampe, J., Wähälä, K., Mäkelä, T., Brunow, G., and Hase, T. 1993, Quantitative determination of lignans and isoflavonoids in plasma of omnivorous and vegetarian women by isotope dilution gas chromatography-mass spectrometry. *Scandinavian journal of clinical and laboratory investigation.* 53: 5-18.

[63] Adlercreutz, H., Fotsis, T., Kurzer, M.S., Wähälä, K., Mäkelä, T., and Hase, T. 1995, Isotope dilution gas chromatographic-Mass Spectrometric method for the determination of unconjugated lignans and isoflavanoids in human feces, with preliminary results in omnivorous and vegetarian women. *Analytical Biochemistry.* 225: 101-108.

[64] Adlercreutz, H., Fotsis, T., Bannwart, C., Hämäläinen, E., Bloigu, S., and Ollus, A. 1986, Urinary estrogen profile determination in young finnish vegetarian and omnivorous women. *Journal of Steroid Biochemistry and Molecular Biology.* 24: 289-296.

[65] Adlercreutz, H., Fotsis, T., Bannwart, C., Wähälä, K., Brunow, K., and Hase, T. 1991, Isotope dilution gas chromatographic-mass spectrometric method for the determination of lignans and isoflavonoids in human urine, including identification of genistein. *Clinica Chimica Acta.* 199: 263-278.

[66] Kuijsten, A., Arts, I.C., Vree, T.B., and Hollman, P.C. 2005, Pharmacokinetics of enterolignans in healthy men and women consuming a single dose of secoisolariciresinol diglucoside. *Journal of Nutrition.* 135: 795-801.

[67] Adlercreutz, H., Fotsis, T., Watanabe, S., Lampe, J., Wähälä, K., Mäkeläa, T., and Hase, T. 1994, Determination of lignans and isoflavonoids in plasma by isotope dilution gas-chromatography-Mass Spectrometry. *Cancer Detection and Prevention.* 18: 259-271.

[68] Jenab, M. and Thompson, L.U. 1996, The influence of flaxseed and lignans on colon carcinogenesis and beta- glucuronidase activity. *Carcinogenesis (London).* 17: 1343-1348.

[69] Kashtan, H., Stern, H.S., Jenkins, D.J., Jenkins, A.L., Thompson, L.U., Hay, K., Marcon, N., Minkin, S., and Bruce, W.R. 1992, Colonic fermentation and markers of colorectal-cancer risk. *American Journal of Clinical Nutrition.* 55: 723-728.

[70] Adlercreutz, H. 1990, Diet, Breast Cancer, and sex hormone metabolism. *Annuals New York Academy of Sciences.* 595: 281-290.

[71] Adlercreutz, H., Lignans and Phytoestrogens. Possible preventative role in cancer. In *Frontiers of Gastrointestinal Research.*, P. Rozen, Ed. Karger: Basel, 1988; Vol. 14, pp 165-176.

[72] Adlercreutz, H. 1984, Does fiber-rich food containing animal lignan precursors protect against both colon and breast cancer? An extension of the "fiber hypothesis". *Gastroenterology.* 86: 761-676.

[73] Rickard, S.E. and Thompson, L.U., The role of flaxseed lignans in hormone-dependent and independent cancer. In *Flax, The genus Linum*, A.D. Muir and N.D. Westcott, Eds. London, 2003; pp 181-204.

[74] Prasad, K. 2000, Oxidative stress as a mechanism of diabetes in diabetic BB prone rats: effect of secoisolariciresinol diglucoside (SDG). *Molecular and Cellular Biochemistry*. 209: 89-96.

[75] Felmlee, M.A., Woo, G., Simko, E., Krol, E.S., Muir, A.D., and Alcorn, J. 2009, Effects of the flaxseed lignans secoisolariciresinol diglucoside and its aglycone on serum and hepatic lipids in hyperlipidemic rats (In press). *British Journal of Nutrition*. 102: 361-369.

[76] Thompson, L.U., Seidl, M.M., Rickard, S.E., Orcheson, L.J., and Fong, H.H. 1996, Antitumorigenic effect of a mammalian lignan precursor from flaxseed. *Nutrition and cancer*. 26: 159-165.

[77] Adlercreutz, H., Lignans and isoflavonoids: Epidemiology and a possible role in prevention of cancer. In *Natural Antioxidants and Food Quality in Atherosclerosis and Cancer Prevention.*, J.T. Kumpulainen and J.T. Salonen, Eds. The Royal Society of Chemistry: London, 1996; pp 349-355.

[78] Adlercreutz, H. In *Phytoestrogens from biochemistry to prevention of cancer and other diseases*, 8th International Congress on the Menopause, Sydney, Australia, Novermber 3-7, 1996, 1996; Maturitas: Sydney, Australia, 1996; pp 12-13.

[79] Adlercreutz, H., Honjo, H., Higashi, A., Fotsis, T., Hämäläinen, E., Hasegawa, T., and Okada, H. 1991, Urinary excretion of lignans and isoflavanoid phytoestrogens in Japanese men and women consuming a traditional Japansese diet. *American Journal of Clinical Nutrition*. 54: 1093-1100.

[80] Serraino, M. and Thompson, L.U. 1992, The effect of flaxseed supplementation on the initiation and promotional stages of mammary tumorigenesis. *Nutrition and cancer*. 17: 153-159.

[81] Sathyamoorthy, N., Wang, T.T., and Phang, J.M. 1994, Stimulation of pS2 expression by diet-derived compounds. *Cancer Research*. 54: 957-961.

[82] Rickard, S.E., Yuan, Y.V., and Thompson, L.U. 2000, Plasma insulin-like growth factor I levels in rats are reduced by dietary supplementation of flaxseed or its lignan secoisolariciresinol diglycoside. *Cancer Letters*. 161: 47-55.

[83] Mousavi, Y. and Adlercreutz, H. 1992, Enterolactone and estradiol inhibit each other's proliferative effect on MCF-7 breast cancer cells in culture. *Journal of Steroid Biochemistry and Molecular Biology*. 41: 615-619.

[84] Morris, D.H. 2001, Essential nutrients and other functional compounds in flaxseed. *Nutrition Today*. 36: 159-162.

[85] Ingram, D., Sanders, K., Kolybaba, M., and Lopez, D. 1997, Case-control study of phyto-oestrogens and breast cancer. *Lancet*. 350: 990-994.

[86] Adlercreutz, H. 1995, Phytoestrogens: Epidemiology and a possible role in cancer protection. *Environmental Health Perspectives*. 103: 103-112.

[87] Saarinen, N.M., Penttinen, P.E., Smeds, A.I., Hurmerinta, T.T., and Makela, S.I. 2005, Structural determinants of plant lignans for growth of mammary tumors and hormonal responses in vivo. *Journal of Steroid Biochemistry and Molecular Biology*. 93: 209-219.

[88]  Saarinen, N.M., Power, K.A., Chen, J., and Thompson, L.U. 2008, Lignans are accessible to human breast cancer xenografts in athymic mice. *Nutr Cancer*. 60: 245-250.

[89]  Power, K.A., Saarinen, N.M., Chen, J.M., and Thompson, L.U. 2006, Mammalian lignans enterolactone and enterodiol, alone and in combination with the isoflavone genistein, do not promote the growth of MCF-7 xenografts in ovariectomized athymic nude mice. *International Journal of Cancer*. 118: 1316-1320.

[90]  Saarinen, N.M., Warri, A., Dings, R.P., Airio, M., Smeds, A.I., and Makela, S. 2008, Dietary lariciresinol attenuates mammary tumor growth and reduces blood vessel density in human MCF-7 breast cancer xenografts and carcinogen-induced mammary tumors in rats. *International Journal of Cancer*. 123: 1196-1204.

[91]  Saarinen, N.M., Warri, A., Airio, M., Smeds, A., and Makela, S. 2007, Role of dietary lignans in the reduction of breast cancer risk. *Mol Nutr Food Res*. 51: 857-866.

[92]  Thompson, L.U., Rickard, S.E., Orcheson, L.J., and Seidl, M.M. 1996, Flaxseed and its lignan and oil components reduce mammary tumor growth at a late stage of carcinogenesis. *Carcinogenesis (London)*. 17: 1373-1376.

[93]  Saarinen, N.M., Warri, A., Makela, S.I., Eckerman, C., Reunanen, M., Ahotupa, M., Salmi, S.M., Franke, A.A., Kangas, L., and Santti, R. 2000, Hydroxymatairesinol, a novel enterolactone precursor with antitumor properties from coniferous tree (Picea abies). *Nutrition and cancer*. 36: 207-216.

[94]  Miura, D., Saarinen, N.M., Miura, Y., Santti, R., and Yagasaki, K. 2007, Hydroxymatairesinol and its mammalian metabolite enterolactone reduce the growth and metastasis of subcutaneous AH109A hepatomas in rats. *Nutr Cancer*. 58: 49-59.

[95]  Bylund, A., Saarinen, N., Zhang, J.X., Bergh, A., Widmark, A., Johansson, A., Lundin, E., Adlercreutz, H., Hallmans, G., Stattin, P., and Makela, S. 2005, Anticancer effects of a plant lignan 7-hydroxymatairesinol on a prostate cancer model in vivo. *Exp Biol Med (Maywood)*. 230: 217-223.

[96]  Wang, C. and Kurzer, M.S. 1997, Phytoestrogen concentration determines effects on DNA synthesis in Human Breast cancer cells. *Nutrition and cancer*. 28: 236-247.

[97]  Fishman, J., Osborne, M.P., and Telang, N.T. 1995, The role of estrogen in mammary carcinogenesis. *Annals of the New York Academy of Sciences*. 768: 91-100.

[98]  Sung, M.K., Lautens, M., and Thompson, L.U. 1998, Mammalian lignans inhibit the growth of estrogen-independent human colon tumor cells. *Anticancer Research*. 18: 1405-1408.

[99]  Adlercreutz, H., Mousavi, Y., and Hockerstedt, K. 1992, Diet and breast cancer. *Acta Oncologica*. 31: 175-181.

[100] Thompson, L.U., Robb, P., Serraino, M., and Cheung, F. 1991, Mammalian lignan production from various foods. *Nutrition and cancer*. 16: 43-52.

[101] Evans, B.A.J., Griffiths, K., and Morton, M.S. 1995, Inhibition of 5 $\alpha$-reductase in genital skin fibroblasts and prostate tissue by dietary lignans and isoflavonoids. *Journal of Endocrinology*. 147: 295-302.

[102] Hall, A.V., Parbtani, A., Clark, W.F., Spanner, E., Keeney, M., Chin-Yee, I., Philbrick, D.J., and Holub, B.J. 1993, Abrogation of MRL/lpr lupus nephritis by dietary flaxseed. *American journal of kidney diseases*. 22: 326-332.

[103] Orcheson, L.J., Rickard, S.E., Seidl, M.M., and Thompson, L.U. 1998, Flaxseed and its mammalian lignan precursor cause a lengthening or cessation of estrous cycling in rats. *Cancer Letters*. 125: 69-76.

[104] Yan, L., Yee, J.A., Li, D., McGuire, M.H., and Thompson, L.U. 1998, Dietary flaxseed supplementation and experimental metastasis of melanoma cells in mice. *Cancer Letters*. 124: 181-186.

[105] Li, D., Yee, J.A., Thompson, L.U., and Yan, L. 1999, Dietary supplementation with secoisolariciresinol diglycoside (SDG) reduces experimental metastasis of melanoma cells in mice. *Cancer Letters*. 142: 91-96.

[106] Serraino, M. and Thompson, L.U. 1992, Flaxseed supplementation and early markers of colon carcinogenesis. *Cancer Letters*. 63: 159-165.

[107] Lin, X., Gingrich, J.R., Bao, W., Li, J., Haroon, Z.A., and Demark-Wahnefried, W. 2002, Effect of flaxseed supplementation on prostatic carcinoma in transgenic mice. *Urology*. 60: 919-924.

[108] Prasad, K. 1999, Reduction of serum cholesterol and hypercholesterolemic atherosclerosis by secoisolariciresinol diglucoside isolated from flaxseed. *Circulation*. 99: 1355-1362.

[109] Prasad, K., Gupta, J.B., Kalra, J., Lee, P., Mantha, S.V., and Bharadwaj, B. 1996, Oxidative stress as a mechanism of cardiac failure in chronic volume overload in canine model. *Journal of Molecular and Cellular Cardiology*. 28: 375-385.

[110] Jenkins, D.J., Kendall, C.W., Vidgen, E., Agarwal, S., Rao, A.V., Rosenberg, R.S., Diamandis, E.P., Novokmet, R., Mehling, C.C., Perera, T., Griffin, L.C., and Cunnane, S.C. 1999, Health aspects of partially defatted flaxseed, including effects on serum lipids, oxidative measures, and ex vivo androgen and progestin activity: a controlled crossover trial. *American Journal of Clinical Nutrition*. 69: 395-402.

[111] Westcott, N.D. and Muir, A.D. 2003, Flax seed lignan in disease prevention and health promotion. *Phytochemistry Reviews*. 2: 401-417.

[112] Prasad, K. 2001, Secoisolariciresinol diglucoside from flaxseed delays the development of type 2 diabetes in Zucker rat. *Journal of Laboratory and Clinical Medicine*. 138: 32-39.

[113] Chen, J., Stavro, P.M., and Thompson, L.U. 2002, Dietary flaxseed inhibits human breast cancer growth and metastasis and downregulates expression of insulin-like growth factor and epidermal growth factor receptor. *Nutrition and cancer*. 43: 187-192.

[114] McIntosh, G.H., Noakes, M., Royle, P.J., and Foster, P.R. 2003, Whole-grain rye and wheat foods and markers of bowel health in overweight middle-aged men. *American Journal of Clinical Nutrition*. 77: 967-974.

[115] Brooks, J.D., Ward, W.E., Lewis, J.E., Hilditch, J., Nickell, L., Wong, E., and Thompson, L.U. 2004, Supplementation with flaxseed alters estrogen metabolism in postmenopausal women to a greater extent than does supplementation with an equal amount of soy. *American Journal of Clinical Nutrition*. 79: 318-325.

[116] Demark-Wahnefried, W., Price, D.T., Polascik, T.J., Robertson, C.N., Anderson, E.E., Paulson, D.F., Walther, P.J., Gannon, M., and Vollmer, R.T. 2001, Pilot study of dietary fat restriction and flaxseed supplementation in men with prostate cancer before surgery: exploring the effects on hormonal levels, prostate-specific antigen, and histopathologic features. *Urology*. 58: 47-52.

[117] Bourlard, T., Bruyant-Vannier, M.P., Schaumann, A., Bruyant, P., and Morvan, C. 2001, Purification of several pectin methyltransferases from cell suspension cultures of flax (Linum usitatissimum L.). *C. R. Acad. Sci.III*. 324: 335-343.

[118] Decker, E.A., Warner, K., Richards, M.P., and Shahidi, F. 2005, Measuring antioxidant effectiveness in food. *J Agric Food Chem*. 53: 4303-4310.

[119] Schwarz, K., Bertelsen, G., Nissen, L.R., Gardner, P.T., Heinonen, M.I., Hopia, A., Tuong, H.B., Lambelet, P., McPhail, D., Skibsted, L.H., and Tijburg, L. 2001, Investigation of plant extracts for the protection of processed foods against lipid oxidation. Comparison of antioxidant assays based on radical scavenging, lipid oxidation and analysis of the principal antioxidant compounds. *Eur. Food Res. Technol.* 212: 319–328.

[120] Kitts, D.D., Yuan, Y.V., Wijewickreme, A.N., and Thompson, L.U. 1999, Antioxidant activity of the flaxseed lignan secoisolariciresinol diglycoside and its mammalian lignan metabolites enterodiol and enterolactone. *Molecular and Cellular Biochemistry*. 202: 91-100.

[121] Eklund, P.C., Langvik, O.K., Warna, J.P., Salmi, T.O., Willfor, S.M., and Sjoholm, R.E. 2005, Chemical studies on antioxidant mechanisms and free radical scavenging properties of lignans. *Org. Biomol. Chem*. 3: 3336-3347.

[122] Ghafoorunissa, Hemalatha, S., and Rao, M.V. 2004, Sesame lignans enhance antioxidant activity of vitamin E in lipid peroxidation systems. *Molecular and Cellular Biochemistry*. 262: 195-202.

In: Bioactive Molecules in Plant Foods
Editor: Florence Ojiugo Uruakpa

ISBN: 978-1-62081-515-1
© 2012 Nova Science Publishers, Inc.

*Chapter IV*

# CHEMISTRY AND BIOACTIVITY OF FOOD PHYTOALEXINS

## *Chibuike C. Udenigwe[1,*] and Rotimi E. Aluko[2]*

[1]Department of Food Science, University of Guelph, Guelph, ON, Canada
[2]Department of Human Nutritional Sciences, and
the Richardson Centre for Functional Foods and Nutraceuticals,
University of Manitoba, Winnipeg, MB, Canada

## ABSTRACT

The enrichment of functional foods with bioactive phytochemicals has emerged as an area of interest to food and nutrition scientists. Recent studies have proposed a subset of functional foods known as "phytoalexin-enriched functional foods". Phytoalexins are low molecular weight compounds produced in plants in response to various forms of biotic and abiotic stress such as microbial infection and ultraviolent radiation. These phytochemicals, mostly polyphenols, terpenoids and alkaloids, function in protecting the damaged or infected plant cells. It has been proposed that the phytoalexinic properties of these compounds can be harnessed in improving the health benefits of established functional foods or for producing novel health-promoting foods. Some plant foods that contain phytoalexins include soybean, peanuts, grapes, pea, beans, potato, crucifers and alfalfa.

This chapter focuses on the different sources, chemical structures and biosynthesis of food phytoalexins as well as their potential human health benefits. The enrichment of foods with bioactive phytoalexins can impact global functional food trends by providing consumers with alternative choice of healthy foods for the prevention and treatment of chronic human diseases and health conditions.

**Keywords:** Phytoalexins, functional foods, phytochemicals, human health

---

* Corresponding author: Dr. Chibuike C. Udenigwe - Department of Food Science, University of Guelph, Guelph, Ontario, N1G 2W1, Canada. Email: cudenigw@uoguelph.ca; Phone: +1 (519) 824-4120 ext. 56585.

# INTRODUCTION

The increased consumer awareness about functional foods two decades ago has added a new dimension to approaches used for the management and treatment of human diseases, especially cardiovascular and neurodegenerative diseases, obesity, diabetes and cancer. Functional foods have also gained particular interest as agents for disease prevention and for maintaining a healthy lifestyle. Most of the pharmacological properties attributed to functional foods are due to their constituent phytochemicals. These are compounds that are not directly involved in primary metabolism of plants, but may play defensive roles against invading organisms or other environmental factors. Phytochemicals are produced in plants from simple precursors such as acetate, shikimate, mevalonate and deoxyxylulose, and can be generally classified as alkaloids, terpenoids and polyphenolic compounds based on their biosynthetic origins and structural features [1]. The biosynthesis of phytochemicals can be constitutive or inducible. Constitutive phytochemicals are produced continuously for plant secondary metabolic functions whereas the inducible compounds are produced as a response to environmental stress or infection. These two groups of phytochemicals can belong to any of the aforementioned classes of compounds. The inducible phytochemicals are known as phytoalexins. The word "phytoalexin" was originally derived from two Greek words, "*phyto*"– plant and "*alexein*"– to ward off or defend. They were initially defined as a group of antibiotic compounds synthesized *de novo* after plants are exposed to infection [2, 3]. Based on this definition, phytoalexins are not pre-formed in plants prior to infection and must function in plant disease resistance. Phytoalexins have also been defined as antimicrobial compounds, synthesized *de novo*, which accumulate in plants in response to microbial infection or stress [4, 5]; therefore, they may not necessarily be involved in disease resistance. These definitions differentiate phytoalexins from another group of compounds known as phytoanticipins, which are constitutively produced by plants to play defensive roles [3]. Moreover, some constitutive phytochemicals are produced by plants in high amounts after exposure to stress or infection; thus, these compounds serve as both phytoalexins and phytoanticipins [6].

Extrinsic factors that induce phytoalexin synthesis in plants are known as elicitors, which are classified as abiotic and biotic. Abiotic elicitors of phytoalexin accumulation include ultraviolet (UV) radiation, freezing or cold weather and physical injury to plants, whereas biotic elicitors include microorganisms and their cell wall extracts, polysaccharides (glycoproteins, chitosans and glucans), peptides (monilicolin A) and ethylene [6–8]. Inorganic salts, e.g. $CuCl_2$, have also demonstrated the ability to elicit phytoalexin production in plants [9]. The induction of phytoalexin production in plant food by elicitors can occur pre-harvest or postharvest. The latter, i.e. postharvest, strategy has been widely studied for enriching foods with bioactive ingredients [6] probably due to the simple approach and unaffected natural composition of the entire plant source. The physiological mechanism of induction of phytoalexin synthesis, in response to elicitor treatments, involves the activation of the expression of genes that code the phytoalexin biosynthetic enzymes [7]. A number of plant foods have been reported to produce appreciable amounts of phytoalexins especially legumes (Table 1). Soy and grapes have been widely studied due to their ability to produce large amounts of phytoalexins with established or potential human health benefits. In addition, accumulation of minor to appreciable amounts of phytoalexins has been reported in stressed garlic, pea, beans, potato, pepper, alfalfa and crucifers. The chemical structures of these compounds are heterogeneous, similar to the backbones of constitutive phytochemicals, and may offer biologically relevant chemical diversity against human disease targets since phytoalexins are biosynthesized in plants for defence. Phytoalexins exists in different structural forms, which include diterpenoids, indole alkaloids, steroidal glycoalkaloids, sesquiterpenoids, isoflavonoids, polyacetylenes, cyclic hydroxamic acids and stilbenes [10]. Some examples of phytoalexins include resveratrol, pterostilbene, glyceollins, glycinol, allixin, capsidiol, α-solanine, α-chaconine and rishitin. The induction of phytoalexin accumulation in foods can be exploited in producing novel functional foods or for improving the health benefits of established functional foods (Figure 1). However, phytoalexin accumulation can create an undesirable sensory attributes that will potentially mar the palatability and quality of food [8]. In addition, there could also be possible toxic effects if levels of phytoalexins are high enough in the body. For example, high amounts of the potato glycoalkaloids (α-solanine and α-chaconine) was reported to induce negative physiological effects such as neurological defects, teratogenicity, interference with trans-membrane transport of calcium and sodium ions, disruption of cholesterol-containing cell membranes as well as toxicity due to induction of hepatic ornithine decarboxylase and even death [11]. Based on the negative effects, the upper limit of the potato glycoalkaloids has been set by the U.S. Food and Drug Administration (FDA) at 20 mg/100 g of fresh potato tubers [11].

**Table 1. Food sources, structural types and some examples of phytoalexins**

| Phytoalexins | Structural type | Food sources |
|---|---|---|
| Resveratrol | Stilbene | Grapes, peanuts, cranberries, mulberries, turmeric, red wines |
| Pterostilbene | Stilbene | Grapes |
| Glycinol | Pterocarpan | Soybeans |
| Glyceollin isomers | Pterocarpan | Soybeans |
| Allixin | Pyrone | Garlic |
| Capsidiol | Terpenoid | Pepper, tobacco |
| Rishitin | Terpenoid | Potato |

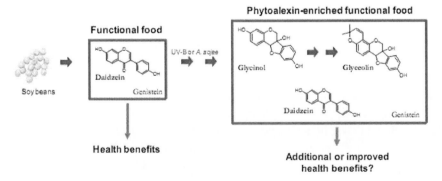

Figure 1. Phytoalexin enrichment of soybeans induced by exposure to abiotic (UV-B radiation) and biotic (*Aspergillius sojae*) elicitors. The accumulation of phytoalexins in plant foods can be exploited in producing novel health-promoting foods or improving the health benefits of established functional foods.

# STRUCTURES, OCCURENCE AND BIOSYNTHESIS OF FOOD PHYTOALEXINS

## Resveratrol and Pterostilbene

Resveratrol (*trans*-3,4′,5-trihydroxystilbene) is a stilbenoid phytoalexin predominantly found in grapevine (*Vitis vinifera*) skin and peanuts (*Arachis hypogaea*). Other dietary sources of resveratrol include blueberries, cranberries, turmeric, hops and mulberries [12]. Minor amounts of resveratrol have also been detected in bilberries, deerberries, partridgeberries, lingonberries and sparkle berries [13]. Resveratrol has also been found in commercial products of these fruits particularly red wine, which contains over 1.5 mg of resveratrol per 100 ml depending on the type of wine, methods of wine-making and resveratrol quantification [14]. Resveratrol has been found in higher amounts in red wines than white wines; it is predominantly synthesized in the grape skin and released into the wine during fermentation [15]. Structurally, resveratrol exists in both its *trans* and *cis* isomers, which are found in varying amounts in foods and commercial red wines. The conversion of the *trans* to *cis* isomers of resveratrol can be induced by UV irradiation, but the *trans* form is more abundant in wines. These isomers of resveratrol can also exist in form of their glucosides known as piceid. Consistent with most polyphenolic compounds, the structure of resveratrol comprises of two aromatic rings joined by an ethylene bridge with the three hydroxyl groups attached to the aromatic rings [14]; the structures of resveratrol and its derivatives are shown in Figure 2. The biosynthesis of resveratrol involves the condensation of one 4-coumaryl-CoA and three malonyl-CoA molecules in a reaction catalyzed by stilbene synthase (STS), a key point in the phenylpropanoid pathway where the precursor can also be used for flavonoid synthesis [1].

Resveratrol is synthesized in plants as an antifungal agent in response to infection [16], but several studies have shown that the induction of resveratrol synthesis can also be elicited by abiotic factors such as UV rays and tissue damage. For example, exposure of grape berries to UV irradiation and postharvest drying process (wilting) resulted in increased synthesis and accumulation of resveratrol in berries [17–19]. Moreover, UV light treatments also led to increase in concentration of resveratrol and its derivatives in peanut plants [20]. In addition, a recent study also showed that short- (less than 1 h) and long-term (up to 13 months) separate and combined UV-ultrasound treatments resulted in increased resveratrol contents in peanuts [21].

A resveratrol dehydrodimer, known as ε-viniferin, was also reported to accumulate in large amounts in response to UV-C irradiation and fungal infection, and has been proposed to be a source of resveratrol in mature berries-derived red wine after extraction and degradation [22, 23]. The synthesis of the stilbene phytoalexins have been attributed to increased expression of STS mRNA in the berries in response to the stress factors [19, 20].

Another type of stilbene phytoalexin found in food is pterostilbene. This compound is the 3,5-O-dimethylated derivative of resveratrol (Figure 2) and is predominant in blueberries, rabbiteye berries, deerberries, and in lower amounts in grapevine berries [13, 17, 23, 24]. Pterostilbene is a minor component of the stress response of grapes but its antifungal activity against pathogens was reported to be better than that of resveratrol, which is produced in higher amount [24]. Although present in small amounts, the synthesis and accumulation of pterostilbene was reported to be elicited by short-term UV irradiation and infection by *Botrytis cinerea* [17, 22, 23]. These stilbene-type phytoalexins may play protective roles in the plants against UV damage.

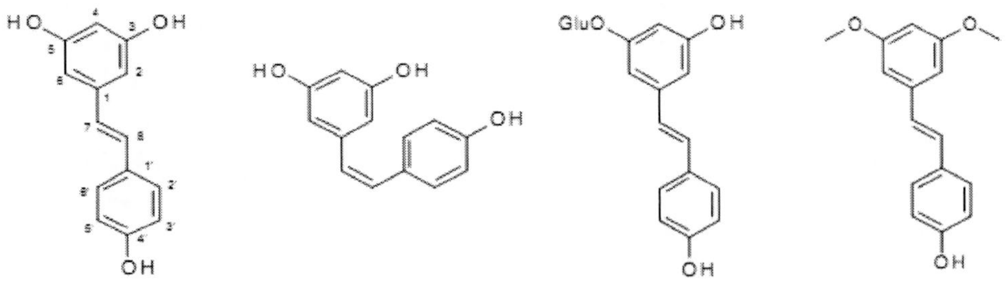

| *trans*-Resveratrol | *cis*-Resveratrol | *trans*-Piceid | Pterostilbene |

Figure 2. Structures of resveratrol and its derivatives found in grapes, peanuts, blueberries, cranberries, turmeric, hops, mulberries and commercial red wines. Resveratrol exists in the form of *trans*- and *cis*-isomers, and as glycosylated derivative known as piceid; pterostilbene is a 3,5-O-dimethylated derivative of resveratrol.

## Pterocarpans

Glyceollins are the major phytoalexins present in soybeans (*Glycine max*) and have been widely studied as agents of plant defence mechanism against pathogens. They belong to the pterocarpan class of phytoalexin and are derived from soy isoflavones. On exposure of soybeans to biotic elicitors, the tricyclic soy isoflavone, daidzein, is transformed into a tetracyclic hydroxylated derivative known as glycinol. This pterocarpan serves as a precursor for the synthesis of pentacyclic glyceollins I, II and III [6]. The structures of soy-derived glycinol and the glyceollins are shown in Figure 3. Several studies have shown that the glyceollins accumulate in soy in response to various pathogenic and food-grade fungi [6, 25–31]. Boue and co-workers found that a number of fungi belonging to the *Aspergillus* species, including *A. sojae*, *A. niger*, *A. oryzae*, *A. flavus*, elicited time-dependent synthesis and accumulation of glyceollins in soybeans compared to uninoculated seeds, which did not contain any detectable amount of the phytoalexins [25]. In this study, glyceollins I, II and III were found in the ratio of 6:2:1 and it was found that *A. sojae* induced the highest amount of glyceollins in the soy seeds evaluated 3 days post-inoculation. The difference in ratio of the biosynthesized glyceollins could be due to differential need for a particular compound required to combat a specific stress factor. The latter observation of phytoalexin ratios can be exploited for the design of functional foods with customized amounts of these phytoalexins. Although the glyceollin biosynthetic pathways have been elucidated, it is not clear whether the phytoalexins are synthesized solely in response to extrinsic stress. Moreover, a combination of physical injury (cutting) and *A. sojae* inoculation have been found to result in the accumulation of over 1.5 mg glyceollins per gram of soybean extract and more than 10-fold increase in the amounts of daidzein and genistein [26]. Another study showed that mincing of soybean seeds elicited the accumulation of more glyceollins than slicing (cutting) the seeds into halves [27], although contradictory observations have also been reported [30]. These observations show that the glyceollins may play protective roles in the plant seeds other than antifungal, and that the biosynthesis of constitutive isoflavones can also be upregulated during stress, perhaps since they serve as precursors to the phytoalexins.

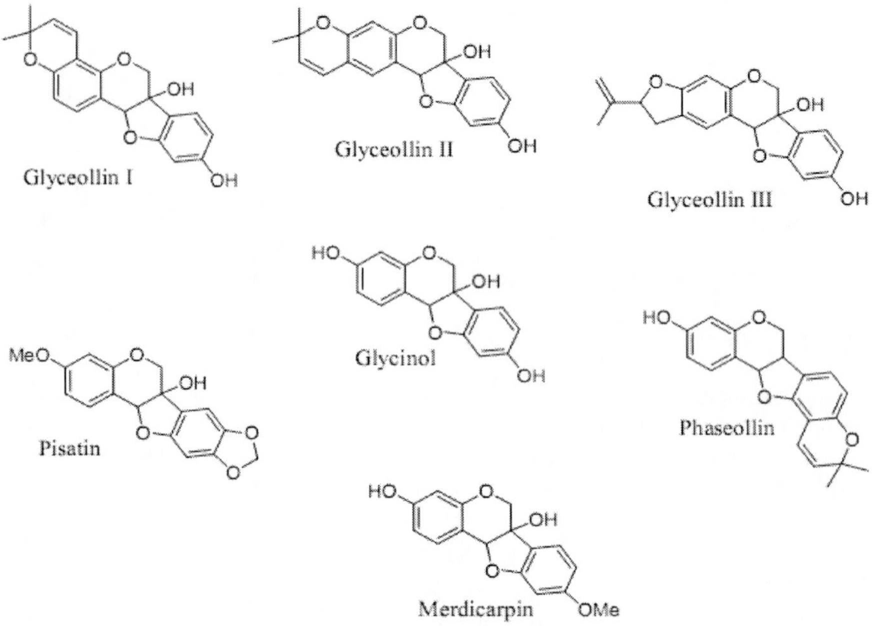

Figure 3. Chemical structures of the pterocarpan phytoalexins derived from different food sources: glycinol, glyceollins I, II and III (soy), pisatin (pea), phaseollin (beans) and medicarpin (alfalfa). These phytoalexins accumulate in plant foods in response to fungal attack and physical factors (e.g. wilting, cutting and seed splitting).

Based on these studies, it is clear that microbes can increase the total amount of phytonutrients in soybeans. For example, fermentation of soybeans with food-grade *Rhizopus microsporus* var. *oligosporus* resulted in the accumulation of the glyceollin isomers (total amount of 1.2 mg/g dry soybeans) and elevated amounts of soy daidzein compared to the untreated soybeans [31].

In addition to soy pterocarpans, other known pterocarpan phytoalexins include pisatin, phaseollin and medicarpin, which are predominant in stressed pea (*Pisum sativum*), common beans (*Phaseolus vulgaris*) and alfalfa (*Medicago sativa*), respectively. The chemical structures of these compounds are shown in Figure 3. Pea pisatin was one of the first phytoalexins to be structurally characterized; it is biosynthesized as a product of acetate-malonate and shikimate pathways [32]. These phytoalexins accumulate in their respective plant sources in response to various stressors especially fungal infection. The amount of accumulated phaseollin over a period of time was reported to be positively correlated with the increased resistance of bean varieties against plant pathogenic fungi [9]. Moreover, a recent study demonstrated that food-grade *A. sojae* elicited the synthesis and accumulation of phaseollin (0.2 mg/g) and another phytoalexin, kievitone (1.2 mg/g), in red kidney bean [33]. Therefore, food processing using microorganisms, e.g. fermentation, can be used for phytoalexin enrichment. Doherty and Buescher [34] had earlier reported that postharvest handling-induced pod damage also elicited the synthesis of phaseollin, which also accumulated in healthy tissue adjacent to the damages area.

## Capsidiol, Rishitin and Allixin

These phytoalexins, structurally different from the stilbenes and glyceollins, have been reported in stressed plant foods. Capsidiol and rishitin belong to the 15-carbon sesquiterpenoid class of phytochemicals.

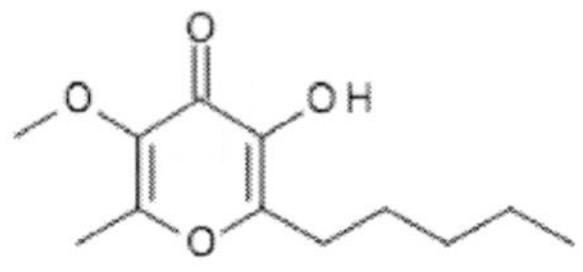

Allixin 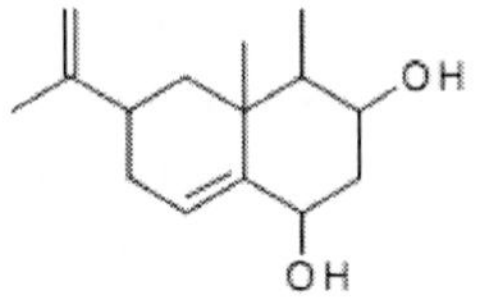                    Capsidiol 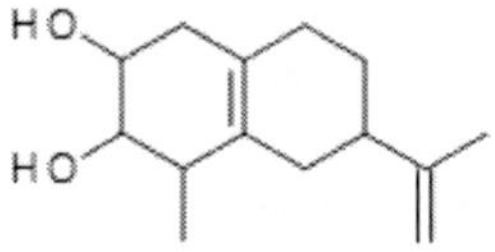                    Rishitin

Figure 4. Chemical structures of food phytoalexins allixin (garlic), capsidiol (pepper) and rishitin (potato); allixin possesses a γ-pyrone structure whereas capsidiol and rishitin belong to the sesquiterpenoid class of phytochemicals.

The chemical structures of these compounds are shown in Figure 4. Capsidiol is a bicyclic sesquiterpene synthesized as the major phytoalexin in chilli pepper (*Capsicum annuum*) and tobacco (*Nicotiana tabacum*) in response to pathogens, especially fungal infection [35, 36]. Capsidiol is synthesized in these plants via the acetate-mevalonate pathway by the conversion of acyclic farnesyl pyrophosphate to cyclic 5-*epi*-aristolochene, which is then converted to capsidiol by double hydroxylation [37]. The other sesquiterpene phytoalexin, rishitin, is a mevalonate-derived antifungal compound found in potato tubers and one of the first phytoalexins to be studied [38]. It accumulates in potato tubers when challenged by infection or physical injury. Rishitin has also been detected in tomato fruits where it accumulated in response to gray mold rot (*Botrytis cinerea*) infection and UV-C treatment; the resistance of the tomato fruit to infection was attributed to rishitin accumulation [39]. Moreover, both rishitin and capsidiol were synthesized in plants during oxidative burst or after exposure to reactive oxygen species, ROS [40, 41]. The production of ROS, e.g. superoxide, hydroxyl radicals and hydrogen peroxide, is considered one of the earliest reactions of plants to stress factors, and these ROS are thought to mediate cell death and pathogenesis induced by the pathogen or elicitors [41]. Therefore, these plant metabolites activated during oxidative burst may play a role in plant defence against oxidative damages. The synthesis of other minor terpenoidal phytoalexins, the phytuberin and vetispirane derivatives, is also induced in different varieties of stressed potato tubers inoculated with pathogenic and non-pathogenic fungi [38, 42]. In contrast to the terpenoids, allixin (3-hydroxy-5-methoxy-6-methyl-2-penthyl-4*H*pyran-4-one) is a non-sulphur-containing phytoalexin that accumulates in garlic (*Allium sativum*) in response to extrinsic stress. As shown in Figure 4, the structure of allixin includes a γ-pyrone skeleton with pentyl, hydroxyl, methyl and methoxy substitutions. Allixin is best known and was the first phytoalexin isolated from garlic [43].

# BIOACTIVITY OF FOOD-DERIVED PHYTOALEXINS

## Resveratrol

Resveratrol was discovered as a chemopreventive agent present in red wine and associated with the "French paradox", an observation of low mortality and coronary heart disease incidence in certain populations that consumed a high-fat diet. It was suggested that this observation was due to red wine consumption within the population [44]. Since then, resveratrol has gained particular interest as a therapeutic agent with many pharmacological activities especially against various cancers, inflammatory and cardiovascular diseases [14, 45–47]. Numerous animal studies and human clinical trials have been conducted to evaluate the health benefits of resveratrol. Figure 5 shows a summary of the various potential human health benefits and mechanisms of physiological activity of resveratrol. The physiological activity and efficacy of resveratrol depends, to a large extent, on its bioavailability and *in vivo* metabolism. Studies have shown that resveratrol is absorbed in rats and humans after oral consumption, and is widely distributed in various forms in the kidneys, stomach, intestine, liver and plasma as well as in the feces, urine and bile [14, 48–50]. The bioavailability of resveratrol is low since it is efficiently metabolized in the liver by phase II enzymes to its sulphate and glucuronide derivatives [50].

The anticancer activity of resveratrol has been extensively studied using cell cultures and animal models. The stilbene phytoalexin exhibits its activity at the initiation, promotion and progression stages of different forms of cancer including lung, prostate, pancreatic, breast, colorectal cancers, leukemia and neuroblastoma. Its primary mechanisms of action involve the inhibition of cell proliferation and metastasis, and induction of programmed cell death (apoptosis) in cancer cells [14]. Resveratrol was found to inhibit cell proliferation by arresting the $G_0/G_1$ phase of the cell cycle and by suppressing the expression of cellular growth factors in human prostate cancer cells [51]. Moreover, resveratrol induced cancer cell apoptosis by down-regulating anti-apoptotic factors such as Bcl-2, cyclin D1 and phosphatidylinositol-3'-kinase/Akt pathway, and also by up-regulating pro-apoptotic factors including Bax, p53 and p21waf [14, 51, 52]. These activities demonstrate the strong potential of resveratrol in cancer treatment. In mice, daily oral administration of 2-50 mg/kg resveratrol in Neobee M5 oil for 5 weeks induced dose-dependent inhibition (up to 80%) of the growth of xenograft neuroblastoma (NGP and SK-N-AS) cells despite low bioavailability of resveratrol [53].

Several other studies have also demonstrated positive effects of resveratrol in animal models of different cancers [14]. In humans, a recent Phase I clinical trial suggested that resveratrol may play a beneficial role in colon cancer prevention due to its inhibitory activity against activation of genes of the Wnt signalling pathway, which plays a role in the aetiology of colon cancer [54]. As indicated in the U.S. National Institutes of Health clinical trials website (http://clinicaltrials.gov), a number of other human intervention studies are in progress to evaluate the role of resveratrol in cancer prevention and treatment.

Resveratrol has also demonstrated promising activities against inflammatory responses. As shown in Figure 5, resveratrol modulates inflammatory processes through various mechanisms, including modulation of gene expression and activity of pro-inflammatory cyclooxygenase (COX)-1, COX-2, lipoxygenase, interleukin (IL)-6, and nitric oxide synthesis via inhibition of inducible nitric oxide synthase [14, 46, 55]. Through suppression of NF-κB and I-κB expression, resveratrol induced a decrease in the production of reactive oxygen species and prostaglandin $E_2$ [56, 57], which are involved in progression of the inflammatory processes. Candelario-Jalil et al. [58] suggested that the effect of resveratrol on prostaglandin synthesis could be due to downregulation of the expression of microsomal prostaglandin synthase (mPGES-1). Resveratrol also exhibits anti-inflammatory activity by inhibiting the secretion of IL-8, vascular cell adhesion molecules, histamine, TNF-α [59] and by suppressing the activity of macrophages, T- and B-cells [57]. These bioactive properties contribute to the value of the stilbene phytoalexin as a potential anti-inflammatory agent in food.

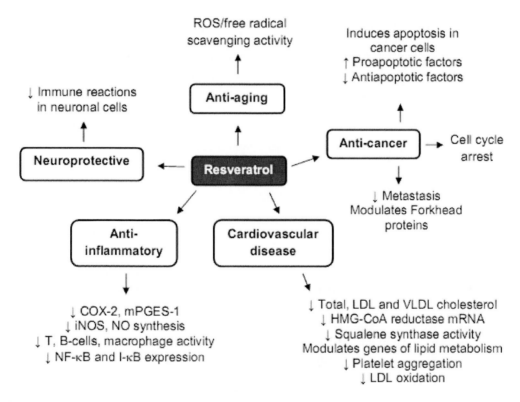

Figure 5. The potential health benefits and mechanisms of the physiological activities of resveratrol. ROS, reactive oxygen species; COX-2, cyclooxygenase-2; iNOS, inducible nitric oxide synthase; NO, nitric oxide; NF-κB, nuclear factor-κB; I-κB, inhibitor of NF-κB; LDL, low-density lipoprotein; VLDL; very low-density lipoprotein; HMG-CoA, 3-hydroxy-3-methylglutaryl-coenzyme A.

In addition to its therapeutic properties against cancers and inflammation, resveratrol exhibited antioxidant activities in cell cultures, and cardioprotective properties via inhibition of low density lipoprotein (LDL) oxidation and platelet aggregation, and modulation of vascular function [46, 47, 60]. Other studies have shown that, at low doses, resveratrol displayed antiatherogenic effects by reducing plasma levels of triglycerides, total-, LDL- and very low density lipoprotein(VLDL)-cholesterol [59, 61–63] although contradictory observations have been reported where resveratrol did not induce these changes [64]. It was suggested that the possible mechanisms of action of resveratrol in cholesterol homeostasis include the inhibition of squalene monooxygenase (SMO) and decrease in mRNA expression of 3-hydroxy-3-methylglutaryl-coenzyme A (HMG-CoA) reductase; both enzymes catalyze the rate-limiting steps of different stages of the pathway that lead to the synthesis of cholesterol [47, 63].

Resveratrol has also been reported to modulate various genes of lipid metabolism and also to induce increase in fecal bile acid excretion with concomitant increase in cholesterol catabolism [62]. The multifunctional physiological activities of resveratrol provide an excellent approach in the control of human diseases with multiple symptoms especially cardiovascular disease, marked with inflammation and oxidative stress.

## Pterostilbene

Pterostilbene has demonstrated multiple potential human health benefits against various cancers, inflammatory diseases, hypercholesterolemia, atherosclerosis and oxidative stress. Like resveratrol, the mechanism of anticancer activity of pterostilbene is mostly through induction of cancer cell apoptosis and cell cycle arrest. For example, Schneider et al. [65] recently reported that treatment of lung cancer cells (NCI-H460 and SK-MES-1) with 20-100 μM pterostilbene decreased cell viability and induced cell death via caspase-3/7-dependent apoptosis. This mechanism was supported by a study that targeted breast cancer cells; this study suggested that pterostilbene induced cell cycle arrest and activated the pro-apoptotic caspases by inducing mitochondrial depolarization and increasing superoxide anion production [66]. In order to induce cell cycle arrest, pterostilbene down-regulated proteins of the cell cycle including cyclin-dependent kinase 2 and 4, cyclin E and D1, retinoblastoma and proliferative cell nuclear antigen [67].

Animal studies have also confirmed these anticancer properties of pterostilbene. In mice, dietary intake of 50 or 250 ppm pterostilbene for 23 weeks suppressed the formation of azoxymethane-induced colonic aberrant crypt foci (ACF) preneoplastic lesions and adenomas via induction of apoptosis and modulation of gene expression of proteins involved in cell proliferation and signalling pathways [68]. These effects were previously demonstrated in rats that received 40 ppm pterostilbene with 57% and 29% inhibition of ACF formation and multiple clusters of aberrant crypts, respectively [69]. These properties are pertinent to the treatment of colon cancer.

Another mechanism of the anticancer activity of pterostilbene is autophagy, a lysosome-mediated degradation of cellular components. Chen et al. [70] reported that pterostilbene induced autophagy in the early stage of growth of human bladder cancer cells, and apoptosis in the later stage.

Pterostilbene was also demonstrated to exhibit additive anticancer properties with anticancer drug, tamoxifen, against breast cancer [71] and natural compound, quercetin, against B16 melanomas [72]. Therefore, pterostilbene can potentially be used as an adjuvant in cancer chemotherapy. Moreover, pterostilbene was found to inhibit DNA synthesis and proliferation of growth factor-induced vascular smooth muscle cells via suppression of Akt kinase activation [67]; Akt plays important roles in cell growth and proliferation. Therefore, pterostilbene can potentially be used for the treatment of vascular diseases such as atherosclerosis.

Although there is a dearth of information on cancer chemopreventive effects of pterostilbene in humans, a clinical trial is conducted at the University of Mississippi Medical

Center to evaluate the effects of pterostilbene on cholesterol, blood pressure and markers of oxidative stress in patients with dyslipidemia. The study planned to administer 50-125 mg pterostilbene orally twice daily with or without grape extract for 6 to 8 weeks (NCT01267227).

The use of pterostilbene as a chemopreventive agent is gaining wide interests because of its potency and higher bioavailability compared to resveratrol. Pterostilbene and its metabolites were found to be more bioavailable than resveratrol after oral administration of equimolar doses of the stilbene phytoalexins to rats for 14 days [73]. This could be due to the hydrophobicity of pterostilbene, compared to resveratrol, which can enhance absorption and transportation to target tissues. Despite all the positive attributes reported for pterostilbene, there is lack of information on the therapeutic potential and bioavailability of the pterostilbene present within the food matrix. This information will be necessary for evaluation of the prospects of the stilbene phytoalexin as a functional ingredient of intact foods.

## Glyceollins

The soy glyceollin isomers have attracted particular interest as food-derived therapeutic agents due to their *in vitro* and *in vivo* bioactive properties (Figure 6). These soybean-derived phytoalexins are widely known for their antiestrogenic activity on estrogen-receptor function as opposed to the estrogenic properties of their isoflavone precursors [74–76]. Glyceollins act by binding to estrogen receptors (ER) and subsequently inhibiting estrogen-induced cellular processes including tumour growth and progression. A study published a decade ago reported that a mixture of the three soy glyceollin isomers induced antiestrogenic effects by suppressing 17β-estradiol-induced proliferation of human breast cancer (MCF-7) cells [74]. This study also demonstrated that the glyceollins had greater dose-dependent affinity and antagonism for ERα than ERβ in human embryonic kidney (HEK 293) cells, although a recent study reported higher affinity for the β-receptors [27]. These observations have been supported by a number of *in vivo* studies using animal disease models. In ovariectomized athymic mice, daily intravenous injection of 20 mg glyceollins/kg body weight suppressed estradiol-stimulated growth of implanted MCF-7 and BG-1 ovarian cancer cells by 53% and 73%, respectively [75]. Recently, competitive binding assays with human ERα and estrogen-responsive elements-based assay showed that the antiestrogenic effects of the glyceollins can be attributed to glyceollin I, which adopted a type II antiestrogenic conformation in binding ERα, as revealed by ligand-receptor docking studies [76]. Moreover, this study demonstrated that glyceollin I alone inhibited ER-mediated gene expressions leading to decreased proliferation of MCF-7 and BG-1 cell lines. Therefore, these studies showed that soy glyceollins can potentially be used as intervention agent towards chemoprevention and treatment of estrogen-dependent cancer progression, particularly breast and ovarian cancers. In addition, the glyceollins showed prospects for application in prostate cancer prevention via mechanisms different from constitutively expressed soy isoflavones.

The soybean phytoalexins inhibited the growth of prostate cancer (LNCap) cells via inhibition of $G_0/G_1$ to S transition phase of the cell cycle, and appeared to be more active than soy genistein [77]. This study also reported that the glyceollins down-regulated expression of androgen responsive genes via modulation of estrogen-mediated pathway. To the best of our knowledge, there is dearth of information about human clinical intervention studies to substantiate the feasibility of the use of these soy phytoalexins in cancer chemoprevention.

In addition to antiestrogenic and anticancer properties, soy glyceollins have shown antioxidant properties *in vitro* and in cell cultures. The accumulation of glyceollins in fungi-inoculated and split soybean seeds correlated with the increased antioxidant activity of the soybean extract [26]. Moreover, isolated glyceollins exhibited strong reducing power, inhibited lipid peroxidation *in vitro*, and scavenged singlet oxygen, superoxide radical as well as synthetic free radicals [28]. In addition to these antioxidant properties, the glyceollins also demonstrated protective roles against oxidative damage peculiar to extended space flight. Exposure of astronauts to protons and high energy particles is of high concern due to cellular damages induced by the radiation; dietary supplements have been developed to ameliorate or prevent such damages [78]. It was reported that glyceollins protected vascular endothelia by inhibiting low dose proton beam-induced reactive oxygen species production and cell death in human umbilical vein endothelial cells [78]. In addition, glyceollin mixture suppressed hydrogen peroxide-induced oxidative stress in murine hepatoma (hepa1c1c7) cells. Therefore, these soy-derived phytoalexins could potentially be used as active ingredients for the treatment of human diseases induced or propagated by radiation and oxidative stress. Soy phytoalexins have also exhibited antifungal activity against several plant fungal pathogens [29] and therefore could be utilized as alternative to synthetic fungicides for ameliorating and treating plant diseases.

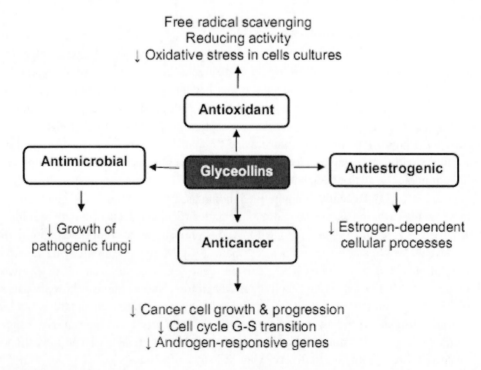

Figure 6. Biological activities of soy glyceollins that can be applied towards the treatment of human diseases.

## Other Phytoalexins

Earlier studies demonstrated that the garlic-derived phytoalexin, allixin, displayed a range of bioactivities that can enhance the use of garlic as functional food. This phytoalexin was reported to possess antioxidant and antimicrobial activities [79], neurotrophic effects [80] and inhibitory activity against the binding of aflatoxin $B_1$ to DNA [81]. In addition, allixin has shown anti-tumour activity by suppressing skin tumour formation in chemical-induced carcinogenesis in mice [82]. The bioavailability of allixin was reported as 13% in a study that detected various levels of the phytoalexin in the brain, lungs, kidneys, liver and serum after intravenous and oral administration to rats [43]. Moreover, red kidney bean-derived phaseollin and kievitone were recently demonstrated to bind both ERα and ERβ to different degrees, which induced estrogenic and antiestrogenic activities in breast cancer (MCF-7) cell culture [33]. Despite their toxicity, the potato glycoalkaloids, α-solanine and α-chaconine, have also been reported to display several beneficial biological properties, in experimental animals, such as anti-inflammatory, anti-allergic, antipyretic, hypocholesterolemic effects and antimicrobial properties against a wide range of pathogenic microorganisms [11]. In addition, the glycoalkaloids exhibited concentration-dependent inhibitory activity against the growth of tumour cells including cervical (HeLa), colon (HT29), lymphomas (U937), liver (HepG2) and stomach (AGS and KATO III) cells, but also slightly decreased the growth of normal liver (Chang) cells [83, 84].

## CONCLUSION

Based on the present literature, it is agreed upon that phytoalexins accumulate in some plant foods in response to biotic and abiotic stress factors, and their presence in sufficient amounts may contribute to the overall health benefits of functional foods. Resveratrol has attracted particular interest as intervention agent against several human diseases including cancer, inflammatory and cardiovascular diseases. Moreover, pterostilbene and soy glyceollins have also shown promising therapeutic properties relevant to human health sustenance. Future research efforts can be focused on conditions (e.g. type and dose of elicitor, timing) for the production of optimum amounts of phytoalexin in foods while not compromising the overall nutritional quality and palatability of foods. Moreover, work should also be conducted on the type and conditions of elicitor exposure in order to produce different types of phytoalexin which may enable manipulation of the type and amounts of phytoalexin in foods for the production of customized functional foods for targeting specific diseases. There is also dearth of detailed information on the bioavailability and pharmacokinetics of most phytoalexins in humans. The concept of phytoalexin-enriched foods may enable the development of functional foods by providing consumers with an alternative choice of healthy foods for the prevention and treatment of chronic human diseases.

# REFERENCES

[1] Dewick, P. M. (2001). *Medicinal Natural Products: A biosynthetic approach* (2nd edition). Chichester, United Kingdom: John Wiley and Sons.

[2] Müller, K. O. and Börger, H. (1940). Experimentelle untersuchungen über die Phytophthora-resistem der kartoffel. *Arb. Biologischen Reichsasnstalt Landw. Forstw.*, 23, 189-231.

[3] VanEtten, H. D., Mansfield, J. W., Bailey, J. A. and Farmer, E. E. (1994). Two classes of plant antibiotics: phytoalexins versus phytoanticipins. *Plant Cell*, 6, 1191-1192.

[4] Paxton, J. D. (1980). A new working definition of the term "phytoalexin". *Plant Disease*, 64, 734.

[5] Paxton, J. D. (1981). Phytoalexins - a working redefinition. *Journal of Phytopathology*, 101, 106-109.

[6] Boué, S. M., Cleveland, T. E., Carter-Wientjes, C., Shih, B. Y., Bhatnagar, D., McLachlan, J. M. et al. (2009). Phytoalexin-enriched functional foods, *Journal of Agricultural and Food Chemistry*, 57, 2614-2622.

[7] Darvill, A. G. and Albersheim, P. (1984). Phytoalexins and their elicitors – a defense against microbial infection in plants. *Annual Review of Plant Physiology*, 35, 243-275.

[8] Shattuck, V. I., Yada, R. and Lougheed, E. C. (1988). Ethylene-induced bitterness in stored parsnips. *HortScience*, 23, 912.

[9] Durango, D., Quiñones, W., Torres, F., Rosero, Y., Gil, J. and Echeverri, F. (2002). Phytoalexin accumulation in colombian bean varieties and aminosugars as elicitors. *Molecules*, 7, 817-832.

[10] Pedras, M. S. C. and Ahiahonu, P. W. K. (2005). Metabolism and detoxification of phytoalexins and analogues by phytopathogenic fungi. *Phytochemistry*, 66, 391-411.

[11] Friedman, M. (2006). Potato glycoalkaloids and metabolites: roles in the plant and in the diet. *Journal of Agricultural and Food Chemistry*, 54, 8655-8681.

[12] Baur, J. A. and Sinclair, D. A. (2006). Therapeutic potential of resveratrol: the in vivo evidence. *Nature Review Drug Discovery*, 5, 493–506.

[13] Rimando, A. M., Kalt, W., Magee, J. B., Dewey, J. and Ballington, J. R. (2004). Resveratrol, pterostilbene, and piceatannol in Vaccinium berries. *Journal of Agricultural and Food Chemistry*, 52, 4713-4719.

[14] Udenigwe, C. C., Ramprasath, V. R., Aluko, R. E. and Jones, P. J. H. (2008). Potential of resveratrol in anticancer and anti-inflammatory therapy. *Nutrition Reviews*, 66, 445-454.

[15] Mercolini, L., Saracino, M. A., Bugamelli, F., Ferranti, A., Malaguti, M., Hrelia, S., et al. (2008). HPLC-F analysis of melatonin and resveratrol isomers in wine using an SPE procedure. *Journal of Separation Science*, 31, 1007-1014.

[16] Jeandet, P., Douillet-Breuil, A. C., Bessis, R., Debord, S., Sbaghi, M. and Adrian, M. (2002). Phytoalexins from the *Vitaceae*: biosynthesis, phytoalexin gene expression in transgenic plants, antifungal activity, and metabolism. *Journal of Agricultural and Food Chemistry*, 50, 2731-2741.

[17] Adrian, M., Jeandet, P., Douillet-Breuil, A. C., Tesson, L. and Bessis, R. (2000). Stilbene content of mature Vitis vinifera berries in response to UV-C elicitation. *Journal of Agricultural and Food Chemistry*, 48, 6103-6105.

[18] Cantos, E., Espín, J. C. and Tomás-Barberán, F. A. (2001). Postharvest induction modeling method using UV irradiation pulses for obtaining resveratrol-enriched table grapes: a new "functional" fruit. *Journal of Agricultural and Food Chemistry*, 49, 5052–5058.

[19] Versari, A., Parpinello, G. P., Tornielli, G. B., Ferrarini, R. and Giulivo, C. (2001). Stilbene compounds and stilbene synthase expression during ripening, wilting, and UV treatment in grape cv. Corvina. *Journal of Agricultural and Food Chemistry*, 49, 5531-5536.

[20] Chung, I. M., Park, M. R., Chun, J. C. and Yun, S. J. (2003). Resveratrol accumulation and resveratrol synthase gene expression in response to abiotic stresses and hormones in peanut plants. *Plant Science*, 164, 103-109.

[21] Potrebko, I. and Resurreccion, A. V. (2009). Effect of ultraviolet doses in combined ultraviolet-ultrasound treatments on trans-resveratrol and trans-piceid contents in sliced peanut kernels. *Journal of Agricultural and Food Chemistry*, 57, 7750-7756.

[22] Bavaresco, L., Petegolli, D., Cantù, E., Fregoni, M., Chiusa, G. and Trevisan, M. (1997). Elicitation and accumulation of stilbene phytoalexins in grapevine berries infected by *Botrytis cinerea*. *Vitis*, 36, 77-83.

[23] Douillet-Breuil, A.-C., Jeandet, P., Adrian, M. and Bessis, R. (1999). Changes in the phytoalexin content of various *Vitis* spp. in response to ultraviolet C elicitation. *Journal of Agricultural and Food Chemistry*, 47, 4456-4461.

[24] Langcake, P., Cornford, C. A. and Pryce, R. J. (1979). Identification of pterostilbene as a phytoalexin from *Vitis vinifera* leaves. *Phytochemistry*, 18, 1025-1027.

[25] Boué, S. M., Carter, C., Ehrlich, K. C. and Cleveland, T. E. (2000). Induction of the soybean phytoalexins coumestrol and glyceollin by *Aspergillus*. *Journal of Agricultural and Food Chemistry*, 48, 2167-2172.

[26] Boué, S. M., Shih, F. F., Shih, B. Y., Daigle, K. W., Carter-Wienties, C. H. and Cleveland, T. E. (2008). Effects of biotic elicitors on enrichment of antioxidant properties and induced isoflavones in soybean. *Journal of Food Science*, 73, H43-H49.

[27] Kim, H. J., Suh, H. J., Kim, J. H., Kang, S. C., Park, S., Lee, C.H. et al. (2010). Estrogenic activity of glyceollins isolated from soybean elicited with *Aspergillus sojae*. *Journal of Medicinal Food*, 13, 382-390.

[28] Kim, H. J., Suh, H. J., Kim, J. H., Park, S., Joo, Y. C. and Kim, J. S. (2010). Antioxidant activity of glyceollins derived from soybean elicited with *Aspergillus sojae*. *Journal of Agricultural and Food Chemistry*, 58, 11633-11638.

[29] Kim, H. J., Suh, H. J., Lee, C. H., Kim, J. H., Kang, S. C., Park, S., et al. (2010). Antifungal activity of glyceollins isolated from soybean elicited with *Aspergillus sojae*. *Journal of Agricultural and Food Chemistry*, 58, 9483-9487.

[30] Lee, M. R., Kim, J. Y., Chun, J., Park, S., Kim, H.J., Kim, J.-S., et al. (2010). Induction of glyceollins by fungal infection in varieties of Korean soybean. *Journal of Microbiology and Biotechnology*, 20, 1226-1229.

[31] Park, S., Ahn, I. S., Kim, J. H., Lee, M. R., Kim, J. S. and Kim, H. J. (2010). Glyceollins, one of the phytoalexins derived from soybeans under fungal stress, enhance insulin sensitivity and exert insulinotropic actions. *Journal of Agricultural and Food Chemistry*, 58, 1551-1557.

[32] Hammerschmidt, R. (1999). Phytoalexins: what have we learned after 60 years? *Annual Review of Phytopathology*, 37, 285-306.

[33] Boué, S. M., Burow, M. E., Wiese, T. E., Shih, B. Y., Elliott, S., Carter-Wientjes, C. H., et al. (2011). Estrogenic and antiestrogenic activities of phytoalexins from red kidney bean (*Phaseolus vulgaris* L.). *Journal of Agricultural and Food Chemistry*, 59, 112-120.

[34] Doherty, J. and Buescher, R. (1978). Occurrence of the phytoalexin phaseollin in pods of *Phaseolus vulgaris*. *Journal of the Science of Food and Agriculture*, 29, 853-856.

[35] Brooks, C. J. W., Watson, D. G. and Freer, I. M. (1986). Elicitation of capsidiol accumulation in suspended callus cultures of *Capsicum annuum*. *Phytochemistry*, 25, 1089-1092.

[36] Betancourt-Jiménez, M. and Lozoya-Gloria, E. (2008). Local and systemic gene expression of sesquiterpene phytoalexin biosynthetic enzymes in plant leaves. *European Journal of Plant Pathology*, 121, 439-449.

[37] Dewick, P. M. (2002). The biosynthesis of C5-C25 terpenoid compounds. *Natural Products Report*, 16, 97-130.

[38] Jadhav, S. J., Mazza, G. and Salunkhe, D. K. (1991). Terpenoid phytoalexins in potatoes: a review. *Food Chemistry*, 41, 195-217.

[39] Charles, M. T., Mercier, J., Makhlouf, J. and Arul, J. (2008). Physiological basis of UV-C-induced resistance to Botrytis cinerea in tomato fruit. I. Role of pre- and post-challenge accumulation of the phytoalexin-rishitin. *Postharvest Biology and Technology*, 47, 10-20.

[40] Noritake, T., Kawakita, K. and Doke, N. (1996). Nitric oxide induces phytoalexin accumulation in potato tuber tissues. *Plant and Cell Physiology*, 37, 113-116.

[41] Araceli A.-C., Elda C.-M., Edmundo L.-G. and Ernesto G.-P. (2007). Capsidiol production in pepper fruits (*Capsicum annuum* L.) induced by arachidonic acid is dependent of an oxidative burst. *Physiological and Molecular Plant Pathology*, 70, 69-76.

[42] Lyon, G. D. (1972). Occurrence of rishitin and phytuberin in potato tubers inoculated with *Erwinia carotovora* var. *atroseptica*. *Physiological Plant Pathology*, 2, 411-416.

[43] Kodera, Y., Ichikawa, M., Yoshida, J., Kashimoto, N., Uda, N., Sumioka, I., et al. (2002). Pharmacokinetic study of allixin, a phytoalexin produced by garlic. *Chemical and Pharmaceutical Bulletin*, 50, 354-363.

[44] de Lange, D. W. (2007). From red wine to polyphenols and back: A journey through the history of the French Paradox. *Thrombosis Research*, 119, 403-406.

[45] Jang, M., Cai, L., Udeani, C. O., Slowing, K. V., Thomas, C. F., Beecher, C. W. W., et al. (1997). Cancer chemopreventive activity of resveratrol, a natural product derived from grapes. *Science*, 275, 218-220.

[46] Ramprasath, V. R. and Jones, P. J. (2010). Phytosterol and resveratrol: fruit compounds and health effects. *Agro Food Industry Hi-Tech.*, 21, 28-31.

[47] Ramprasath, V. R. and Jones, P. J. (2010). Anti-atherogenic effects of resveratrol. *European Journal of Clinical Nutrition*, 64, 660-668.

[48] Boocock, D. J., Faust, G. E. S., Patel, K. R., Schinas, A. M., Brown, V. A., Ducharme, M. P., et al. (2007). Phase I dose escalation pharmacokinetic study in healthy volunteers of resveratrol, a potential cancer chemopreventive agent. *Cancer Epidemiology, Biomarkers and Prevention*, 16, 1246-1252.

[49] Wenzel, E., Soldo, T., Erbersdobler, H. and Somoza, V. (2005). Bioactivity and metabolism of *trans*-resveratrol orally administered to Wister rats. *Molecular Nutrition and Food Research*, 49, 482-494.

[50] Wenzel, E. and Somoza, V. (2005). Metabolism and bioavailability of *trans*-resveratrol. *Molecular Nutrition and Food Research*, 49, 472-481.

[51] Benitez, D. A., Pozo-Guisado, E., Alvarez-Barrientos, A., Fernandez-Salguero, P. M. and Castellón, E. A. (2007). Mechanisms involved in resveratrol-induced apoptosis and cell cycle arrest in prostate cancer-derived cell lines. *Journal of Andrology*, 28, 282-293.

[52] Bhardwaj, A., Sethi, G., Vadhan-Raj, S., Bueso-Ramos, C., Takada, Y., Gaur, U., et al. (2007). Resveratrol inhibits proliferation, induces apoptosis, and overcomes chemoresistance through down-regulation of STAT3 and nuclear factorkB- regulated antiapoptotic and cell survival gene products in human multiple myeloma cells. *Blood*, 109, 2293-2302.

[53] van Ginkel, P. R., Sareen, D., Subramanian, L., Walker, Q., Darjatmoko, S. R., Lindstrom, M. J., et al. (2007). Resveratrol inhibits tumor growth of human neuroblastoma and mediates apoptosis by directly targeting mitochondria. *Clinical Cancer Research*, 13, 5162-5169.

[54] Nguyen, A. V., Martinez, M., Stamos, M. J., Moyer, M. P., Planutis, K., Hope, C., et al. (2009). Results of a phase I pilot clinical trial examining the effect of plant-derived resveratrol and grape powder on Wnt pathway target gene expression in colonic mucosa and colon cancer. *Cancer Management and Research*, 1, 25-37.

[55] Das, S. and Das, D. K. (2007). Anti-inflammatory responses of resveratrol. *Inflammation and Allergy - Drug Targets*, 6, 168-173.

[56] Kim, Y. A., Kim, G. Y., Park, K. Y. and Choi, Y. H. (2007). Resveratrol inhibits nitric oxide and prostaglandin E2 production by lipopolysacharideactivated C6 microglia. *Journal of Medicinal Food*, 10, 218-224.

[57] Sharma, S., Chopra, K., Kulkarni, S. K. and Agrewala, J. N. (2007). Resveratrol and curcumin suppress immune response through CD28/CTLA-4 and CD80 co-stimulatory pathway. *Clinical and Experimental Immunology*, 147, 155-163.

[58] Candelario-Jalil, E., Pinheiro De Oliveira, A.C., Gräf, S., Bhatia, H.S., Hüll, M., Muñoz, E., et al. (2007). Resveratrol potently reduces prostaglandin E2 production and free radical formation in lipopolysaccharide-activated primary rat microglia. *Journal of Neuroinflammation*, 4, 25.

[59] Rivera, L., Morón, R., Zarzuelo, A. and Galisteo, M. (2009). Long-term resveratrol administration reduces metabolic disturbances and lowers blood pressure in obese Zucker rats. *Biochemical Pharmacology*, 77, 1053-1063.

[60] Bradamante, S., Barenghi, L. and Villa, A. (2004). Cardiovascular protective effects of resveratrol. *Cardiovascular Drug Reviews*, 22, 169-188.

[61] Nihei, T., Miura, Y. and Yagasaki, K. (2001). Inhibitory effect of resveratrol on proteinuria, hypoalbuminemia and hyperlipidemia in nephritic rats. *Life Sciences*, 68, 2845-2852.

[62] Ahn, J., Cho, I., Kim, S., Kwon, D. and Ha, T. (2008). Dietary resveratrol alters lipid metabolism-related gene expression of mice on an atherogenic diet. *Journal of Hepatology*, 49, 1019-1028.

[63] Cho, I. J., Ahn, J. Y., Kim, S., Choi, M. S. and Ha, T. Y. (2008). Resveratrol attenuates the expression of HMG-CoA reductase mRNA in hamsters. *Biochemical and Biophysical Research Communications*, 367, 190-194.

[64] Frémont, L. (2000). Minireview: Biological effects of resveratrol. *Life Sciences*, 66, 663-673.

[65] Schneider, J. G., Alosi, J. A., McDonald, D. E. and McFadden, D. W. (2010). Pterostilbene inhibits lung cancer through induction of apoptosis. *Journal of Surgical Research*, 161, 18-22.

[66] Alosi, J. A., McDonald, D. E., Schneider, J. S., Privette, A. R. and McFadden, D.W. (2010). Pterostilbene inhibits breast cancer in vitro through mitochondrial depolarization and induction of caspase-dependent apoptosis. *Journal of Surgical Research*, 161, 195-201.

[67] Park, E.-S., Lim, Y., Hong, J.-T., Yoo, H.-S., Lee, C.-K., Pyo, M.-Y., et al. (2010). Pterostilbene, a natural dimethylated analog of resveratrol, inhibits rat aortic vascular smooth muscle cell proliferation by blocking Akt-dependent pathway. *Vascular Pharmacology*, 53, 61-67.

[68] Chiou, Y.-S., Tsai, M.-L., Wang, Y.-J., Cheng, A.-C., Lai, W.-M., Badmaev, V., et al. (2010). Pterostilbene inhibits colorectal aberrant crypt foci (ACF) and colon carcinogenesis via suppression of multiple signal transduction pathways in azoxymethane-treated mice. *Journal of Agricultural and Food Chemistry*, 58, 8833-8841.

[69] Suh, N., Paul, S., Hao, X., Simi, B., Xiao, H., Rimando, A. M. et al. (2007). Pterostilbene, an active constituent of blueberries, suppresses aberrant crypt foci formation in the azoxymethane-induced colon carcinogenesis model in rats. *Clinical Cancer Research*, 13, 350-355.

[70] Chen, R., Ho, C. and Wang, Y.-J. (2010). Pterostilbene induces autophagy and apoptosis in sensitive and chemoresistant human bladder cancer cells. *Molecular Nutrition and Food Research*, 54, 1819-1832.

[71] Mannal, P., McDonald, D. and McFadden, D. (2010). Pterostilbene and tamoxifen show an additive effect against breast cancer *in vitro*. *American Journal of Surgery*, 200, 577-580.

[72] Ferrer, P., Asensi, M., Segarra, R., Ortega, A., Benlloch, M., Obrador, E., et al. (2005). Association between pterostilbene and quercetin inhibits metastatic activity of B16 melanoma. *Neoplasia*, 7, 37-47.

[73] Kapetanovic, I. M., Muzzio, M., Huang, Z., Thompson, T. N. and McCormick, D. L. (2011). Pharmacokinetics, oral bioavailability, and metabolic profile of resveratrol and its dimethylether analog, pterostilbene, in rats. *Cancer Chemotherapy and Pharmacology*, 68, 593-601.

[74] Burow, M. E., Boue, S. M., Collins-Burow, B. M., Melnik, L. I., Duong, B. N. and Carter-Wientjes, C. H. (2001). Phytochemical glyceollins, isolated from soy, mediate antihormonal effects through estrogen receptor α and β. *Journal of Clinical Endocrinology and Metabolism*, 86, 1750-1758.

[75] Salvo, V. A., Boué, S. M., Fonseca, J. P., Elliott, S., Corbitt, C., Collins-Burow, B. M., et al. (2006). Antiestrogenic glyceollins suppress human breast and ovarian carcinoma tumorigenesis. *Clinical Cancer Research*, 12, 7159-7164.

[76] Tilgham, S. L., Boue, S. M. and Burow, M. E. (2010). Glyceollins, a novel class of antiestrogenic phytoalexins. *Molecular and Cellular Pharmacology*, 2, 155-160.

[77] Payton-Stewart, F., Schoene, N. W., Kim, Y.S., Burow, M.E., Cleveland, T.E., Boue, S.M., et al. (2009). Molecular effects of soy phytoalexin glyceollins in human prostate cancer cells LNCaP. *Molecular Carcinogenesis*, 48, 862-871.

[78] Jung, M. H., Han, S. M., Lee, S. H., Lee, Y. M. and Kim, Y.-H. (2009). Glyceollins protection against vascular endothelial cell death caused by a low-dose proton beam. *Korean Journal of Physical Society*, 54, 2129-2132.

[79] Kodera, Y., Matuura, H., Yoshida, S., Sumida, T., Itakura, Y., Fuwa, T., et al. (1989). Allixin, a stress compound from garlic. *Chemical and Pharmaceutical Bulletin*, 37, 1656-1658.

[80] Moriguchi T., Matsuura H., Itakura Y., Katsuki H., Saito H. and Nishiyama N. (1997). Allixin, a phytoalexin produced by garlic, and its analogues as novel exogenous substances with neurotrophic activity. *Life Sciences*, 61, 1413-1420.

[81] Yamasaki T., Teel R. W. and Lau B. H. S. (1991). Effect of allixin, a phytoalexin produced by garlic, on mutagenesis, DNA-binding and metabolism of aflatoxin $B_1$. *Cancer Letters*, 59, 89-94.

[82] Nishino, H., Nishino, A., Takayama, J., Iwashima, A., Itakura, Y., Kodera, Y., et al. (1990). Antitumor-promoting activity of allixin, a stress compound produced by garlic. *Cancer Journal*, 3, 20-21.

[83] Lee, K. R., Kozukue, N., Han, J. S., Park, J. H., Chang, E. Y., Baek, E. J., et al. (2004). Glycoalkaloids and metabolites inhibit the growth of human colon (HT29) and liver (HepG2) cancer cells. *Journal of Agricultural and Food Chemistry*, 52, 2832-2839.

[84] Friedman, M., Lee, K. R., Kim, H. J., Lee, I. S. and Kozukue, N. (2005). Anticarcinogenic effects of glycoalkaloids from potatoes against human cervical, liver, lymphoma, and stomach cancer cells. *Journal of Agricultural and Food Chemistry*, 53, 6162-6169.

In: Bioactive Molecules in Plant Foods
Editor: Florence Ojiugo Uruakpa

ISBN: 978-1-62081-515-1
© 2012 Nova Science Publishers, Inc.

*Chapter V*

# BIOACTIVITY OF ALKYLRESORCINOLS

## *Rania Agil and Farah S. Hosseinian**

Department of Chemistry, Food Science and Nutrition, Carleton University,
Ottawa, ON, Canada

## ABSTRACT

Although 5-n-alkylresorcinols can be isolated from a wide array of sources, alkylresorcinols (ARs) in edible food sources are of the greatest advantage. The abundance of ARs in wholegrain cereals and their exclusive presence in the bran fraction, allows for ARs to be an excellent candidate as biomarkers of wholegrain intake. The role of ARs as biomarkers is extremely important for validation of the disease preventative properties and health benefits resulting from the inclusion of whole grains in the diet. Numerous studies on the pharmacokinetics of ARs in *in vivo* and *in vitro* have determined that levels of whole grains consumed in the diet correlate with levels of intact ARs measured in the faeces as well as AR metabolites extracted from urine samples of these individuals. Recently, it has been suggested that ARs can also be used as long-term biomarkers of whole grain intake. A small percentage of ARs consumed from whole grains often reside in the adipose tissue and accumulated proportions correlate with long term intake.

In addition to the role of ARs as biomarkers, these phenolic lipids owe to their amphiphillic structure their varying degree of biological effects. ARs possess antimicrobial, antioxidant, and cytotoxic activity, as well as inhibitory or stimulatory effects on enzymes, and stabilizing or disruptive effects on the phospholipid bilayer of cell membranes. These effects are dependent on the chain length, degree of saturation, chain or ring constituents, and the concentration of AR homologues present; these factors affect their hydrogen donating capacity, amphiphillic or lipophilic nature, polarity, hydrophobicity, binding capacity, as well as their ease of integration and interaction with enzymes, proteins and membranes.

The ability of ARs to reduce or inhibit triglyceride accumulation, tumour cell formation, thromboxane synthesis, and enhance liposome stability, makes them suitable for respective applications of obesity, cancer, and cardiovascular disease prevention

---

* Corresponding author: Fax (613) 520-3749; telephone (613) 520-2600 ext.2048; E-mail farah_hosseinian@ carleton.ca.

(CVD), as well as liposomal drug delivery. However, future research, particularly that of *in vivo* studies, need to be conducted on the biological effects and health benefits of ARs before their potential application can be employed. Furthermore, a common trend is evident in studies on the bioactivity of ARs such that homologs of 15 to 17 carbon chains have more pronounced biological effects than their shorter and longer chain counterparts; Thus, emphasis should be placed on these chain lengths for future *in vivo* studies.

## ABBREVIATIONS

| | |
|---|---|
| AA | ascorbic acid |
| AAPH | 2,2'-azobis (2-amidinopropane) dihydrochloride |
| AChE | acetylcholinesterase |
| AR(s) | Alk(en)ylresorcinol(s) |
| BER | base excision repair |
| C15:0-C25:0 | alkylresorcinols with respective carbon chain lengths |
| CEAD | Coulometric Electrode Array Detector |
| CHD | coronary heart disease |
| CVD | cardiovascular diseases |
| DHBA | 3,5-dihydroxybenzoic acid |
| DHPPA | 3-(3,5-Dihydroxyphenyl)-1-propanoic acid |
| DM | dry matter |
| DPPH | 2,2diphenyl1picrylhydrazyl |
| EBV-EA | Epstein-Barr virus early antigen |
| FA | ferulic acid |
| FID | flame ionisation detector |
| FTC | ferric thiocyanate |
| FRAP | ferric reduction ability of plasma |
| GPDH | glycerol-3-phosphate dehydrogenase |
| GC | Gas Chromatography |
| GC-MS | Gas Chromatography- Mass Spectrometry |
| HDL | high-density lipoprotein |
| HPLC | High Performance Liquid Chromatography |
| LDL | low-density lipoprotein |
| NAD | Nicotinamide adenine dinucleotide |
| NER | nucleotide excision repair |
| PDA | photodiode array |
| PUFA | poly-unsaturated fatty acids |
| RBC | red blood cells |
| ROS | reactive oxygen species |
| SC-$CO_2$ | supercritical carbon dioxide |
| SH | sulfhydryl |
| TX | thromboxane |
| TLC | thin layer chromatography |
| TPA | 12-Otetradecanoylphorbol-13-acetate |

| TSE | traditional solvent extraction |
| VLDL | very low-density lipoprotein |

# 1. INTRODUCTION

Studies have shown that consumption of whole grain cereals have beneficial health effects, including a reduced risk of diabetes, obesity, coronary heart disease (CHD), and cancer [1-4]. Some of these health benefits may be attributed to the presence of alkylresorcinols (ARs) [1, 3, 5, 6]. For example, alkylresorcinols have exhibited radical scavenging and hydrogen donation properties [7, 8]. In addition, they have been suggested as biological markers for human intake of whole grains [9, 10].

5-*n*-alkylresorcinols are phenolic lipids possessing a polar aromatic ring and a hydrophobic alkyl chain generally at the C5 position [11]. ARs from cereal grains are commonly extracted using hydrophobic organic solvents such as acetone, ethyl acetate, methanol, ethanol, diethyl ether and hexane with a solid to solvent ratio generally between 1:40 and 1:50 (w/v) [12, 13].

ARs are mainly found in the bran fraction (not endosperm) of whole grain cereals. Rye is richest in ARs, followed by triticale and wheat, while barley has a poor AR content [14-17]. Reviewed in this chapter are the bioactivity and pharmacokinetics of alkylresorcinols, with a focus on 5-*n*-alkylresorcinols found in whole grains.

# 2. ALKYLRESORCINOLS STRUCTURE AND SOURCES IN NATURE

ARs, also known as resorcinolic lipids, were first discovered in *Ginkgo biloba* (Ginkgoaceae) in 1989 but have since been isolated from various sources in nature, including families of higher plants, fungi, algae, mosses, bacteria and one source from the animal family; the marine sponge. *Haliclona sp.* [18].

The amount of resorcinolic lipids varies greatly across different families and species, however, the richest consumable sources of ARs are found in cereal grains of the Gramineae family [19]. The most recent finding of ARs occurrence was in the woodland plant, *Mercurialis perennis,* of the Euphorbiaceae family; a mixture of saturated AR homologues (C15:0-C27:0) were identified where C19:0, C21:0 and C23:0 were the major homologues present [20].

These 1, 3-dihydroxy-alkylbenzene derivatives consist of a polar aromatic ring and hydrophobic alkyl chain generally at the C-5 position (Figure 1). Depending on the source, the structure of ARs can vary in degrees of unsaturation, chain length, ring or chain substituted functional groups on the alkyl chain or aromatic ring and the position of the alkyl chain. [18, 21].

Oftentimes, these isoprenoid phenolic lipids are present as mixtures of several homologues and derivatives. In cereal grains, saturated 5-*n*-alkylresorcinol homologues ranging in chain length from C15-C25 are most common; however, mono-unsaturated (5-alkenylresorcinols) and substituted derivatives (5-oxoalkyl-, 5-oxoalkenyl, and 5-hydroxyalkylresorcinols) have also been identified [11, 15, 22-24].

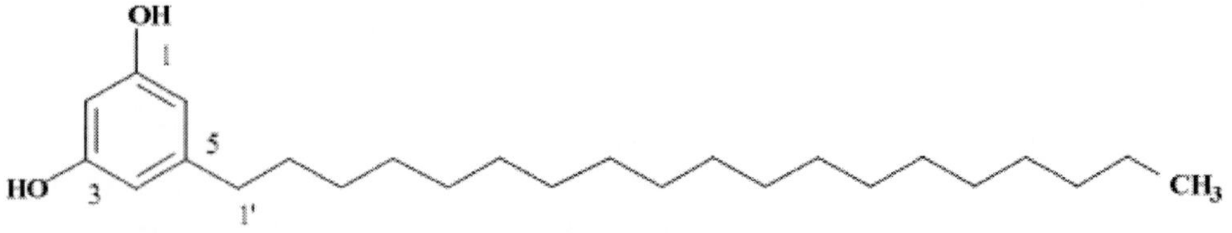

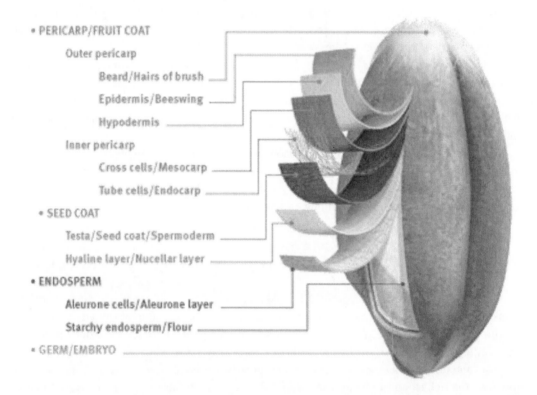

Figure 1. Chemical structure of 5-alkylresorcinols represented by C19:0.

- PERICARP/FRUIT COAT
    Outer pericarp
        Beard/Hairs of brush
        Epidermis/Beeswing
        Hypodermis
    Inner pericarp
        Cross cells/Mesocarp
        Tube cells/Endocarp
- SEED COAT
    Testa/Seed coat/Spermoderm
    Hyaline layer/Nucellar layer
- ENDOSPERM
    Aleurone cells/Aleurone layer
    Starchy endosperm/Flour
- GERM/EMBRYO

Figure 2. The majority of ARs reside in the bran, predominantly the seed coat [29].

Alkylresorcinols contribute 0.01-0.15% of the whole kernel dry weight [25] and are found almost exclusively in the bran, particularly the seed coat (testa); only trace levels have been detected in the endosperm and germ layers (Figure 2) [10, 15, 19, 26]. Due to the occurrence of ARs in the outer layer of cereal grains, extractability of ARs from intact kernels has been found to be greater than that of milled whole-grain flour based on the higher AR yields obtained with fewer unwanted co-extractives [27]. However, no variation in the ease of AR extractability and content was detected when comparing non-milled and finely milled rye bran [28].

As mentioned previously, the highest levels of ARs are found in rye, followed by wheat and triticale, with low levels reported in barley [11, 14, 15, 17, 19, 25, 30, 31]. Although past studies have found trace amounts of ARs in rice, millet, oat, corn and sorghum [32] [33-37] other studies found no ARs to be present in these grains [15, 19, 38]. The content of alkylresorcinols is reported to vary widely within and between species due to environmental, agricultural and genetic factors [16, 39, 40]. Additionally, cereal grain maturity has been found to have an impact whereby AR content is highest during the early stages of grain development and decreases as the grain matures [41]. During baking and processing however, alkylresorcinols are stable throughout and AR levels remain relatively unchanged [28]. Although ARs are not destroyed by heat from baking, ARs complex with the hydrophobic regions of starch, thus requiring the application of a stronger solvent, particularly hot 1-propanol, for their complete extraction [19].

**Table 1. Wholegrain food sources of alkylresorcinols, their content range (µg/g DM) in fractions of wholegrain, bran and flour, predominant homologues, and C17:0/C21:0 ratios**

| References | Cereal | Cereal Fraction | Range (µg/g DM) | Predominant Homologues | AR C17:0/C21:0 ratio |
|---|---|---|---|---|---|
| [14, 15, 19, 26, 27, 39, 44] | Rye | Whole Grain | 560-1444 | C19, C21 | 0.8-1.3 |
| | | Bran | 2400-4108 | | |
| | | Flour (endosperm) | 69-79 | | |
| [14, 15, 19, 26, 30, 39, 41, 42] | Common Wheat | Whole Grain | 264-943 | C21, C19 | 0.09-0.24 |
| | | Bran | 2210-3225 | | |
| | | Flour (endosperm) | 29-45 | | |
| [11, 12, 19, 33, 35, 45] | Triticale | Whole Grain | 430-700 | C21, 19 | 0.18-0.55 |
| | | Bran | 2780-3080 | | |
| [14, 16, 17, 30, 31] | Barley | Whole Grain | 41-74 | C25, C21 | 0.05-0.46 |
| | | Bran | 210 | | |

The AR content in the bran fractions of a given cereal is often two to five times higher than its respective whole grain content [15, 19]. The ratio of the AR homologues C17 and C21 are distinct for all cereal grain types, a useful tool when distinguishing amongst consumed grains (Table 1). The ratio of the homologues C17:0/C21:0 are approximately 0.2 in triticale, 0.1 in wheat and 1.0 in rye bran [14, 21, 42]. In future studies, it would be interesting to know whether ARs are in conjugation with other compounds such as sugars or phenolics and if the application of acid or alkaline hydrolysis may aid in the liberation of these bound constituents, as is the case with other phenolic compounds such as the isolation of SECO (aglycones portion) from SDG in flaxseed [43].

# 3. PHARMACOKINETICS OF ALKYLRESORCINOLS

Determining the fate of a substance ingested or administered externally to a living organism, whether it be a drug, nutrient, hormone or toxin, is also known as the study of its pharmacokinetics. Pharmacokinetics has four main focuses of study which include: the extent and rate of absorption, distribution, metabolism and excretion. Absorption is best described as the process of a substance entering the bloodstream; from the site of administration to the site of measurement. Distribution is the transfer of substances from the circulatory system to the fluids and tissues of the body, a reversible process. Metabolism is the irreversible transformation of parent compounds into daughter metabolites while excretion is the elimination of the substances from the body [46]. Both animal and human studies have been conducted and contribute to our current understanding of AR pharmacokinetics [47-55].

## 3.1. Intake and Digestibility

Based on studies conducted in 2005, the average daily consumption of alkylresorcinols in Sweden and the UK was found to be 22.9 mg/day and 11.8 mg/day respectively. This variation amongst regions is largely owing to their differences in cultural habits wherein the British population ordinarily consume whole grain products low in ARs such as white wheat bread (much like the U.S.), and Swedes generally consume AR rich products such as dark rye bread [56]. Depending on the dose and source (e.g. pericarp/testa vs. aleurone layer), AR digestibility and absorption varies between 60-79%, wherein AR uptake decreases with increasing levels consumed [55, 57], [54]. AR digestibility may also be affected by other foods administered, as suggested by a study demonstrating AR absorption increased when subjects were served an AR free meal 4h after AR intake [52]. The effect of nibbling (7 small meals/day) and ordinary (3 large meals/day) meal frequencies on AR digestibility has also been studied with no variations detected amongst them [54].

## 3.2. Absorption

The absorption pathway of ARs is theoretically similar (Figure 3) to that of structurally related fat soluble compounds such as tocopherols. Bile acids in the gut allow for the solubilization of such hydrophobic molecules as tocopherols and ARs into micelles [58]. Through passive diffusion, micelles cross the unstirred layer and release their contents into the enterocyte membrane where ARs are packaged into chylomicrons and secreted into the lymphatic system [51, 53, 55]. In a study where pigs were given a single or prolonged feeding of AR rich diets, absorption was measured at both the portal vein and mesenteric artery. Since the level of absorption at both sites did not differ from each other, it was concluded that ARs are indeed absorbed by the lymphatic system [49].

Furthermore, Ross et al. (2003) conducted a study in which pigs were fed three diets consisting of varying degrees of ARs; whole grain aleurone, pericarp-testa, or the endosperm fraction of rye. Ileal recoveries representing unabsorbed ARs of the large intestine ranged between 21-40% and remaining levels representing absorbed ARs of the small intestine, positively correlated with the level of AR consisting in the diets. Therefore, it is held that the remaining 60-79% of ARs not recovered, were absorbed by the upper intestine. These results were in agreement with human ileostomy studies conducted where a 40% recovery was found, suggesting 60% absorption of ARs [54]. Variation in uptake patterns of short and long chain AR homologues could not be distinguished in studies on pig plasma kinetics and ileal recovery results in both humans and pigs [49, 54, 55]. However, studies on the human plasma kinetics of ARs found there to be a variation in the absorption of patterns of AR homologues such that relative bioavailability increased with increasing chain length [52].

In a secondary portion of this study, C21:0 radiolabelled ARs were fed to rats and traced in blood, urine, feces and body tissues. Peak activity was at 24 h in the feces and urine and of the 92% radioactivity recovered, 61% was found in the feces and 31% in the urine. The maximum amount of radioactivity in blood was detected at 7-12 h, declined quickly soon after, with the majority of ARs cleared from the blood at 60h and less than 1% remained at 144h [55]. Thus, AR levels never fully reach zero as seen in this study and other studies measuring AR concentrations in plasma [6, 10, 52, 53, 59, 60]. This is likely due to enterohepatic circulation or slow turnover of ARs liberated from storage in body tissues [50, 61]. Similar studies found two absorption peak times at 3-4 h and 6-9 h in pigs and 2-3.2 h and 6.6-6.8 h in humans; further evidence to suggest enterohepatic circulation or individual and species dependent differences in the mechanism by which ARs are metabolized, stored or released after intake [49, 52]. Although research findings are indicative of enterohepatic circulation of ARs, the exact mechanism and structural compositions of compounds which may be present in bile have yet to be elucidated [50]. Furthermore, studies have shown that increasing intake of ARs from the diet correlates with plasma and urine AR concentrations systemically rather than dose-dependently [6, 10, 51, 60, 62-64].

## 3.3. Distribution

Once ARs are absorbed by the small intestine and packaged into chylomicrons, they are released into the capillaries of the lymph system where they are broken down by lipoprotein lipase; ARs and other related compounds are then transported in the blood by lipoproteins, HDL, VLDL, and LDL [25, 51]. ARs transferred from chylomicrons can be i) transferred to HDL and transported directly in the blood to various tissues or ii) remaining ARs in chylomicron remnants may be taken up by the liver, incorporated into VLDL which transfers ARs to HDL and through this process VLDL can be converted to LDL by lipoprotein lipases; HDL and LDL from the liver thereby carry ARs through the blood to various tissues in the body (Figure 3).

In a study measuring AR concentrations in plasma, erythrocytes, and lipoproteins, 70-80% of total ARs were found in the lipoprotein fractions, suggesting that the majority of ARs in plasma are transported by lipoproteins in unconjugated form. Amongst the lipoprotein classes isolated and examined for AR occurrence, VLDL, HDL, and LDL contained approximately 46%, 33%, and 20% of the lipoprotein AR respectively. Thus VLDL and HDL are the primary carriers of AR, rather than LDL which is the main carrier of cholesterol in humans [50, 51]. Non-modified ARs have been detected in the adipose tissue of rats, pigs and humans at concentrations of 2.4, 1.5, and 0.54 ug AR/g of fresh tissue [1, 65]. As previously mentioned, less than 1% of radiolabelled AR homologues remained in body tissues after 144 h, particularly that of the gut, lungs, kidneys, peri-renal fat, heart, spleen, brain, and carcass [55].

Due to the amphiphillic nature of ARs, they are easily incorporated into biological membranes as seen in both *in vitro* [18, 66] as well as *in vivo* studies [51, 53] whereby longer-chain AR homologues (C17:0 and C19:0) exhibited a greater ease of integration into membranes than their shorter-chain counterparts. Erythrocyte AR membrane levels increase with wholegrain consumption and remain stable in fasting blood samples; this correlation suggests that ARs are incorporated into and potentially stored in erythrocyte membranes [53].

## 3.4. Metabolism

The proposed mechanism of ARs metabolism is based on the metabolic stages of structurally similar tocopherols and is summarized in Figure 4.

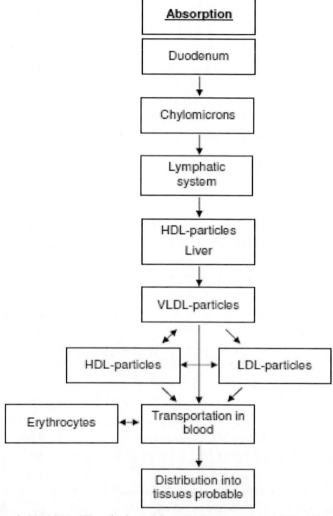

Proposed by Ross et al. 2004 [25, 67] and adapted from Linko, A.M. 2006 [50] with permission.

Figure 3. Absorption and distribution pathways of alkylresorcinols.

ARs metabolism is initiated by a cytochrome P450 enzyme whereby hydroxyl groups on the phenolic ring are conjugated then undergo ω-oxidation, followed by shortening of the alkyl chain and conversion of the ω-hydroxyl group to a carboxylic acid. Lastly, a series of stages of β-oxidation follow resulting in the formation of metabolites, DHPPA (3-(3,5-Dihydroxyphenyl)-1-propanoic acid) and DHBA (3,5-dihydroxybenzoic acid). A proportion of these metabolites may undergo a second phase of metabolism prior to urinary excretion, where they are conjugated to glucuronides and sulfates to increase their polarity and water solubility [25]. AR metabolites, DHPPA and DHBA, have been detected in both conjugated and free form in rat urine [55], human urine [6, 48, 67-71] and human plasma [9, 63, 64, 72].

Metabolism and conjugation of ARs was first evidenced when recovery of radiolabelled AR in urinary samples of rats was greatly increased through application of enzymatic hydrolysis. This suggested that metabolites of AR were present in urine, while this was not the case in feces [55]. It was later determined that the more hydrophilic metabolite DHBA is mainly unconjugated in urine in comparison with DHPPA [71]. The extent of this variation was found mainly in glucuronide conjugates where 67% of total DHBA were present in urine as free aglycones versus only 46% of total DHPPA existing as such. In the case of sulfate conjugates of DHPPA and DHBA, no apparent variations in the extent of conjugation amongst the two metabolite forms were found [69].

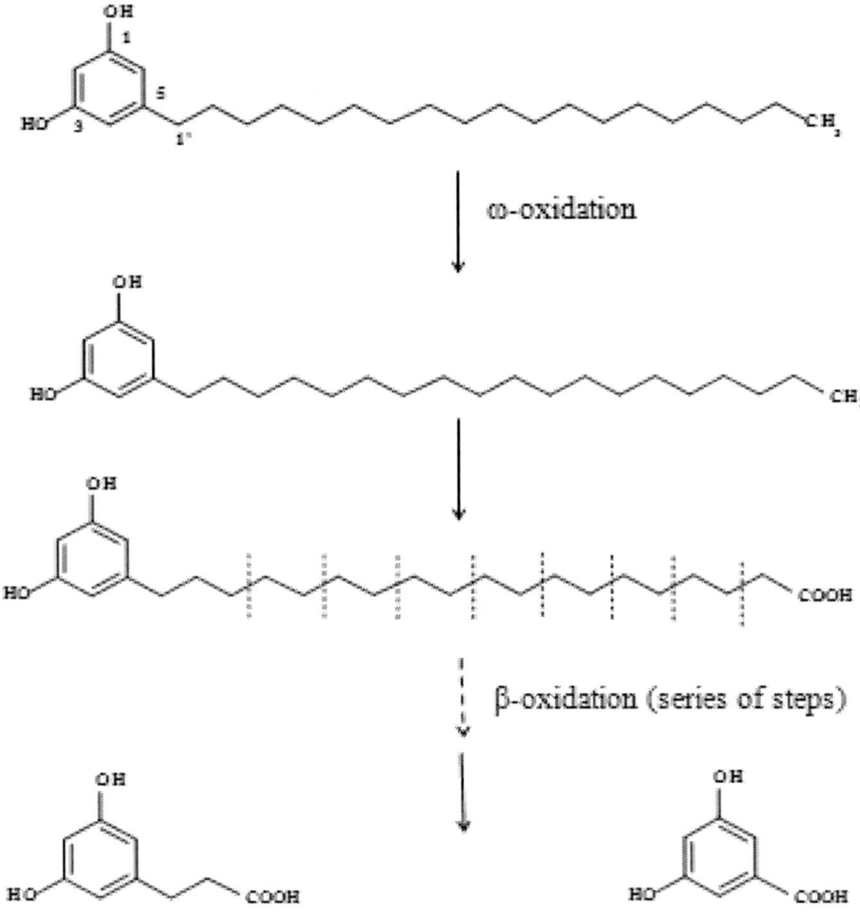

DHPPA

DHBA

(3-(3,5-Dihydroxyphenyl)-1-propanoic acid)

(3,5-dihydroxybenzoic acid)

Adapted from Ross et al. 2004 [25].

Figure 4. Mechanism of alkylresorcinol metabolism by example of C19:0.

## 3.5. Elimination

ARs not absorbed by the small intestine pass through the digestive tract and are eliminated mainly as unchanged ARs in fecal waste [55].

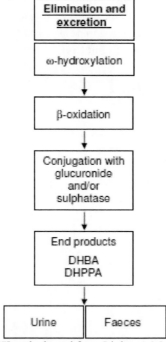

Proposed by Ross et al. 2004 [25, 67] and adapted from Linko, A.M. 2006 [50] with permission.

Figure 5. Potential mode of AR elimination and excretion.

Absorbed ARs are likely secreted into bile where they are metabolized to more water soluble forms due to the highly insoluble nature of ARs in water, DHPPA and DHBA, to be carried by the bloodstream to the kidney and then excreted as conjugated and free forms in urinary waste [25, 71] as seen in Figure 5. A small proportion of absorbed ARs may also be stored and accumulated in body tissues (adipose tissue and/or biological membranes); this is mainly evident in cases of prolonged feeding of AR-rich diets, as opposed to a single dose feeding [25, 53, 55, 65].

## 4. BIOLOGICAL EFFECTS OF ALKYLRESORCINOLS

### 4.1. Antimicrobial Activity

Numerous studies have demonstrated the antimicrobial capacities of alkylresorcinols and related resorcinolic lipids, as reviewed by Kozubek and Tyman (1999) [18]. Due to their strong antibacterial and antifungal activity, these compounds are biosynthesized specifically during the seedling stage to protect the plant against predators [18, 31, 73]. 5-n-alkylresorcinols isolated from cereal grains [73, 74], the waxy epicuticular layer of barley [75], and the peel of mango fruits [76, 77] have all exhibited antifungal activity against a number of types and strains of pathogenic fungi. These pathogens include but are not limited to, *Aspergillus niger, Penicillium chrysogenum, Fusarium culmorum* as well as *Alternaria alternata*. The antibacterial potential of alkylresorcinols is dependent on various factors where greater inhibitory activity is seen with more hydroxyl groups, increasing chain length, a greater degree of unsaturation as well as higher activity against gram positive bacteria versus gram negative bacteria [78]. Alkylresorcinols also exhibit antiparasitic activity against *Briomphalaria glabrata* (mollusks) [79] and *Filaria* (worms) [80], particularly by ARs with longer and more saturated chains [18].

## 4.2. Antioxidant Activity

Reactive oxygen species (ROS) are standard products of aerobic metabolism generated as a host cell defense mechanism against foreign invaders [81]. Oxidative stress is the result of an imbalance of ROS in which the level of oxidants exceeds that of antioxidants and leads to cell damage [82]. Compounds capable of preventing or delaying oxidative degradation at concentrations much lower than those of an oxidizable substrate are classified as antioxidants. The degree of antioxidant activity of a compound is dependent on its structural properties which determine whether it can donate hydrogen atoms or electrons to free radicals to produce a stable chain breaking product [83].

Lipid peroxidation (Figure 6) involves hydrogen abstraction to form a lipid radical ($L^{\cdot}$) (equation 1), which can react with oxygen to form a lipid peroxyl radical (equation 2). The peroxyl radical propagates the chain reaction by abstracting hydrogen from another lipid (equation 3), usually the rate-limiting step in lipid peroxidation [84]. Ideally, antioxidants work by blocking the propagation step through hydrogen atom donation (Figure 7). Antioxidants can also interfere with the oxidation process by chelating catalytic metals and acting as free radical scavengers [85].

Vitamin E components, tocopherols, are well established natural antioxidants in living systems. They possess a hydrophobic phytyl chain that allows for their solubility in membranes and a hydroxy group that serves as the main source of their radical scavenging and hydrogen donation abilities [87] (Figure 8a). ARs structural resemblance to tocopherols has been cause for speculation that they too hold antioxidant potential *in vitro* due to their hydroxyl groups attached to the aromatic ring at C1 and C3, as well as *in vivo* antioxidant membrane protection due to their lipophilic alkyl tail that eases incorporation into cell membranes (Figure 8b) [8, 88]. Although they are considered weak antioxidants in comparison to tocopherols, they do possess antioxidant properties which are more evident *in vivo* than *in vitro* [7, 8, 89-92].

Lipid peroxidation is a self-propagation reaction that leads to the generation of lipid radicals and peroxides [93]. Cell membrane constituents, phospholipids and proteins, are the direct targets of lipid oxidation [93, 94]. As lipid oxidation of cell membranes progresses, the polarity of the lipid-phase and oligomer protein formation increases. However, the molecular mobility of lipids, number of sulfhydryl (SH) groups, and resistance to thermo-denaturation decrease [94]. Increased levels of lipid oxidation products are associated with diabetes and atherosclerosis [93, 94]. Oxidation of low-density LDL has been reported to be involved in the development of atherosclerosis and cardiovascular disease [93-95]. Oxidized cholesterol or fatty acid moieties in plasma LDL can lead to the development of atherosclerosis [93].

$$R^{\bullet} + LH \longrightarrow RH + L^{\bullet} \quad \text{(equation 1)}$$

$$L^{\bullet} + O2 \longrightarrow LOO^{\bullet} \quad \text{(equation 2)}$$

$$LOO^{\bullet} + LH \longrightarrow LOOH + L^{\bullet} \quad \text{(equation 3)}$$

Figure 6. Lipid peroxidation steps, adapted from Hosseinian 2010 [86].

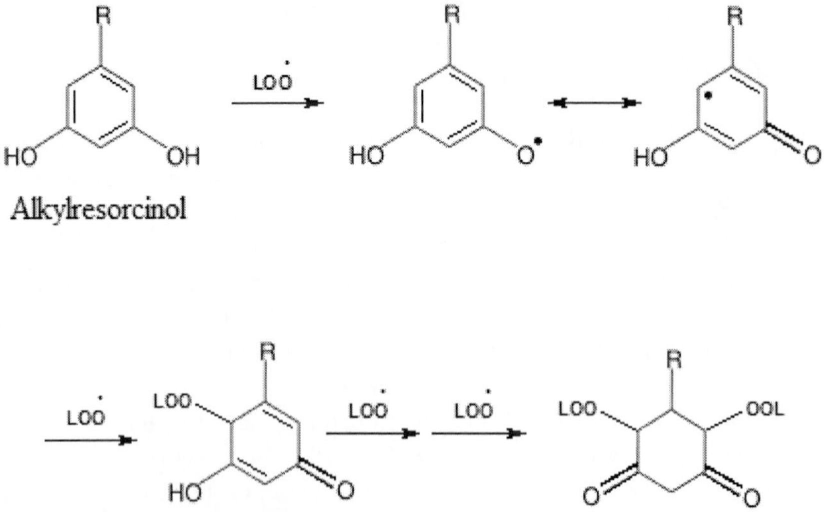

Figure 7. Theoretical formation of stable non-radical products using antioxidant AR.

In suspensions of erythrocyte injected with hydrogen peroxide and homologs of 5-n-alkylresorcinols, ARs were found to decrease peroxidation products induced by hydrogen peroxide at micromolar concentrations. Homolog C15:0 had the greatest antioxidant effect followed by C19:0, C23:0 while C5:0 (olivetol) had on minimal effects. In addition, the degree of peroxidation inhibition increased with longer incubation times up to 10 minutes with no marked difference thereafter that time. These results suggested that the antioxidant potential of AR homologs is dependent on their incorporation into the lipid bilayer (Figure 9) and their ease of incorporation is determined by their chain length [7]. In liposomal emulsions of phosphatidyl choline, AR homologues extracted from rye protected lipids and fatty acids of the membrane bilayer against $Fe^{2+}$ induced peroxidation at micromolar concentrations; the level of protection by ARs positively correlated with AR chain length [96].

Lipid peroxidation can also cause rancidity of food products such as fats and oils, which affects odour, taste and nutritional value of these products [84, 98]. The main purpose of using antioxidants in foods is to delay, retard, or prevent the autoxidation process and thus to extend the shelf life of foodstuffs and to minimize nutritional losses [98]. Winata and Lorenz (1996) found that AR homologue, pentadecylresorcinol (C15:0), effectively slowed the rate of oxidative rancidity in oils as well as lipid oxidation in cereal products at AR concentrations of 0.050-0.075% [89]. A recent study also identified that AR derivative, 1,3-dihydroxy-5-

(tridec-4′,7′-dienyl), effectively inhibited lipid peroxidation of linoleic acid measured by an FTC (ferric thiocyanate) method [99]. These findings suggest that ARs may prove to be useful as natural antioxidants in the food industry [87].

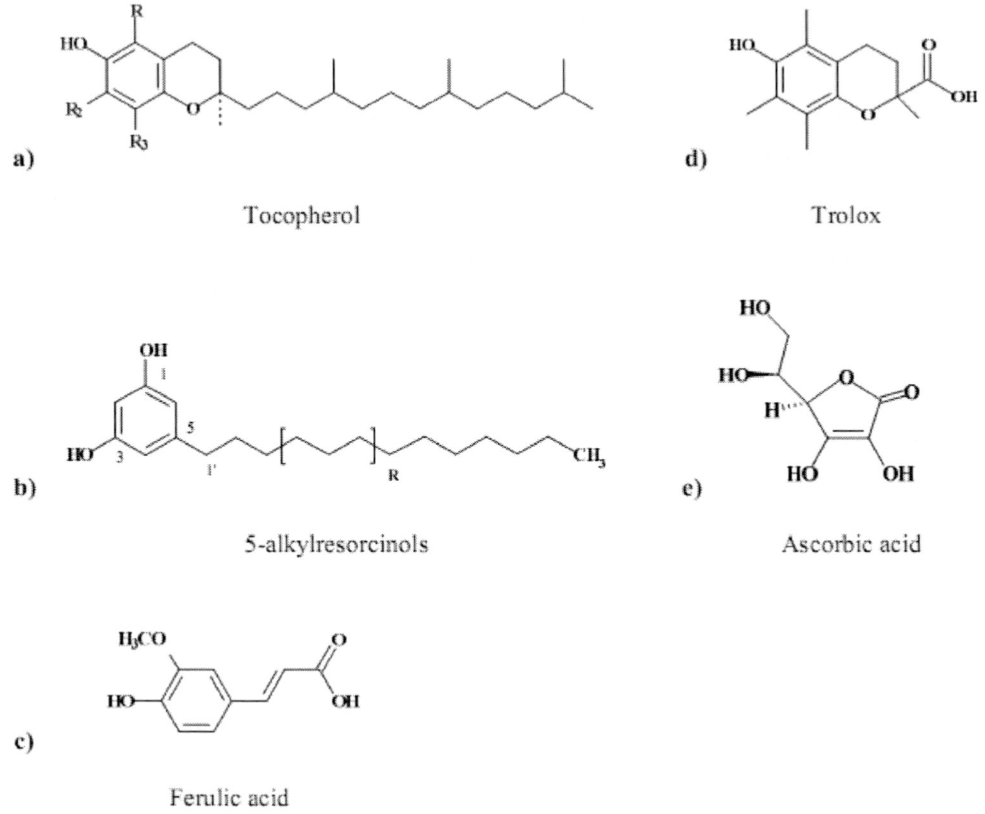

a) Tocopherol

d) Trolox

b) 5-alkylresorcinols

e) Ascorbic acid

c) Ferulic acid

Figure 8. Chemical structures of standard antioxidants compared to that of 5-alkylresorcinols.

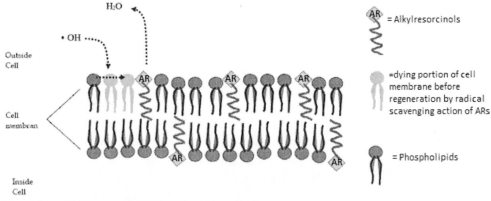

Adapted from Williams et al. 2007 [97] with permission.

Figure 9. Theoretical illustration of a hydroxyl radical (•OH) scavenged or converted to water (H20) by ARs in the membrane.

DPPH is a stable free radical commonly used in studies to measure the kinetics and hydrogen donating potential of AR homologues in comparison to well-known antioxidants, vitamin E tocopherols, trolox, ferulic acid (FA), and ascorbic acid (AA) (Figure 8b-e) [8, 91, 92, 99, 100]. From this method, it was found that ARs (C15:0-C25:0) and tocopherols decreased the initial DPPH concentration by 50% at $EC_{50}$ concentrations of 157-195 µM and 16-27 µM respectively [92]. This study and others employing such methods as the AAPH induced chemiluminescence method, FRAP (ferric reduction ability of plasma) and autoxidation of triacylglycerol/PUFA substrates, found ARs were only effective at higher concentrations that were double that of FA or AA [8, 99], triple that of trolox [92, 100] and over ten times that of tocopherols [91], making them comparatively weak antioxidants. Nevertheless, ARs possess enough antioxidant power to be used as natural antioxidants for food industry applications [92]. The antioxidative potential of ARs in preventing oxidation of lipoproteins induced by copper (II) was measured in human plasma LDL by measuring conjugated diene complex formation over time. Results showed that ARs, particularly C15:0, effectively delayed LDL oxidation by 65 min at concentrations of 25 µM; thus AR antioxidant activity is more prevalent in the event of lipophilic interaction in a biological system [101].

Studies demonstrated that ARs, particularly cereal bran isolates, act as antioxidants in food and biological systems. However, the details of the behaviour and action of ARs in the membranes, their behaviour in different emulsion or food systems, the potential of ARs to act as preventative antioxidants and whether or not ARs exhibit a synergistic effect, are only a few of many questions which remain to be established in regards to the antioxidant activity of ARs.

## 4.3. Anticarcinogenic Activity

Cancer occurs as a result of DNA damage or mutation incurred by cells due to exposure to carcinogenic substances. Anticarcinogens can act at the three stages of cancer development: initiation, promotion, and progression; They do so by blocking agents during the initiation phase and inhibit the formation of reactive intermediates or by suppressing agents acting during the promotion or progression phases thereby preventing interaction with DNA, RNA, and proteins [102].

Several studies, although in vitro, have demonstrated the effectiveness of ARs and related resorcinolic lipids as cytotoxic agents against murine breast cancer cell lines (FM3A), LNCaP human prostate adenocarcinoma cell lines, BT-20 breast cancer cells, HeLa epithelioid cervix carcinoma cells, human tumour squamous carcinoma A431 cells, A549, MCF-7, and PANC-1 cells lines, human promyelocytic leukaemia HL60 cells, KB cell lines, murine lymphoma cells, as well as Sarcoma 180 ascites and P-388 lymphocytic leukemia in mice [79, 99, 100, 103-108]. In one particular study, AR homologues C15:0 and C17:0 exhibited a greater potential than C19:0-C23:0 to inhibit DNA damage acquired by HT29 human colon cancer cells due to exposure to genotoxic substances: hydrogen peroxide ($H_2O_2$) and fecal water. AR homologues, particularly C15:0, effectively inhibited DNA damage by 40% under conditions of 24 h incubation time at AR concentrations of 100 µM against $H_2O_2$ and 50 µmol/L against fecal water [8]. In an initial screening test for antitumor agents, 5-n-alk(en)ylresorcinols extracted from wheat and rye bran oils inhibited 80-85% of Epstein-Barr virus early antigen (EBV-EA) induction by 12-Otetradecanoylphorbol-13-acetate (TPA) in Raji cells at $1 \times 10^3$ mol ratio/TPA; AR homologues C17:0-C25:0 exhibited reduced inhibition power with increasing chain length above that of C17:0 [109]. 5-*n*-alkylresorcinol analogue, 1,3-dihydroxy-5-(tridec-4',7'-dienyl) benzene isolated from *Lithraea molleoides*, a South American tree from the Anacardiaceae family, had an antiproliferative effect on murine lymphoma cells in comparison to that of normal lymphocytes in which ARs stimulated cell proliferation [99].

As suggested earlier for the antioxidant activity of ARs, the hydroxylation at C-1 and C-3 and chain length at C-5 are also significant structural properties responsible for and effect the level of cytotoxic potential of ARs [104]. In a series of studies conducted by Gasiorowski et al., it was determined that ARs possess antimutagenic activity in lymphocytes cultures against direct acting genotoxic compounds (Mitomycin C, MMS and DRC) and indirect promutagens (benzo[a]pyrene and 2-AF) by stimulating apoptosis of highly damaged cells [110-112]. Later studies confirmed these results, such that ARs exhibited cytotoxic effects against human colon tumour, promyeloid leukemia, hepatocellular carcinoma cell lines and squamous carcinoma cells by inducing programmed cell death [107, 113, 114].

In addition to increasing apoptotic elimination of cells damaged by mutagens, ARs also employ another mechanism of cytotoxic action known as DNA cleavage. Cancer cells often develop resistance mechanisms to anticarcinogenic agents by adopting the ability to repair DNA damaged by such agents, thereby lessening their effects. Therefore, the solution to this particular predicament is to target the proteins involved in the DNA repair pathways such as base excision repair (BER), nucleotide excision repair (NER), and DNA mismatch repair [115]. In this context, ARs have been reported as mediators of DNA damage by strand scission in the presence of Cu (II), and in some cases $O_2$, as well as inhibiting DNA polymerase $\beta$ from repairing the damaged strands [115-117]. Once again, chain length was found to have an impact whereby the success of DNA cleavage by ARs was greater with increasing chain length of up to 17 carbons [115, 117]. Therefore, findings from the aforementioned studies on the anticarcinogenic effects of ARs suggest the optimal chain length for cytotoxic action to be that of 15 to17 carbons in the alkyl chain. Details on the suggested mechanisms involved in DNA scission by ARs are described in the reviews by Kozubek and Tyman (1999), and Ross et al. (2004) [18, 25].

## 4.4. Membrane, Protein and Enzyme Interactions

Similarly to phospholipids, resorcinolic lipids consist of a hydrophilic head (polar aromatic ring) and a hydrophobic tail (alkyl chain at C-5). This amphiphillic nature of ARs allows them to easily incorporate into cell membranes resulting in changes in membrane structure and properties such as phospholipid mobility, membrane stability, fluidity and permeability, even to the extent of lipid bilayer disruption and cell rupture. Effects of ARs on cell membranes is dependent on the chain length, degree of saturation, presence of chain substituents, and concentration of alk(en)ylresorcinols that incorporate into liposomal and erythrocyte membranes [18, 25, 53, 101, 118].

In an effort to mimic biological membranes, liposomes have been constructed from various mixtures of phospholipids and compared to similar systems incorporating ARs. The resulting effect of utilising ARs for liposomal membranes was enhanced stabilization of the bilayer as well as effective entrapment and retention of aqueous solutions. These effects of ARs were further enhanced by the presence of other lipophilic compounds (i.e. cholesterol, fatty acids) in the membrane and when ARs were incorporated prior to bilayer formation [118-121].

In a recent study investigating methods to improve sphingomyelin–cholesterol liposomes for drug delivery purposes, it was found that the incorporation of ARs enhanced solute encapsulation *in vitro* and reduced the elimination rate of the liposome from circulation *in vivo* [4]. Siwko et al. (2009) conducted a study to determine the effects of resorcinolic lipid incorporation before and after bilayer formation of liposomes using atomistic molecular dynamics simulations. Results of these simulations show that when ARs are integrated during liposome formation, the outcome is improved such that reduced bilayer permeability and an enhanced order of lipid chains is exhibited. However, the opposite is true when ARs are integrated into preformed liposomes such that the newly added ARs have a disruptive effect on the bilayer. Stimulation of pore development, leakiness, and potential rupturing have all been observed [122]. Due to the enhancing effects of ARs on liposome stability, the application of ARs in liposomal drug delivery has been proposed [25, 123].

ARs also interact with enzymes and proteins through direct binding to their hydrophobic domains, altering their properties and activity [18, 25] The transportation of ARs by lipoproteins in human plasma is a recent example of the direct binding interactions of ARs and proteins *in vivo* [51]. ARs and their derivatives have shown to be inhibitors of various enzymes including but not limited to, prostaglandin $H_2$-synthetase, glycerol-3-phosphate dehydrogenase, erythrocyte membrane acetylcholinesterase (AChE), lipoxygenase, $\alpha$-glucosidase, aldose reductase, mushroom tyrosinase, $Ca^{2+}$-ATPase, as well as stimulation of $Ca^{2+}$ calmodulin-ATPase at an AR concentration of 50 $\mu$M [18, 25, 101, 124-128]. Potency of enzyme inhibition was dependent on chain length, degree of saturation, and concentration of ARs as is the case for their antioxidant and anticarcinogenic potential.

## 4.5. Effects on Metabolism

As a result of the interaction of ARs with various enzymes, a range of metabolic effects have been documented. Glycerol-3-phosphate dehydrogenase (GPDH) is a membrane enzyme essential for lipid and carbohydrate metabolism in addition to sustaining the membrane potential across the inner mitochondrial membrane during glycolysis [129]. Triglyceride synthesis and storage in adipose tissue is dependent on the generation of its precursor glycerol-3-phosphate which is controlled by the activity of the dehydrogenase enzyme, GPDH. The activity of this enzyme is most pronounced during cell differentiation into adipocytes. NAD is a substrate which binds to the coenzyme domain of GPDH (glycerol-3-phosphate dehydrogenase) causing changes in its conformation resulting catalyzed enzyme activity. *In vitro* studies suggest that ARs inhibit triglyceride synthesis by competing with NAD for the GPDH binding site, thereby inhibiting enzyme activity. This in turn prevents triglyceride synthesis as seen *in vivo* by the reduced accumulation of triglycerides during 3T3-L1 cell differentiation. [124, 130, 131].

ARs have also been found to elevate $\gamma$-tocopherol levels in the liver and lungs of rats fed an AR diet, therefore it was suspected that ARs block the tocopherol-$\omega$–hydroxylase pathway responsible for $\gamma$-T metabolism, thereby inhibiting its elimination. Through a hepatic culture assay, it was determined that ARs did in fact inhibit synthesis of $\gamma$-T metabolites (hydroxychromans) in a dose-dependent manner in Hep G2 cells; this effect was also compared to that of the positive control sesamin. Synthesis of γ-T metabolites was reduced by 47%, 84%, and 95%, for rye ARs at 20 μM, synthetic pentadecylresorcinol at 20 μM, and sesamin at 2 μM respectively. Since the effects of ARs were dose-dependent and substantially weaker than that of sesamin, it is proposed that ARs act as substrates competing with γ-tocopherols for their metabolism and elimination [65].

Leptin is an adipose derived hormone that regulates energy intake and metabolism; It acts to stimulate glycogen synthesis by inhibition of phosphorylase *a*. In the presence of AR related compound, resorcinol (1,3-Dihydroxybenzene), the inhibitory effect of leptin has been found to be enhanced [132]. ARs and their relative analogues have also shown to reduce insulin absorption in intestinal loops isolated from anesthetized dogs [133].

## 4.6. Effects on Growth

It has been speculated that ARs cause appetite suppression in animals by observation of farm animals on a rye-rich feed, therefore a feed rich in ARs, showed poor growth in comparison to those consuming other cereals such as wheat or maize. Although several animal studies have been conducted on this basis, results remain inconclusive due to contradicting findings. Some studies have found a direct correlation between diets rich in rye with antinutritional effects whereas others have found no such effect on growth by ARs. It has been proposed that the effect of ARs on reducing animal growth has been attributed to soluble fibers in rye as the causative factor, particularly arabinoxylans. These studies are discussed in greater detail in the review by Ross et al. (2004) [25].

## 4.7. Other Effects

Arachidonic acid is an unsaturated fatty acid present in cell membranes and is freed from attachment to phospholipids of the bilayer by $Ca^{2+}$ stimulation of phospholipase enzymes. This release initiates a cascade of metabolic events resulting in the production of various eicosanoids such as thromboxane (TX) which induce platelet aggregation [134]. ARs can inhibit human platelet TX production by blocking phospholipase activity or enhance TX synthesis by increasing membrane permeability at higher AR concentrations. This increase in membrane permeability allows cations such as $Ca^{2+}$ to pass through; thereby stimulating phospholipase activity that leads to an increase in TX levels *in vivo* [135].

# 5. METHODS

## 5.1. Extraction Methods

### 5.1.1. Traditional Solvent Extraction (TSE)

Resorcinolic lipids are generally amphiphillic compounds and with increasing chain length (>10 carbon alkyl chain) they are rendered insoluble in water [18]. For this reason,

ARs from cereal grains are commonly extracted using hydrophobic organic solvents such as acetone, ethyl acetate, methanol, ethanol, diethyl ether and hexane [21]. Although most ARs are soluble in methanol and ethanol, the longer chain homologues are not extractable to the same extent as they are in acetone and ethyl acetate. The solid to solvent ratio is generally between 1:40 to 1:50 (w/v) with an extraction time of 16-24hr for optimal recovery of ARs from cereal grains [12, 13].

### 5.1.2. Soxhlet Extraction

In 2004, R. Zarnowski and Y. Suzuki (2004) successfully established an alternative to previously published TSE procedures. This new method involved the application of a Soxhlet apparatus whereby lipids were isolated and yielded extracts of varying resorcinolic lipid contents, homologue compositions and contaminating co-extractives depending on the solvent used. This variation in extracts was dependent on the polarity of the solvent. Cyclohexane was found to be the ideal extraction solvent for Soxhlet extraction because it produced the highest yield of total resorcinolic lipids with the least amount of undesirable lipids and other co-extractives. This procedure is more time efficient when compared to TSE due to the reduced extraction time of 2-6hr [136].

### 5.1.3. Super Critical Carbon Dioxide Extraction SC-Co$_2$

In 2005, Francisco et al. developed a new method to effectively extract ARs by using supercritical carbon dioxide (SC-CO$_2$) whereby conditions of pressure, temperature, and co-solvent type could be set [137]. When carbon dioxide gas is both heated and compressed above its critical point in a synchronized fashion, SC-CO$_2$ is the result. These super-critical conditions can act as an extraction solvent and its effectiveness is dependent upon conditions of pressure, temperature, and co-solvent [138]. This method is attractive in comparison to past procedures due to its non-toxic, non-flammable, inexpensive and environmentally friendly properties [11, 138-140]. In addition, it is more time efficient, allows for the separation of high and low molecular weight AR components, and yields qualitatively cleaner bran fractions due to the utilization of co-solvents ethanol and methanol, rather than the traditional organic solvents acetone and ethyl acetate [11, 138-141]. The current optimal settings and conditions for this procedure were found to be at temperature 70 °C, pressure 35 MPa, with a flow rate of 25 g/min for 4 h (primary extraction step), and 5 g/min for 4 h (secondary fractionation step) using 95% ethanol as a co-solvent [11]. While past studies by Francisco et al. (2005) have found SC-CO$_2$ [138, 140] to yield 8-80% more ARs when compared with traditional extraction using acetone, recent studies found no significant difference in total AR content amongst the two methods when comparing against traditional extraction with ethyl acetate [11, 141].

## 5.2. Methods of Analysis

### 5.2.1. Colorimetry

A colorimetric method of analysis has been used in several studies to quantify total AR concentrations by measuring the intensity of electromagnetic radiation in the visible spectrum transmitted through AR extracts [40, 142-146] [147, 148]. This method of analysis was first developed by Musehold in 1973 and has been adapted since to produce more accurate results that are in agreement with other methods. This method is based on a diazonium salt which reacts with phenolic compounds to form an azo-complex that develops a reddish violet colour with a maximum absorption peak ($\lambda$=520nm) distinct for 5-alk(en)ylresorcinols [144, 148]. Various diazotized compounds have been used as reagents for this method, such as sulfonic acid [40, 149, 150], *p*-nitroaniline [151], Fast Blue B BF4 [142, 145], Fast Blue B Zn [144, 147], and Fast Blue RR salt [147]. Current methods employ either one of the three Fast Blue salts; however, the methods employed vary depending on the type of salt used. It is important to note that colorimetry does not distinguish amongst the various AR homologues present in the extract as it only quantifies based on the sum of aromatic rings reacting with the diazonium salt [145]. Therefore, this method is ideal for rapid, simple, cost-effective detection and quantification of total ARs [144, 146, 147]. Further analysis by chromatography is recommended for confirmation of the results obtained by colorimetry and to differentiate between the different AR homologues [21, 136].

### 5.2.2. Thin Layer Chromatography (TLC)

TLC has been used a qualitative method for the identification and separation of ARs [30, 136, 139, 141, 152]. In this method, a plate coated with a layer of silica gel or aluminum oxide, acts as the stationary phase.Once the sample is applied on the plate, a solvent mixture is drawn up the plate causing different analytes to separate at different rates, thereby allowing for separation of the compound of interest. The plate is sprayed with a reagent such as Fast Blue that reacts with the separated bands of ARs to form colors that range in intensity; bands vary from pink to deep crimson depending on the chain length [21]. TLC is an ideal preliminary method for detection, isolation and purification of AR homologues, as it is a rapid and simple procedure. However, further analysis by HPLC or GC is essential for the quantitative determination of ARs [18] [136] [21] [101].

### 5.2.3. High Performance Liquid Chromatography (HPLC) and Gas Chromatography (GC)

For a more in depth analysis of the AR homologue composition of extracts, either HPLC [13, 15, 22, 33, 139, 152-154] and/or GC have been employed [13, 14, 27, 30, 69, 147, 148, 152, 155-159] HPLC separates, identifies, and quantifies AR homologues based on their characteristic retention times that are dependent on AR-chain length and degree of unsaturation [33, 38, 68, 154]. Given that the majority of AR homologues extracted from cereal grains are non-polar, a reverse-phase HPLC with a non-polar C18 column as the stationary phase and a polar solvent mobile phase is generally used [33, 38, 139, 154] [138]. Use of a gradient system produces optimal results with clear peak separation points and reduced background noise in the resultant chromatogram; a combination of methanol and water (v/v) or a step-wise gradient of 70-99% MeOH have been commonly used [72, 139]. The characteristic retention times of the AR homologues are made available by a UV detector set at 280 nm [33, 138, 139, 152], a photodiode array (PDA) detector [13, 26] or a coulometric electrode array detector (CEAD) [68, 153] set at a scanning range of 250-350 nm. Other parameters such as the flow-rate of the mobile phase, column temperature, pump pressure, and the exact ratio of solvent gradient used varies depending on the specific system used. HPLC coupled to an atmospheric pressure chemical ionization multistage mass spectrometer (DAD-APcI-MSn) effectively characterizes substituted AR homologues with saturated, monoenoic, dienoic, and/or oxygenated side-chains [22] and HPLC-CEAD allows for sensitive analysis and maximum recovery of 98-107% AR homologues [153].

Gas chromatography separates and quantifies the relative amounts of AR homologues based on their individual boiling points, thus their retention times, which are visualized by a flame ionization detector (FID) or mass spectrometer (MS) [160]. While GC alone does not positively identify all components of an AR extract, GC-MS identifies AR components with high accuracy through their characteristic ionized fragments of mass to charge ratio (m/z) and retention times [11, 27]. The characteristic ion peaks are generally 320, 348, 376, 404, 432 and 460 m/z for respective AR homologues C15:0, C17:0, C19:0, C21:0, C23:0 and C25:0 [161]. Alternative methods such as gas chromatography/tandem mass spectrometry (GC/MS/MS) and normal-phase liquid chromatography/tandem mass spectrometry have been used for rapid analysis of ARs in human plasma and red blood cells (RBC) and exhibited lower limits of detection and quantification in comparison to that of GC-MS [156, 162].

## CONCLUSION

Although 5-n-alkylresorcinols can be isolated from a wide array of sources, ARs in food sources are of the greatest advantage. The abundance of ARs in wholegrain cereals and their exclusive presence in the bran fraction, allows for ARs to be an excellent candidate as biomarkers of wholegrain intake. The role of ARs as biomarkers is extremely important for validation of the disease preventative properties and health benefits resulting from the inclusion of whole grains in the diet. Numerous studies on the pharmacokinetics of ARs *in vivo* and *in vitro* have determined that levels of whole grains consumed in the diet correlate with levels of intact ARs measured in the faeces as well as AR metabolites extracted from urine samples of these individuals. Recently, Jansson et al. (2010) suggested that ARs can also be used as long-term biomarkers of whole grain intake as a small percentage of ARs consumed from whole grains often reside in the adipose tissue and accumulated proportions correlate with long term intake [1].

In addition to the role of ARs as biomarkers, these phenolic lipids owe to their amphiphillic structure their varying degree of biological effects of antimicrobial, antioxidant, cytotoxic activity as well as their inhibitory or stimulatory effects on enzymes, and their stabilizing or disruptive effects on the phospholipid bilayer of cell membranes. These effects are dependent on the chain length, degree of saturation, chain or ring constituents, and the concentration of AR homologues present; these factors affect their hydrogen donating capacity, amphiphillic or lipophilic nature, polarity, hydrophobicity, binding capacity, as well as their ease of integration and interaction with enzymes, proteins and membranes.

## REFERENCES

[1]   Jansson, E., Landberg, R., Kamal-Eldin, A., Wolk, A., Vessby, B., and Aman, P. 2010, Presence of alkylresorcinols, potential whole grain biomarkers, in human adipose tissue. *British Journal of Nutrition.* 1-4.

[2]     Landberg, R., Andersson, S. O., Zhang, J. X., Johansson, J. E., Stenman, U. H., Adlercreutz, H., Kamal-Eldin, A., Aman, P., and Hallmans, G. 2010, Rye whole grain and bran intake compared with refined wheat decreases urinary C-peptide, plasma insulin, and prostate specific antigen in men with prostate cancer. *J. Nutr.* 140: 2180-6.

[3]     Olsen, A., Landberg, R., Aman, P., Kamal-Eldin, A., Christensen, J., Johnsen, N. F., Overvad, K., and Tjonneland, A. 2010, Plasma levels of alkylresorcinols and incidence of endometrial cancer. *European journal of cancer prevention.* 19: 73-7.

[4]     Zant-Przeworska, E., Stasiuk, M., Gubernator, J., and Kozubek, A. 2010, Resorcinolic lipids improve the properties of sphingomyelin-cholesterol liposomes. *Chemistry and Physics of Lipids.* 163: 648-54.

[5]     Kulawinek, M. and Kozubek, A. 2007, 5-n-alkylresorcinols of whole grain cereals and whole grain cereal products as biomarkers of healthy food. *Postepy Biochemii.* 53: 287-96.

[6]     Landberg, R., Aman, P., Friberg, L. E., Vessby, B., Adlercreutz, H., and Kamal-Eldin, A. 2009, Dose response of whole-grain biomarkers: alkylresorcinols in human plasma and their metabolites in urine in relation to intake. *American Journal of Clinical Nutrition.* 89: 290-6.

[7]     Kozubek, A. and Nienartowicz, B. 1995, Cereal grain resorcinolic lipids inhibit H2O2-induced peroxidation of biological membranes. *Acta Biochimica Polonica.* 42: 309-15.

[8]     Parikka, K., Rowland, I. R., Welch, R. W., and Wahala, K. 2006, In vitro antioxidant activity and antigenotoxicity of 5-n-alkylresorcinols. *J. Agric. Food Chem.* 54: 1646-50.

[9]     Aubertin-Leheudre, M., Koskela, A., Samaletdin, A., and Adlercreutz, H. 2010, Plasma and urinary alkylresorcinol metabolites as potential biomarkers of breast cancer risk in Finnish women: a pilot study. *Nutr. Cancer.* 62: 759-64.

[10]   Landberg, R., Kamal-Eldin, A., Andersson, A., Vessby, B., and Aman, P. 2008, Alkylresorcinols as biomarkers of whole-grain wheat and rye intake: plasma concentration and intake estimated from dietary records. *The American journal of clinical nutrition.* 87: 832-8.

[11]   Athukorala, Y., Hosseinian, F. S., and Mazza, G. 2010, Extraction and fractionation of alkylresorcinols from triticale bran by two-step supercritical carbon dioxide *LWT - Food Science and Technology* 43: 660-5.

[12]   Hosseinian, F. S., Agil, R., Oomah, D. B., and Mazza, G. 2011, Optimization of alkylresorcinols extraction from triticale bran using response surface methodology. *Food and Bioprocess Technology.* not yet published.

[13]   Mullin, W. J., Wolynetz, M. S., and Emery, J. P. 1992, A comparison of methods for the extraction and quantitation of Alk(en)ylresorcinols. *Journal of Food Composition and Analysis.* 5: 216-23.

[14]   Chen, Y., Ross, A. B., Aman, P., and Kamal-Eldin, A. 2004, Alkylresorcinols as markers of whole grain wheat and rye in cereal products. *J. Agric. Food Chem.* 52: 8242-6.

[15]   Mattila, P., Pihlava, J. M., and Hellstrom, J. 2005, Contents of phenolic acids, alkyl- and alkenylresorcinols, and avenanthramides in commercial grain products. *J. Agric. Food Chem.* 53: 8290-5.

[16]   Zarnowski, R. and Suzuki, Y. 2004, 5-n-Alkylresorcinols from grains of winter barley (Hordeum vulgare L.). *Z. Naturforsch. C.* 59: 315-7.

[17] Andersson, A. A., Lampi, A. M., Nystrom, L., Piironen, V., Li, L., Ward, J. L., Gebruers, K., Courtin, C. M., Delcour, J. A., Boros, D., Fras, A., Dynkowska, W., Rakszegi, M., Bedo, Z., Shewry, P. R., and Aman, P. 2008, Phytochemical and dietary fiber components in barley varieties in the HEALTHGRAIN Diversity Screen. *J. Agric. Food Chem.* 56: 9767-76.

[18] Kozubek, A. and Tyman, J. H. P. 1999, Resorcinolic lipids, the natural non-isoprenoid phenolic amphiphiles and their biological activity. *Chemical Reviews.* 99: 1-25.

[19] Ross, A. B., Shepherd, M. J., Schüpphaus, M., Sinclair, V., Alfaro, B., Kamal-Eldin, A., and Åman, P. 2003, Alkylresorcinols in Cereals and Cereal Products. *Journal of Agricultural and Food Chemistry.* 51: 4111-8.

[20] Lorenz, P., Knodler, M., Bertrams, J., Berger, M., Meyer, U., and Stintzing, F. C. 2010, n-Alkylresorcinol occurrence in Mercurialis perennis L. (Euphorbiaceae). *Z. Naturforsch. C.* 65: 174-9.

[21] Ross, A. B., Aman, P., Andersson, R., and Kamal-Eldin, A. 2004, Chromatographic analysis of alkylresorcinols and their metabolites. *J. Chromatogr. A.* 1054: 157-64.

[22] Knodler, M., Kaiser, A., Carle, R., and Schieber, A. 2008, Profiling of Alk(en)ylresorcinols in cereals by HPLC-DAD-APcI-MSn. *Anal. Bioanal. Chem.* 391: 221-8.

[23] Suzuki, Y., Esumi, Y., and Yamaguchi, I. 1999, Structures of 5-alkylresorcinol-related analogues in rye. *Phytochemistry.* 52: 281-9.

[24] Seitz, L. M. 1992, Identification of 5-(2-oxoalkyl)resorcinols and 5-(2-oxoalkenyl)resorcinols in wheat and rye grains. *Journal of Agricultural and Food Chemistry.* 40: 1541-6.

[25] Ross, A. B., Kamal-Eldin, A., and Aman, P. 2004, Dietary alkylresorcinols: absorption, bioactivities, and possible use as biomarkers of whole-grain wheat- and rye-rich foods. *Nutr. Rev.* 62: 81-95.

[26] Kulawinek, M., Jaromin, A., Kozubek, A., and Zarnowski, R. 2008, Alkylresorcinols in selected Polish rye and wheat cereals and whole-grain cereal products. *J. Agric. Food Chem.* 56: 7236-42.

[27] Ross, A. B., Kamal-Eldin, A., Jung, C., Shepherd, M. J., and Åman, P. 2001, Gas chromatographic analysis of alkylresorcinols in rye (Secale cereale L) grains. *Journal of the Science of Food and Agriculture.* 81: 1405-11.

[28] Hedkvist, S. 2009. *Bread volume and Alkylresorcinol content in rye bread baked with high and low levels of Alkylresorcinols.* Swedish University of Agricultural Sciences, Uppsala. 34 pp.

[29] Layers of a wheat kernel. In *Grain Gallery*, ed. http://grain-gallery.com/media/wheat/renderings/02.png. Hamburg, Germany: KAMPFFMEYER Food Innovation GmbH.

[30] Landberg, R., Kamal-Eldin, A., Salmenkallio-Marttila, M., Rouau, X., and Åman, P. 2008, Localization of alkylresorcinols in wheat, rye and barley kernels. *Journal of Cereal Science.* 48: 401-6.

[31] Zarnowski, R., Suzuki, Y., Yamaguchi, I., and Pietr, S. J. 2002, Alkylresorcinols in barley (Hordeum vulgare L. distichon) grains. *Z. Naturforsch. C.* 57: 57-62.

[32] Bouillant, M. L., Jacoud, C., Zanella, I., Favre-Bonvin, J., and Bally, R. 1994, Identification of 5-(12-heptadecenyl)-resorcinol in rice root exudates. *Phytochemistry.* 35: 768-71.

[33] Hengtrakul, P., Lorenz, K., and Mathias, M. 1991, Alkylresorcinol homologs in cereal grains. *Journal of Food Composition and Analysis.* 4: 52-7.

[34] Evans, L. E., Dedio, W., and Hill, R. D. 1973, Variability in the alkylresorcinol content of rye grain. *Canadian Journal of Plant Science.* 53: 485-8.

[35] Verdeal, K. and Lorenz, K. 1997, Alkylresorcinols in wheat, rye and triticale. *Cereal Chemistry.* 54: 475-83.

[36] Gembeh, S. V., Brown, R. L., Grimm, C., and Cleveland, T. E. 2001, Identification of Chemical Components of Corn Kernel Pericarp Wax Associated with Resistance to Aspergillus flavus Infection and Aflatoxin Production. *Journal of Agricultural and Food Chemistry.* 49: 4635-41.

[37] Fate, G. D. and Lynn, D. G. 1996, Xenognosin Methylation Is Critical in Defining the Chemical Potential Gradient That Regulates the Spatial Distribution in Striga Pathogenesis. *Journal of the American Chemical Society.* 118: 11369-76.

[38] Mullin, W. J. and Emery, J. P. H. 1992, Determination of alkylresorcinols in cereal-based foods. *J. Agric. Food Chem.* 40: 2127-30.

[39] Andersson, A. A., Kamal-Eldin, A., and Aman, P. 2010, Effects of Environment and Variety on Alkylresorcinols in Wheat in the HEALTHGRAIN Diversity Screen (dagger). *J. Agric. Food Chem.* 58: 9299-92305.

[40] Musehold, J. 1975, 5-Alkylresorcinol content influenced through grain size, genetical and environmental conditions. *Hodowla Rosl. Aklim. Nasienna.* 19: 603–4.

[41] Hengtrakul, P., Lorenz, K., and Mathias, M. 1990, Alkylresorcinols in U.S. and Canadian wheats and flours. *Cereal Chemistry.* 67: 413-7.

[42] Andersson, A. A. M., Kamal-Eldin, A., Fraś, A., Boros, D., and Åman, P. 2008, Alkylresorcinols in Wheat Varieties in the HEALTHGRAIN Diversity Screen. *Journal of Agricultural and Food Chemistry.* 56: 9722-5.

[43] Touré, A. and Xueming, X. 2010, Flaxseed Lignans: Source, Biosynthesis, Metabolism, Antioxidant Activity, Bio-Active Components, and Health Benefits. *Comprehensive Reviews in Food Science and Food Safety.* 9: 261-9.

[44] Nyström, L., Lampi, A.-M., Andersson, A. A. M., Kamal-Eldin, A., Gebruers, K., Courtin, C. M., Delcour, J. A., Li, L., Ward, J. L., Fraś, A., Boros, D., Rakszegi, M., Bedő, Z., Shewry, P. R., and Piironen, V. 2008, Phytochemicals and Dietary Fiber Components in Rye Varieties in the HEALTHGRAIN Diversity Screen. *Journal of Agricultural and Food Chemistry.* 56: 9758-66.

[45] Al-Ruqaie, I. and Lorenz, K. 1992, Alkylresorcinols in extruded cereal brans. *Cereal Chemistry.* 69: 472- 5.

[46] Rolan, P. and Molnar, V. 2007. Clinical Pharmacokinetics. In *The Textbook of Pharmaceutical Medicine*, pp. 176-97: Blackwell Publishing Ltd.

[47] Soderholm, P. P., Koskela, A. H., Lundin, J. E., Tikkanen, M. J., and Adlercreutz, H. C. 2009, Plasma pharmacokinetics of alkylresorcinol metabolites: new candidate biomarkers for whole-grain rye and wheat intake. *The American journal of clinical nutrition.* 90: 1167-71.

[48] Soderholm, P. P., Lundin, J. E., Koskela, A. H., Tikkanen, M. J., and Adlercreutz, H. C. 2011, Pharmacokinetics of alkylresorcinol metabolites in human urine. *The British journal of nutrition.* 1-5.

[49] Linko, A. M., Ross, A. B., Kamal-Eldin, A., Serena, A., Kjaer, A. K., Jorgensen, H., Penalvo, J. L., Adlercreutz, H., Aman, P., and Knudsen, K. E. 2006, Kinetics of the

appearance of cereal alkylresorcinols in pig plasma. *British Journal of Nutrition.* 95: 282-7.

[50] Linko-Parvinen, A. M. 2006. *Cereal alkylresorcinols as dietary biomarkers-Absorption and occurrence in biological membranes.* Dissertation thesis. University of Helsinki, Helsinki. 1-84 pp.

[51] Linko-Parvinen, A. M., Landberg, R., Tikkanen, M. J., Adlercreutz, H., and Peñalvo, J. L. 2007, Whole-grain alkylresorcinols are transported in human plasma lipoproteins, and their intake corresponds to plasma concentrations. *Journal of Nutrition* 137:1137-42.

[52] Landberg, R., Linko, A. M., Kamal-Eldin, A., Vessby, B., Adlercreutz, H., and Åman, P. 2006, Human Plasma Kinetics and Relative Bioavailability of Alkylresorcinols after Intake of Rye Bran. *J. Nutr.* 136: 2760-5.

[53] Linko, A. M. and Adlercreutz, H. 2005, Whole-grain rye and wheat alkylresorcinols are incorporated into human erythrocyte membranes. *British Journal of Nutrition.* 93: 11-3.

[54] Ross, A. B., Kamal-Eldin, A., Lundin, E. A., Zhang, J. X., Hallmans, G., and Aman, P. 2003, Cereal alkylresorcinols are absorbed by humans. *J. Nutr.* 133: 2222-4.

[55] Ross, A. B., Shepherd, M. J., Bach Knudsen, K. E., Glitso, L. V., Bowey, E., Phillips, J., Rowland, I., Guo, Z. X., Massy, D. J., Aman, P., and Kamal-Eldin, A. 2003, Absorption of dietary alkylresorcinols in ileal-cannulated pigs and rats. *British Journal of Nutrition.* 90: 787-94.

[56] Ross, A. B., Becker, W., Chen, Y., Kamal-Eldin, A., and Aman, P. 2005, Intake of alkylresorcinols from wheat and rye in the United Kingdom and Sweden. *British Journal of Nutrition.* 94: 496-9.

[57] Tłuścik, F., Kupiec, R., and Rakowska, M. 1990, Studies on antinutritive components of the rye grain. II. Balance and metabolism of 5-n-alkylresorcinols in rats. *Acta Aliment Pol.* 16: 119–28.

[58] Herrera, E. and Barbas, C. 2001, Vitamin E: action, metabolism and perspectives. *J. Physiol. Biochem.* 57: 43-56.

[59] Landberg, R., Kamal-Eldin, A., Andersson, S. O., Johansson, J. E., Zhang, J. X., Hallmans, G., and Aman, P. 2009, Reproducibility of plasma alkylresorcinols during a 6-week rye intervention study in men with prostate cancer. *Journal of Nutrition.* 139: 975-80.

[60] Linko, A., Juntunen, K., Mykkanen, H., and Adlercreutz, H. 2005, Whole-grain rye bread consumption by women correlates with plasma alkylresorcinols and increases their concentration compared with low-fiber *Journal of Nutrition* 135: 580-3.

[61] Landberg, R. 2009. *Alkylresorcinols as Biomarkers of Whole Grain Wheat and Rye Intake.* Doctoral Thesis thesis. Swedish University of Agricultural Sciences, Uppsala.

[62] Landberg, R., Kamal-Eldin, A., Aman, P., Christensen, J., Overvad, K., Tjønneland, A., and Olsen, A. 2011, Determinants of plasma alkylresorcinol concentration in Danish post-menopausal women. *European journal of clinical nutrition.* 65: 94-101.

[63] Aubertin-Leheudre, M., Koskela, A., Samaletdin, A., and Adlercreutz, H. 2010, Responsiveness of Urinary and Plasma Alkylresorcinol Metabolites to Rye Intake in Finnish Women. *Cancers.* 2: 513-22.

[64] Aubertin-Leheudre, M., Koskela, A., Samaletdin, A., and Adlercreutz, H. 2010, Plasma alkylresorcinol metabolites as potential biomarkers of whole-grain wheat and rye cereal fibre intakes in women *British Journal of Nutrition.* 103: 339-43.

[65]  Ross, A. B., Chen, Y., Frank, J., Swanson, J. E., Parker, R. S., Kozubek, A., Lundh, T., Vessby, B., Aman, P., and Kamal-Eldin, A. 2004, Cereal alkylresorcinols elevate gamma-tocopherol levels in rats and inhibit gamma-tocopherol metabolism in vitro. *Journal of Nutrition.* 134: 506-10.

[66]  Kozubek, A. 1987, The effect of 5-(n-alk(en)yl)resorcinols on membranes. I. Characterization of the permeability increase induced by 5-(n-heptadecenyl)resorcinol. *Acta Biochim. Polon.* 34: 357–67.

[67]  Ross, A. B., Aman, P., and Kamal-Eldin, A. 2004, Identification of cereal alkylresorcinol metabolites in human urine-potential biomarkers of wholegrain wheat and rye intake. *J. Chromatogr. B Analyt. Technol. Biomed. Life Sci.* 809: 125-30.

[68]  Marklund, M., Landberg, R., Åman, P., and Kamal-Eldin, A. 2011, Comparison of gas chromatography-mass spectrometry and high-performance liquid chromatography with coulometric electrode array detection for determination of alkylresorcinol metabolites in human urine. *Journal of Chromatography B.* 879: 647-51.

[69]  Marklund, M., Landberg, R., Aman, P., and Kamal-Eldin, A. 2010, Determination of alkylresorcinol metabolites in human urine by gas chromatography-mass spectrometry. *J. Chromatogr. B Analyt. Technol. Biomed. Life Sci.* 878: 888-94.

[70]  Guyman, L. A., Adlercreutz, H., Koskela, A., Li, L., Beresford, S. A. A., and Lampe, J. W. 2008, Urinary 3-(3,5-dihydroxyphenyl)-1-propanoic acid, an alkylresorcinol metabolite, is a potential biomarker of whole-grain intake in a U.S. population. *J. Nutr.* 138.

[71]  Koskela, A., Linko-Parvinen, A.-M., Hiisivuori, P., Samaletdin, A., Kamal-Eldin, A., Tikkanen, M. J., and Adlercreutz, H. 2007, Quantification of Alkylresorcinol Metabolites in Urine by HPLC with Coulometric Electrode Array Detection. *Clin. Chem.* 53: 1380-3.

[72]  Koskela, A., Samaletdin, A., Aubertin-Leheudre, M. n., and Adlercreutz, H. 2008, Quantification of Alkylresorcinol Metabolites in Plasma by High-Performance Liquid Chromatography with Coulometric Electrode Array Detection. *Journal of Agricultural and Food Chemistry.* 56: 7678-81.

[73]  Zarnowski, R. and Kozubek, A. 1999, Alkylresorcinol homologs in Pisum sativum L. varieties. *Z. Naturforsch. C.* 54c: 44–8.

[74]  Reiss, J. 1989, Influence of alkylresorcinols from rye and related compounds on the growth of food-borne moulds. *Cereal Chem.* 66: 491–3.

[75]  García, S., García, C., Heinzen, H., and Moyna, P. 1997, Chemical basis of the resistance of barley seeds to pathogenic fungi. *Phytochemistry.* 44: 415-8.

[76]  Droby, S., Prusky, D., Jacoby, B., and Goldman, A. 1987, Induction of antifungal resorcinols in flesh of unripe mango fruits and its relation to latent infection by Alternaria alternata. *Physiological and Molecular Plant Pathology.* 30: 285-92.

[77]  Cojocaru, M., Droby, S., Glotter, E., Goldman, A., Gottlieb, H. E., Jacoby, B., and Prusky, D. 1986, 5-(12-heptadecenyl)-resorcinol, the major component of the antifungal activity in the peel of mango fruit. *Phytochemistry.* 25: 1093-5.

[78]  Himejima, M. and Kubo, I. 1991, Antibacterial agents from the cashew Anacardium occidentale (Anacardiaceae) nut shell oil. *Journal of Agricultural and Food Chemistry.* 39: 418-21.

[79] Kubo, I., Ochi, M., Vieira, P. C., and Komatsu, S. 1993, Antitumor agents from the cashew (Anacardium occidentale) apple juice. *Journal of Agricultural and Food Chemistry.* 41: 1012-5.

[80] Suresh, M. and Kaleysa, R. K. 1990, Cardol: the antifilarial principle from Anacardium occidentale. *Current Science.* 59: 477–9.

[81] Halliwell, B. 1996, Mechanisms involved in the generation of free radicals. *Pathologie-biologie.* 44: 6-13.

[82] Halliwell, B. 1996, Free radicals, proteins and DNA: oxidative damage versus redox regulation. *Biochemical Society transactions.* 24: 1023-7.

[83] Niki, E. 2010, Assessment of antioxidant capacity of natural products. *Current pharmaceutical biotechnology.* 11: 801-9.

[84] Shahidi, F. and Wanasundara, P. K. 1992, Phenolic antioxidants. *Crit. Rev. Food Sci. Nutr.* 32: 67-103.

[85] Niki, E. 1987, Antioxidants in relation to lipid peroxidation. *Chemistry and physics of lipids.* 44: 227-53.

[86] Hosseinian, F. 2010. Flaxseed Lignans: Properties and Health Benefits. In *Flaxseed Lignans, mechanism of activity using in vitro and in vivo models*: LAP LAMBERT Academic Publishing.

[87] Leopoldini, M., Russo, N., and Toscano, M. 2011, The molecular basis of working mechanism of natural polyphenolic antioxidants. *Food Chemistry.* 125: 288-306.

[88] Fardet, A., Rock, E., and Rémésy, C. 2008, Is the in vitro antioxidant potential of whole-grain cereals and cereal products well reflected in vivo? *Journal of Cereal Science.* 48: 258-76.

[89] Winata, A. and Lorenz, K. 1996, Antioxidant potential of 5-n-pentadecylresorcinol. *Journal of Food Processing and Preservation.* 20: 417-29.

[90] Hładyszowski, J., Zubik, L., and Kozubek, A. 1998, Quantum mechanical and experimental oxidation studies of pentadecylresorcinol, olivetol, orcinol and resorcinol. *Free Radic Res.* 4.

[91] Kamal-Eldin, A., Pouru, A., Eliasson, C., and Åman, P. 2001, Alkylresorcinols as antioxidants: hydrogen donation and peroxyl radical-scavenging effects. *Journal of the Science of Food and Agriculture.* 81: 353-6.

[92] Korycinska, M., Czelna, K., Jaromin, A., and Kozubek, A. 2009, Antioxidant activity of rye bran alkylresorcinols and extracts from whole-grain cereal products. *Food Chemistry.* 116: 1013-8.

[93] Halliwell, B. and Chirico, S. 1993, Lipid peroxidation: its mechanism, measurement, and significance. *American Journal of Clinical Nutrition.* 57 715S-24S.

[94] Smith, C., Mitchinson, M. J., Aruoma, O. I., and Halliwell, B. 1992, Stimulation of lipid peroxidation and hydroxyl-radical generation by the contents of human atherosclerotic lesions. *Biochem. J.* 286: 901–5.

[95] Gutteridge, J. M. C. and Halliwell, B. 2000, Free Radicals and Antioxidants in the Year 2000: A Historical Look to the Future. *Annals of the New York Academy of Sciences.* 899: 136-47.

[96] Hladyszowski, J., Zubik, L., and Kozubek, A. 1998, Quantum mechanical and experimental oxidation studies of pentadecylresorcinol, olivetol, orcinol and resorcinol. *Free Radic. Res.* 28: 359-68.

[97]   C.A., W., Atherly, L. E., and Hirsch, J. D. 2007. Antioxidants and Your Horse Rutgers, The State University of New Jersey.

[98]   Shahidi, F. 2000, Antioxidant factors in plant foods and selected oilseeds. *Biofactors.* 13: 179-85.

[99]   López, P., Ferraro, G., and Anesini, C. 2011, Comparative antioxidant activity of an extract of Lithraea molleoides and an isolated 5-alkyl resorcinol derivative. Effects on the proliferation of normal and tumoral lymphocytes. *Phytotherapy Research.* 25:271-6.

[100] Sumino, M., Sekine, T., Ruangrungsi, N., Igarashi, K., and Ikegami, F. 2002, Ardisiphenols and other antioxidant principles from the fruits of Ardisia colorata. *Chem. Pharm. Bull. (Tokyo).* 50: 1484-7.

[101] Parikka, K. 2007. *Antioxidative long chain Alkylresorcinols. Synthesis and deuterium labelling of bioactive compounds present in whole grains.* Academic dissertation thesis. University of Helsinki, Helsinki. 1-64 pp.

[102] Farombi, E. O. 2004, Diet-related cancer and prevention using anticarcinogens. *African Journal of Biotechnology* 3: 651-61.

[103] Bylund, A., Zhang, J.-X., Bergh, A., Damber, J.-E., Widmark, A., Johansson, A., Adlercreutz, H., Åman, P., Shepherd, M. J., and Hallmans, G. 2000, Rye bran and soy protein delay growth and increase apoptosis of human LNCaP prostate adenocarcinoma in nude mice. *The Prostate.* 42: 304-14.

[104] Arisawa, M., Ohmura, K., Kobayashi, A., and Morita, N. 1989, A cytotoxic constituent of Lysimachia japonica THUNB. (Primulaceae) and the structure-activity relationships of related compounds. *Chem. Pharm. Bull. (Tokyo).* 37: 2431-4.

[105] Itokawa, H., Totsuka, N., Nakahara, K., Maezuru, M., Takeya, K., Kondo, M., Inamatsu, M., and Morita, H. 1989, A quantitative structure-activity relationship for antitumor activity of long-chain phenols from Ginkgo biloba L. *Chem. Pharm. Bull. (Tokyo).* 37: 1619-21.

[106] Itokawa, H., Totsuka, N., Nakahara, K., Takeya, K., Lepoittevin, J., and Asakawa, Y. 1987, Antitumor principles from Ginkgo biloba L. *Chem. Pharm. Bull. (Tokyo).* 35: 3016-20.

[107] Buonanno, F., Quassinti, L., Bramucci, M., Amantini, C., Lucciarini, R., Santoni, G., Iio, H., and Ortenzi, C. 2008, The protozoan toxin climacostol inhibits growth and induces apoptosis of human tumor cell lines. *Chemico-Biological Interactions.* 176: 151-64.

[108] Bao, L., Wang, M., Zhao, F., Zhao, Y., and Liu, H. 2010, Two New Resorcinol Derivatives with Strong Cytotoxicity from the Roots of Ardisia brevicaulisDiels. *Chemistry and Biodiversity.* 7: 2901-7.

[109] Iwatsuki, K., Akihisa, T., Tokuda, H., Ukiya, M., Higashihara, H., Mukainaka, T., Iizuka, M., Hayashi, Y., Kimura, Y., and Nishino, H. 2003, Sterol Ferulates, Sterols, and 5-Alk(en)ylresorcinols from Wheat, Rye, and Corn Bran Oils and Their Inhibitory Effects on Epstein–Barr Virus Activation. *Journal of Agricultural and Food Chemistry.* 51: 6683-8.

[110] Gasiorowski, K., Brokos, B., Kulma, A., Ogorzałek, A., Sk, oacute, and rkowska, K. 2001. *Impact of four antimutagens on apoptosis in genotoxically damaged lymphocytes in vitro.* 649-75 pp.

[111] Gasiorowski, K., Brokos, B., Kozubek, A., and Oszmian'ski, J. 2000, The antimutagenic activity of two plant-derived compounds. A comparative cytogenetic study. *Cellular and Molecular Biology Letters*. 5: 171-90.

[112] Gasiorowski, K., Szyba, K., Brokos, B., and Kozubek, A. 1996, Antimutagenic activity of alkylresorcinols from cereal grains. *Cancer Letters*. 106: 109-15.

[113] Filip, P., Anke, T., and Sterner, O. 2002, 5-(2'-oxoheptadecyl)-resorcinol and 5-(2'-oxononadecyl)-resorcinol, cytotoxic metabolites from a wood-inhabiting basidiomycete. *Z. Naturforsch. C*. 57: 1004-8.

[114] Barbini L, L. P., Ruffa J, Martino V, Ferraro G, Campos R, Cavallaro L. 2006, Induction of apoptosis on human hepatocarcinoma cell lines by an alkyl resorcinol isolated from Lithraea molleoides. *World J. Gastroenterol*. 12: 5959-63.

[115] Starck, S. R., Deng, J.-Z., and Hecht, S. M. 2000, Naturally Occurring Alkylresorcinols That Mediate DNA Damage and Inhibit Its Repair†. *Biochemistry*. 39: 2413-9.

[116] Lytollis, W., Scannell, R. T., An, H., Murty, V. S., Reddy, K. S., Barr, J. R., and Hecht, S. M. 1995, 5-Alkylresorcinols from Hakea trifurcata, that cleave DNA. *Journal of the American Chemical Society*. 117: 12683-90.

[117] Barr, J. R., Murty, V. S., Yamaguchi, K., Singh, S., Smith, D. H., and Hecht, S. M. 1988, 5-Alkylresorcinols from Hakea amplexicaulis that cleave DNA. *Chemical Research in Toxicology*. 1: 204-7.

[118] Stasiuk, M. and Kozubek, A. 2008, Membrane perturbing properties of natural phenolic and resorcinolic lipids. *FEBS letters*. 582: 3607-13.

[119] Bitkov, V. V., Nenashev, V. A., Pridachina, N. N., and Batrakov, S. G. 1992, Membrane-structuring properties of bacterial long-chain alkylresorcinols. *Biochimica et Biophysica Acta (BBA) - Biomembranes*. 1108: 224-32.

[120] Przeworska, E., Gubernator, J., and Kozubek, A. 2001, Formation of liposomes by resorcinolic lipids, single-chain phenolic amphiphiles from Anacardium occidentale L. *Biochimica et Biophysica Acta (BBA) - Biomembranes*. 1513: 75-81.

[121] Gubernator, J., Stasiuk, M., and Kozubek, A. 1999, Dual effect of alkylresorcinols, natural amphiphilic compounds, upon liposomal permeability. *Biochimica et Biophysica Acta (BBA) - Biomembranes*. 1418: 253-60.

[122] Siwko, M. E., de Vries, A. H., Mark, A. E., Kozubek, A., and Marrink, S. J. 2009, Disturb or Stabilize? A Molecular Dynamics Study of the Effects of Resorcinolic Lipids on Phospholipid Bilayers. *Biophysical Journal*. 96: 3140-53.

[123] Kozubek, A., Gubernator, J., Przeworska, E., and Stasiuk, M. 2000, Liposomal drug delivery, a novel approach: PLARosomes. *Acta Biochimica Polonica*. 47: 639-49.

[124] Rejman, J. and Kozubek, A. 2004, Inhibitory Effect of Natural Phenolic Lipids upon NAD-Dependent Dehydrogenases and on Triglyceride Accumulation in 3T3-L1 Cells in Culture. *Journal of Agricultural and Food Chemistry*. 52: 246-50.

[125] Stasiuk, M., Bartosiewicz, D., and Kozubek, A. 2008, Inhibitory effect of some natural and semisynthetic phenolic lipids upon acetylcholinesterase activity. *Food Chemistry*. 108: 996-1001.

[126] Stasiuk, M., Kleta, M., and Kozubek, A. 2011, Dual effect of free and liposomal forms of phenolic lipids on the activity of GPI-anchor-deprived acetylcholinesterase from erythrocytes. *Food Chemistry*. 125: 508-12.

[127] Tocco, G., Fais, A., Meli, G., Begala, M., Podda, G., Fadda, M. B., Corda, M., Attanasi, O. A., Filippone, P., and Berretta, S. 2009, PEG-immobilization of cardol and soluble

polymer-supported synthesis of some cardol-coumarin derivatives: Preliminary evaluation of their inhibitory activity on mushroom tyrosinase. *Bioorganic and medicinal chemistry letters.* 19: 36-9.

[128] Zhuang, J.-X., Hu, Y.-H., Yang, M.-H., Liu, F.-J., Qiu, L., Zhou, X.-W., and Chen, Q.-X. 2010, Irreversible Competitive Inhibitory Kinetics of Cardol Triene on Mushroom Tyrosinase. *Journal of Agricultural and Food Chemistry.* 58: 12993-8.

[129] Harding, J., Joseph, W., Pyeritz, E. A., Copeland, E. S., and White, H. B. 1975, Role of Glycerol 3-Phosphate Dehydrogenase in Glyceride Metabolism - Effect of Diet on Enzyme Activities in Chicken Liver. *Biochemistry.* 146.

[130] Tsuge, N., Mizokami, M., Imai, S., Shimazu, A., and Seto, H. 1992, Adipostatins A and B, new inhibitors of glycerol-3-phosphate dehydrogenase. *The Journal of antibiotics.* 45: 886-91.

[131] Rejman, J. and Kozubek, A. 1997, Longchain orcinol homologs from cereal bran are effective inhibitors of glycerophosphate dehydrogenase *Cell. Mol. Biol. Lett.* 2: 411-9.

[132] Aiston S, A. L. 1999, Leptin enhances glycogen storage in hepatocytes by inhibition of phosphorylase and exerts and additive effect with insulin. *Diabetes.* 48.

[133] Sealock, R., Murlin, J., and Driver, R. 1939, A comparative study of the effect of alkylresorcinols and related compounds upon the absorption of insulin from isolated intestinal loops of anesthetized dogs. *J Physiol.* 128: 92–6.

[134] Baynes, J. W. and Marek, H. D. 2005. Medical Biochemistry 2nd. Edition. pp. p. 555 Elsevier Mosby.

[135] Hengtrakul, P., Mathias, M., and Lorenz, K. 1991, Effects of cereal alkylresorcinols on human platelet thromboxane production. *J. Nutr. Biochem.* 2: 20-4.

[136] Zarnowski, R. and Suzuki, Y. 2004, Expedient Soxhlet extraction of resorcinolic lipids from wheat grains. *Journal of Food Composition and Analysis.* 17: 649-63.

[137] Fatouh, A. E., Mahran, G. A., El-Ghandour, M. A., and Singh, R. K. 2007, Fractionation of buffalo butter oil by supercritical carbon dioxide. *LWT - Food Science and Technology.* 40: 1687-93.

[138] Francisco, J. d. C., Danielsson, B., Kozubek, A., and Dey, E. S. 2005, Application of supercritical carbon dioxide for the extraction of alkylresorcinols from rye bran. *The Journal of supercritical fluids.* 35: 220-6.

[139] Dey, E. S. and Mikhailopulo, K. 2009, A food grade approach for the isolation of major alkylresorcinols (ARs) from rye bran applying tailored supercritical carbon dioxide (scCO2) extraction combined with HPLC. *The Journal of supercritical fluids.* 51: 167-73.

[140] Francisco, J. d. C., Danielsson, B., Kozubek, A., and Dey, E. S. 2005, Extraction of Rye Bran by Supercritical Carbon Dioxide: Influence of Temperature, CO2, and Cosolvent Flow Rates. *Journal of Agricultural and Food Chemistry.* 53: 7432-7.

[141] Landberg, R., Dey, E. S., Francisco, J. D. C., Åman, P., and Kamal-Eldin, A. 2007, Comparison of supercritical carbon dioxide and ethyl acetate extraction of alkylresorcinols from wheat and rye. *Journal of Food Composition and Analysis.* 20: 534-8.

[142] Tluscik, F., Kozubek, A., and Mejbaum-Katzenellenbogen, W. 1981 Alkylresorcinols in rye (Secale cereale L.) grains. VI. Colorimertic micromethod for the determination of alkylresorcinols with the use of diazoniu salt, Fast Blue B. *Acta Soc. Bot. Pol.* 50.

[143] Kozubek, A. and Nienartowicz., B. 1994 The colorimetric estimation of phenolic lipids by stable diazonium salt Fast Blue BxBF4. *XXX PTBioch Congress, Szczecin.* p.228.

[144] Gajda, A., Kulawinek, M., and Kozubek, A. 2008, An improved colorimetric method for the determination of alkylresorcinols in cereals and whole-grain cereal products. *Journal of Food Composition and Analysis.* 21: 428-34.

[145] Kulawinek, M. and Kozubek, A. 2008, Quantitative Determination Of Alkylresorcinols In Cereal Grains: Independence Of The Length Of The Aliphatic Side Chain. *Journal of Food Lipids.* 15: 251-62.

[146] Sampietro, D. A., Vattuone, M. A., and Catalán, C. A. N. 2009, A new colorimetric method for determination of alkylresorcinols in ground and whole-cereal grains using the diazonium salt Fast Blue RR. *Food Chemistry.* 115: 1170-4.

[147] Landberg, R., Andersson, A. A. M., Aman, P., and Kamal-Eldin, A. 2009, Comparison of GC and colorimetry for the determination of alkylresorcinol homologues in cereal grains and products. *Food Chemistry.* 113: 1363-9.

[148] Landberg, R., Kamal-Eldin, A., Andersson, A. M., and Aman, P. 2009 Analytical procedures for determination of alk(en)ylresorcinols in cereals and cereal products. *AACC International.* 4 25-40.

[149] Musehold, J. 1973, Zur quantitativen bestimmung einer toxischen phenolartigen substanz des roggenkornes. *Zeitschrift Pflanzenzuchtg* 69: 102–6.

[150] Musehold, J. 1974 Zur methodik der selektion auf 5-alkyl-resorcin-arme pflanzen beim roggen. *Zeitschrift Pflanzenzuchtg* 71: 124–9.

[151] Mejbaum-Katzenellenbogen, W., Tluscik, F., Kozubek, A., Sikorski, A., and Maresz, Z. 1975, Alkylresorcinols in rye (Secale cereale L.) grains. I: micromethod for determination of alkyl derivatives of resorcinol in rye grain. *Acta Societas Botanica Polonica* 44: 479–89.

[152] Mullin, W. J. and Collins, F. W. 1991, Purification and Identification of Alk(en)ylresorcinols. *Journal of Food Composition and Analysis.* 4: 270-5.

[153] Ross, A. B. and Kochhar, S. 2009, Rapid and sensitive analysis of alkylresorcinols from cereal grains and products using HPLC-Coularray-based electrochemical detection. *J. Agric. Food Chem.* 57: 5187-93.

[154] Kozubek, A., Geurts van Kessel, W. S. M., and Demel, R. A. 1979, Separation of 5-N-alkylresorcinols by reversed-phase high-performance liquid chromatography. *Journal of Chromatography.* 169: 422-5.

[155] Landberg, R., Man, P., and Kamal-Eldin, A. 2009, A rapid gas chromatography-mass spectrometry method for quantification of alkylresorcinols in human plasma. *Analytical Biochemistry.* 385: 7-12.

[156] Nagy, K., Ross, A. B., Fay, L. B., Bourgeois, A., and Kussmann, M. 2008, Gas chromatography/tandem mass spectrometry analysis of alkylresorcinols in red blood cells. *Rapid communications in mass spectrometry: RCM.* 22: 4098-104.

[157] Landberg, R., Kamal-Eldin, A., Andersson, R., and Aman, P. 2006, Alkylresorcinol content and homologue composition in durum wheat (Triticum durum) kernels and pasta products. *Journal of Agricultural and Food Chemistry.* 54: 3012-4.

[158] Kozubek, A., Tluscik, F., and Mejbaum, K. W. 1981, Alkylresorcinols in rye (Secale cereale L.) grains. V. Chromatographic analysis of 5nalk(en)ylresorcinols during their preparation. *Acta Biochimica Polonica.* 50 637-43.

[159] Gohil, S., Pettersson, D., Salomonsson, A.-C., and Åman, P. 1988, Analysis of alkyl- and alkenylresorcinols in triticale, wheat and rye. *Journal of the Science of Food and Agriculture.* 45: 43-52.

[160] McNair, H. M. and Miller, J. M. 2008. Frontmatter. In *Basic Gas Chromatography*, pp. i-xiii: John Wiley and Sons, Inc.

[161] Deszcz, L. and Kozubek, A. 2000, Higher cardol homologs (5-alkylresorcinols) in rye seedlings. *Biochimica et biophysica acta.* 1483: 241-50.

[162] Ross, A. B., Redeuil, K., Vigo, M., Rezzi, S., and Nagy, K. 2010, Quantification of alkylresorcinols in human plasma by liquid chromatography/tandem mass spectrometry. *Rapid Communications in Mass Spectrometry.* 24: 554-60.

In: Bioactive Molecules in Plant Foods
Editor: Florence Ojiugo Uruakpa

ISBN: 978-1-62081-515-1
© 2012 Nova Science Publishers, Inc.

*Chapter VI*

# SEABUCKTHORN (*HIPPOPHAE RHAMNOIDES* L) AND ITS PRODUCTS: A POWERHOUSE OF PHYTOCHEMICALS

## *Florence O. Uruakpa*[1,*] *and Alphonsus Utioh*[2,†]
[1]Indiana State University, Department of Applied Health Sciences,
Terre Haute, IN, US
[2]Food Development Centre, Portage la Prairie, MB, Canada

## ABSTRACT

Seabuckthorn (*Hippophae rhamnoides* L.) product streams (fruits, oils, pulp, leaves, seeds, puree) are rich sources of functional compounds with reported benefits on health and wellness. These products can find application in the food, nutraceutical, pharmaceutical and cosmetic industries. Seabuckthorn fruits high in vitamins, minerals, flavonoids, carotenoids and fatty acids can be processed into juice, dried/infused fruits or fractionated into puree, seed and pulp. Its juice rich in antioxidants, iron and vitamins A and C may be used to produce single-strength juice or juice blends used as nutritional or sport beverage. Supercritical fluid extraction may be used to produce bioactive oil fractions for target use. Its seed oil contains 6-7% palmitoleic acid (ω-7), 11-12% palmitic acid, 15-18% oleic acid, 31-32% linoleic acid (ω-6) and 29-32% linolenic acid (ω-3). The high amount of palmitoleic acid (ω-7) in its pulp gives it a unique characteristic. Dried pulp ingredient can be used in nutrition bars and bakery products to enhance their nutritional value and provide attractive aroma and color. The pulp and seed oils are the most valuable products due to their good fat-soluble vitamins, sterols and fatty acid profile – this makes them valuable raw materials in food, pharmaceutical and cosmetic manufacture. Its leaves and barks may be crushed for extraction of essential oil, flavonoids and proanthocyanidins. This chapter highlights some nutritional and physiological benefits of seabuckthorn product streams.

---

[*] Tel: 812 237 8753; Fax: 812 237 8607. Ojiugou@yahoo.com.
[†] Tel: 2042393179; Toll-free: 1 800 870 1044; Fax: 204 239 3180. Alphonsus.Utioh@gov.mb.ca; www.manitoba.ca/fdc.

# INTRODUCTION

Seabuckthorn (*Hippophae rhamnoides* L.) is a thorny shrub of Elaeagnaceae family [1] with very high nutraceutical and therapeutical values. It originated from China, Mongolia, Russia and Eurasia; and has been spread by humans to Europe and North America for food, therapeutic and pharmaceutical purpose [2]. The most economically valuable *H. rhamnoides* is commonly called seabuckthorn (SB). China, Russia, and Mongolia are currently the largest producers of SB. In China, fruits are harvested from over one million hectares of wild SB and about 300,000 hectares of cultivated plants [3].

The commercial value of SB lies in its nutritional, cosmetic and medicinal qualities. It has been harvested mainly as a medicinal plant for at least 12 centuries in China. Oil and extracts mostly from SB berries have been incorporated into commercial medicinal and cosmetic products in Europe in the last half century.

In North America, interest has been generated in the development of SB as a commercial crop in the last decade. Chinese SB (*H. rhamnoides* subspecies *sinensis*), the most important species of *Hippophae*, adapts to harsh ecological conditions and is widely distributed in a large area of north and North-West China. An estimated total area of Chinese SB is approximately 2.13 million hectares including wild and cultivated plants which account for 90% of total SB resources worldwide [4]. Chinese SB is the main resource for the SB industry in China.

SB is resistant to cold, drought, salt and alkali. The vigorous vegetative reproduction and the strong, complex root system with nitrogen-fixing nodules make SB an optimal pioneer plant in soil and water conservation and reforestation of eroded areas.

**Table 1. Proanthocyanidin polymers in seabuckthorn\***

| Degree of polymerization | | | |
|---|---|---|---|
| 1 | 2 | 3 | 4 |
| Structure acronyms | | | |
| EC | EC-EC | EC-EC-EC | DNI |
| EGC | EC-EGC | EC-EC-EGC | |
| | EGC-EGC | EC-EGC-EGC | |
| | GC-GC | EGC-EGC-EGC | |
| | C-C | EGC-EGC-EC | |
| | C-GC | EC-EGC-EC | |
| | C-EGC | EGC-EC-EC | |
| | GC-C | | |
| | C-EC | | |

\* Rösch *et al.* [8]. EC = epicatechin; EGC = epigallocatechin.
GC = gallocatechin; C = catechin; DNI = detected not identified.

SB is a dioecious species (its male and female reproductive organs are borne on separate parts of the same species) and buds in 3-4 years after seeding. Its flowers are formed mostly on 2 year old wood differentiated during the previous growing season [5]. The pollination of its female flowers depends solely on the wind because neither the male nor female flowers produce nectar, and does not attract insects [6]. SB berries are rich source of polyphenols and vitamins and they contain large amounts of the potent antioxidant quercetin, and other flavonols in various glycosidic forms [7, 8]. The proanthocyanidin structural components of SB are shown in Table 1 [8]. The flavonol glycosides are characterised by a specific UV absorption maximum of $\lambda=370$ nm as the main group of polyphenols [7].

## SEABUCKTHORN PRODUCTION UPDATES IN CANADA

Over 20 varieties of SB exist worldwide. More than 50 tons of SB fruits are produced annually in Canada [9]. Its products include oil, juice, skins and pulp for use in cosmetics, food and pet food; with over 50 different products available in the market including frozen berries for food service. Canadian institutions/establishments with research programs on SB include University of Laval in Quebec City, Food Development Centre in Portage La Prairie, Agriculture and Agri-Food Canada Research Centres and University of Manitoba.

### Seabuckthorn Fractions

The fractions include tea leaves, fruits, seeds, dry pulp, pulp oil, seed oil and puree (Figure 1, 2).

SB fruits contain bioactives such as vitamin C, vitamin E, flavonoids, and carotenoids. SB seeds and pulp oils contain fat-soluble vitamins, plant sterols, and essential fatty acids [9].

### Seabuckthorn and its Functional Components

A functional food is similar in appearance to (or may be) a conventional food, is consumed as part of a usual diet, and is demonstrated to have physiological benefits and/or reduce the risk of chronic disease beyond basic nutritional functions [10].

SB berries and leaves have a long history of applications as a food and medicinal ingredient in Eastern countries (e.g., Tibet, Mongolia). For example, SB berries are used in Tibetan and Mongolian medicines for treating sputum and cough, and for improving blood circulation and the function of the digestive system [11]. Both seeds and the soft parts (fruit flesh and skin) of SB berry are rich in lipids. The oils isolated from the two fractions differ in fatty acid composition and both are abundant in fat-soluble vitamins and plant sterols [12].

Ripe SB berries/fruits have colors ranging from yellow to orange to red. They are 10-15 mm in diameter with soft, fleshy edible outer tissue enclosing a hard seed. The nutritional value of SB fruits embodies the importance of SB plant. For centuries the fruits have been used for food, therapeutic and pharmaceutical purposes in Europe and Asia [2]. They contain essential oil and high concentration of vitamins A and B-complex (B1, B2 and B6). Other fruit components which are of therapeutic importance are carotene, fatty acids (palmitin, palmitoleic acids), bioactive lipids (e.g., β-sitosterol), and are rich in flavonoids, polyphenols, carotenoid, and water- and fat-soluble vitamins [13, 14, 15, 16, 17].

SB berries are rich in vitamin C (360 mg/100 g fruit wt), vitamin E (203 mg/100 g fruit wt), β-carotene (249 mg/100 g). They have high antioxidant activity similar to that of blueberries and have potential therapeutic effects [18, 19].

The concentration of vitamin C in SB berries is higher compared to other berries such as strawberry, raspberry and blackberry. The composition of combined pulp and seed oil of SB berry is unusual including nutritionally important fatty acids and sterols, and a high antioxidative capacity including vitamins and carotenoids [20, 21]. The major fatty acids in the seed and pulp oil of SB berry are shown in Table 2.

**Table 2. Composition of seabuckthorn berry pulp and seed oil**

| Fatty acids | Seed oil | Pulp oil |
|---|---|---|
| Linoleic | 34%; 18:2 n-6 | ND |
| α-Linolenic | 25%; 18:3 n-3 | ND |
| Oleic | 19%; 18:1 n-9 | 26%; 18:1 n-9 |
| Palmitic | ND | 33%; 16:0 |
| Palmitoleic | ND | 25%; 16:1 n-7 |

Source: Yang et al. [22]; ND = No data.

Seabuckthorn leaves are small and narrow with a length of 2-6 cm. The leaves are very rich in polyphenolic compounds and are reported to have antitumor, antiviral and antioxidant properties [23]. SB leaves have been used in the preparation of Hiporamin, a phytochemical drug with wide spectrum of antiviral activities [23]. There is a growing interest in the use of SB berries and leaves for medicinal and cosmetic applications.

More than 200 products including nutraceuticals, cosmetics and pharmaceuticals, based on SB plant parts are currently available on the market. Phenolics, including flavonols, flavones, phenolic acids, proanthocyanidins and hydrolysable tannins, are reported as the major contributors to the biological properties like antioxidant activities of SB berries and leaves [14]. Quercetin, kaempherol, and isorhamnetin are the major flavonoid compounds reported in SB berries [24].

Phenolic acids are simple compounds of non-flavonoid family, which constitute a large group of phenolic compounds in plants. Phenolic acids are reported to have a wide spectrum of pharmacological activities including antioxidant, antimutagenic, antitumor and anticarcinogenic properties [25]. Phenolic acids include two main groups namely, hydroxybenzoic acid and hydroxycinnamic acid derivatives with different number and position of hydroxylation and methoxylation in the aromatic ring (Figure 3). Phenolic acids are distributed as their free and bound forms in nature, more often bound forms occur as their esters and glycosides.

A reverse phase-HPLC with diode array detector (DAD) analytical method was used to quantify nine phenolic acids (gallic acid, protocatechuic acid, p-hydroxybenzoic acid, vanillic acid, salicylic acid, p-coumaric acid, cinnamic acid, caffiec acid, ferulic acid) in SB leaves and berries [26]. Phenolic acid derivatives in anatomical parts of SB berries and leaves were separated into free phenolic acids, phenolic acids bound as esters and phenolic acids bound as glycosides and profiled in HPLC.

Figure 3. Structures of phenolic acids.

Hydroxybenzoic acid derivatives

| R$_1$ | R$_2$ | R$_3$ | R$_4$ | |
|------|------|------|------|---|
| OH | H | H | H | Salicylic acid |
| H | H | OH | H | p-hydroxy benzoic acid |
| H | OH | OH | H | 3,4-dihydroxy benzoic acid |
| H | OH | OH | OH | Gallic acid |
| H | OH | OCH$_3$ | H | Vanillic acid |

Hydroxycinnamic acid derivatives

| R$_1$ | R$_2$ | |
|------|------|---|
| H | H | Cinnamic acid |
| H | OH | p-coumaric acid |
| OH | OH | Caffiec acid |
| OH | OCH$_3$ | Ferulic acid |

The total phenolic acids content in SB parts are 1068 mg/kg for berry pulp; 5741 mg/kg for seed kernel; 448 mg/kg for seed coat; and 4988 mg/kg for leaves. The major fraction (approximately 70%) of phenolic acids in SB berries was found to be concentrated in the seeds. Gallic acid was the predominant phenolic acid both in free and bound forms in SB berries and leaves. The number of scientific research publications supporting claims for the therapeutic values of SB has increased significantly over the last 5 decades [6].

## Bioactivity of Seabuckthorn – Why it Is Good for you

There is a century-old tradition in Chinese medicine to utilize seabuckthorn; and beneficial effects of its oil (e.g., in the treatment of cardiovascular disease) have been reported [27, 28]. Seabuckthorn berry fractions have been used in treating cardiovascular disease (CVD) both in animal experiments and clinical investigations in China [27, 28]. The health benefits of SB are attributed to the pharmacological functions of the oil. It has anti-inflammatory, antimicrobial, analgesic properties and promotes tissue regeneration [29]. SB berries are rich in vitamin C (360 mg/100 g fruit wt), vitamin E (203 mg/100 g fruit wt), β-carotene (249 mg/100 g), flavonoids and other phytochemicals. They have high antioxidant activity similar to that of blueberries [30] and hence may have similar therapeutic effects. According to Li and Tan [31], seabuckthorn is regarded as a mild medicine for its efficacy in lowering fever, diminishing inflammation, counteracting toxicity and reducing abscesses, treating cough and colds, having mild laxative effect, treating tumors (mainly of the stomach and esophagus) and treating different kinds of gynecological diseases in Tibetan medicine.

The characteristic signs of atopic dermatitis include dry, scaly, itchy skin with eczematous inflammation and typical distribution of lesions. Although genetic factors play an important role, disturbed epidermal barrier function, aberrant immune response, and increased production of immunoglobulin E (IgE) are actively involved in the process of disease development [32]. In a placebo-controlled, double-blind study, Yang et al. [22] examined the effects of seed and pulp oils of seabuckthorn on atopic dermatitis. The study group included 49 atopic dermatitis patients who took 5 g (10 capsules) of seed oil, pulp oil, or paraffin oil daily for 4 months. In the seed oil group, after supplementation for 1 month, positive correlations were found between symptom improvement and the increase in proportions of α-linolenic acid in plasma phospholipids (Rs = 0.84; P = 0.001) and neutral lipids (Rs = 0.68; P

= 0.02). In the pulp oil group, a significant increase in the level of high density lipoprotein (HDL) cholesterol (from 1.38 to 1.53 Mmol/L) was observed.

A small-scale preliminary cross-over study assessed the effects of supercritical $CO_2$-extracted SB berry oil (SBO) on some risk factors of cardiovascular disease [33]. Twelve healthy normolipidemic (normal or standard level of lipids in the blood) men were recruited and each volunteer consumed SBO and fractionated coconut oil (control) 5 g per day for a period of 4 weeks in a random order (wash-out 4–8 weeks). SBO supplementation showed a clear decrease in the rate of adenosine-5′-diphosphate-induced platelet aggregation and maximum aggregation were found; suggesting the beneficial effects of SBO on blood clotting. Both the rate of platelet aggregation reaction (% aggregation/min) and maximum platelet aggregation (% aggregation at 4 min) were reduced by SBO supplementation [33]. This intervention study suggested that SBO could be of value when treating persons with increased tendency to blood clotting.

Supplementation of hyperlipidemic (abnormal high level of lipids in the blood) subjects with SBO has been reported to normalize the plasma lipid levels [34]. Antioxidant supplements have been found to decrease the adenosine-5′-diphosphate (ADP)-induced platelet aggregation in humans [35]. SBO contains about 1% sterols, with sitosterol being the most abundant individual component [20, 36]. Sitosterol has been reported to inhibit platelet aggregation [37]. Phytosterols including sitosterol are also known to reduce plasma total and low-density lipoprotein (LDL) cholesterol levels by mechanisms affecting both the absorption and synthesis of cholesterol [38, 39]. Oil of seabuckthorn berries contains high concentrations of palmitoleic acid (>17%) that may have cholesterol- and triglyceride-lowering as well as stroke-suppressing effects [40, 41].

## Seabuckthorn Inhibits Lipid Oxidation (in Foods too)

A wide spectrum of physiological effects of SB berries including inhibition of oxidation of low-density lipoprotein (LDL) [42], antioxidant and immunomodulation (adjustment of the immune response to a desired level) effects [43] have been reported. Oral consumption of SB berry oil has been reported to inhibit platelet aggregation [33] and reduce atopic dermatitis [22] in human; and protect rats from gastric ulcers [44].

Health-promoting functional foods prepared from meat are becoming popular. Mechanically deboned (or recovered) meat (MDM) is economically substantiated as a raw material for preparation of these products. The main potential health problems accompanied with consumption of MDM are an elevated risk of bacterial intoxication and higher ingested doses of oxidized/peroxidized, potentially mutagenic and carcinogenic fatty acids in comparison with use of hand deboned meat (HDM). Oxygen bound to the meat mass, enzymes, heme released due to extensive stress and aeration during mechanical grinding catalyze peroxidation of the polyunsaturated fatty acids (PUFA) and hence accelerate the oxidative deterioration of the MDM, especially of turkey origin [45]. As a result of the inclusion of the bone marrow, there is also a higher content of cholesterol and phospholipids in MDM [46] than in respective hand deboned meat (HDM). Polyphenols contained in plant supplements may help to reduce these adverse effects, contributing an extra antibacterial and antioxidant capacity to the MDM [47].

MDM contains about 10 times more PUFAs and also more hemoproteins than HDM, and is essentially more susceptible to both chemical and biochemical oxidation. The oxidation, leading to the formation of potentially mutagenic and carcinogenic derivatives of PUFAs, can be inhibited by berry extracts rich in antioxidant polyphenols. Using the 2-thiobarbituric acid reactive substances (TBARS) and liquid chromatography-DAD-tandem mass spectrometry (LC-DAD-ESI-MS/MS) method, Püssa et al. [48] established that the ethanol slurry of the juice-free solid residue of SB berries inhibited oxidation of unsaturated fatty acids of both chicken and turkey MDM. The polyphenols, mainly flavonols, responsible for this inhibition, are comparatively stable during short-term cooking and 6-day storage of cooked SB-MDMs at +6 °C. About half of the polyphenols are lost, obviously oxidised, during the storage of the uncooked samples of turkey 2% SB-MDM at +6 °C. The loss of polyphenols is much smaller in the case of chicken MDM, which is characterised by an in situ lower content of fatty acids, including the polyunsaturated ones.

## Highlights of Research Findings on Seabuckthorn from Food Development Centre (FDC), Portage la Prairie, Manitoba, Canada

### *Seabuckthorn Processing*

Food Development Centre (FDC) has developed an integrated process (operated on a pilot scale) for SB as shown in the flow chart (Figure 4). SB fruits can be air/freeze dried to produce dried fruits or sugar-infused fruits. The fruits are processed by a pulper/finisher to produce puree, skin and seeds. Puree is clarified to clear juice by centrifugation and processed to single strength juice or blended juice, beverage, jelly and wine. Skin and seeds are separated by air-drying and sifting through a properly sized screen. The skin (dried pulp) may be incorporated into nutritional bar or used to extract the pulp oil and yellow pigment.

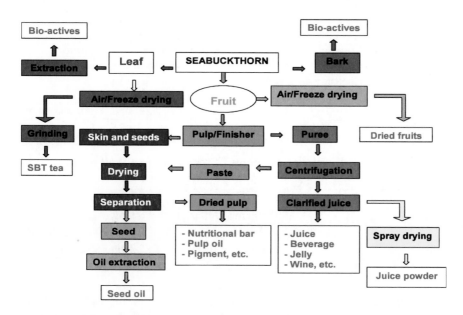

Figure 4. Flowchart of seabuckthorn processing at Food Development Centre (Manitoba, Canada).

The pigment is extracted and concentrated by spray drying to yield a yellow powder which contains mainly flavonoids and low levels of carotene and vitamin E. This product may be used as a natural food colorant and/or as a supplement to boost nutritional values. The seeds are used to extract seed oil by different processing methods. The leaves of seabuckthorn are dried to make tea, and some bioactive components are extracted from the leaves [49]. Bioactive components in the bark are extracted by different methods [50].

### Seabuckthorn Uses

Seabuckthorn plant is unique in its chemical composition for nutritional, medical and cosmetic uses. Almost all parts of the plant (fruits, leaves, and bark) have uses in the food, pharmaceutical, and cosmetic industries due to their content of essential nutrients and bioactives. The component and uses of the plant parts are shown in Table 3. Research has indicated that extracts isolated from the bark of seabuckthorn may inhibit tumour growth and there are reports that it has successfully treated gingivitis [50]. The leaves of the seabuckthorn plant also contain many nutrients and bioactive substances [51]. Leaves harvested from the male plant can be used to produce tea, tea extracts, tea powder and animal feed [52]. The extensive root system of seabuckthorn plant offers environmental benefits in soil conservation and land reclamation. The vitamin C content is dependent on the species, varieties [53], plant location, maturity of the fruits, harvesting time, altitude of growing environment and processing method of SB, and is among the highest in the plant kingdom. Health Canada's recommended daily intake (RDI) of vitamin C for adult is 60 mg/day (Table 4); which means an average Canadian only needs to consume 2.4-40 gram of fruit to meet the vitamin C requirement.

### Table 3. Components and uses of plant parts of seabuckthorn

| SB parts | Component | Uses |
|---|---|---|
| Fruits | Pulp, seed, juice | Food, drink, pharmaceuticals |
| Pulp | Oil | Pharmaceuticals, cosmetics, pigments |
| Seeds | Oil | Pharmaceuticals, cosmetics |
| Leaves | Sterols, flavonoids, carotenoids | Pharmaceuticals, cosmetics, tea |
| Bark | Hippophan (5-hydroxytryptamine), Proanthocyanidins | Pharmaceuticals |
| Roots | - | Soil conservation, land reclamation |

Source: Utioh [9], FDC data.

### Table 4. Unique components of seabuckthorn fruit or oil

| Components | Amount/100g fruit or oil | Health Canada's RDI * |
|---|---|---|
| Vitamin C | 500-1000 mg (700 mg) | 60 mg (<10 g fruit) |
| Folic acid | Up to 0.08 mg | 0.18-0.20 mg (250 g fruit) |
| Vitamin E | Up to 200 mg (300 IU) | 8-10 mg (5 g oil) |

Source: Utioh [9], FDC data. *RDI = Recommended daily intake.

SB is known for its high content of α-tocopherol (vitamin E) in its seed oil. An average adult needs to take about 5 g of SB seed oil to meet the daily vitamin E requirement. Tocopherol is recognized as the natural antioxidant in the human body. It is believed that high levels of tocopherol minimize skin oxidation, which helps to maintain skin integrity and reduce skin toughening and wrinkling. SB oils are also believed to have a biological protective capacity. The tocopherols and carotenoids can trap and reduce the formation of UV-B induced toxic products in skin cells. Due to these UV-B absorptive properties, SB oils may be used by industry as a natural sun screen [54]. Other unique constituents of SB are relatively high amount of unsaturated fatty acids, especially high amount of ω-3 fatty acid in its seed oil. The palmitoleic acid (ω-7) in SB pulp oil is known to be the highest in plant kingdom to date [55]. The palmitoleic acid and carotenoid contents found in SB oils are claimed to promote healing of skin burns and the relief of other skin ailments such as eczema and dermatitis. Furthermore, Table 5 shows the unique constituent in SB fruit or oils. High amounts of carotenoids, flavonoids and sterols in SB contribute to the unique color and antioxidant capacity of its fruits while high organic acid content contributes to the unique tart flavor of its fruits.

#### Table 5. Unique components of seabuckthorn fruits continued

| Component | Amount |
|---|---|
| Lipids, made up of: | 6-15% of seed |
| Unsaturated: oleic acid (ω-9), palmitoleic acid (ω-7), palmitic acid and linoleic acid (ω-6), and linolenic acid (ω-3), | |
| Saturated: Sterols (mainly β-sitosterol) | |
| Carotenoids, including β-carotene, lycopene, zeaxanthin | 30-40 mg/100g fruits |
| Flavonoids (mainly isorhamnetin, quercetin glycosides, and kaempferol) | 100-1000 mg/100g fruits |
| Organic acids (malic and quinic acids) | 3.5-4.4 (% malic acid) |

Source: Food Development Centre, Manitoba, Canada.

#### Table 6. Comparison of nutritional composition of seabuckthorn juice with other common fruit juices*

| Nutrients | Seabuckthorn (Indian Summer) raw | Orange raw | Grapefruit raw | Cranberry canned unsweetened | Prune canned | Tomato canned no salt |
|---|---|---|---|---|---|---|
| Energy (kcal/100g) | 53 | 45 | 39 | 46 | 71 | 17 |
| Protein (g/100g) | 0.60 | 0.70 | 0.50 | 0.39 | 0.61 | 0.76 |
| Fat (g/100g) | 1.40 | 0.20 | 0.10 | 0.13 | 0.03 | 0.05 |
| Carbohydrates (g/100g)** | 9.50 | 10.40 | 9.20 | 12.20 | 17.45 | 4.24 |
| Calcium (mg/100g) | 11 | 11 | 9 | 8 | 12 | 10 |
| Iron (mg/100g) | 1.10 | 0.20 | 0.20 | 0.25 | 1.18 | 0.43 |
| Vitamin A (IU/100g) | 636 | 200 | 440 | 45 | 3 | 450 |
| Vitamin C (mg/100g) | 187 | 50 | 38 | 9.3 | 4.1 | 18.3 |

* Seabuckthorn data is from the Food Development Centre and data for the other fruit juices is from USDA Nutrient Database for Standard Reference (http://www.ars.usda.gov/Services/docs.htm?docid=8964) [56].
** Contributes to °Brix.

A comparison of the nutritional composition of SB juice and other common fruit juices is shown in Table 6. The nutritional composition of SB juice is unique compared to other commonly consumed fruit juices as SB juice contains more fat, vitamins A and C and a significant amount of iron.

## Chemical Composition of Juice

The chemical composition of seabuckthorn juice varies with the fruit origin and climate, as well as the method of extraction. The juice yield by a pulper/finisher is about 65% for *sinensis* and 70% for Indian summer [57]. The typical characteristics of Indian summer seabuckthorn juice are shown in Table 7 [58].

**Table 7. Typical characteristics of Indian summer seabuckthorn juice**

| Component | Characteristic/Content |
|---|---|
| Colour | Yellow |
| Yield | 57 - 75% |
| Soluble solids | 9.3- 15.5 °Brix* |
| pH | 2.7-3.13 |
| Vitamin C | 150-1500 mg/100mL |
| Organic acid (% malic acid) | 3.5 - 4.4 |
| Potassium | 100-806 mg/mL |
| Sodium | 17.7-89.8 mg/mL |
| Zinc | 0.43-6.31 mg/mL |

* °Brix is an approximate measure of total soluble solids (see Table 6).
Source: Food Development Centre, Manitoba, Canada.

**Table 8. Composition of raw seabuckthorn juice**

| | Seabuckthorn variety | |
|---|---|---|
| Nutrient | Indian Summer | *Sinensis* |
| Protein (g/100g) | 0.6 | 0.6 |
| Fat, Total (g/100g) | 1.4 | 0.8 |
| Saturated | 0.6 | 0.3 |
| Omega 6 | 0.1 | 0.1 |
| Omega 7 | 0.5 | 0.2 |
| Omega 9 | 0.2 | 0.2 |
| Vitamin A (IU/100g) | 636 | 308 |
| Vitamin C (mg/100g) | 187 | 450 |

Source: Food Development Centre, Manitoba, Canada.

## Nutritional Composition of Juice

The nutritional composition of raw SB juice is shown in Table 8. SB juice from the Indian summer variety had a higher total fat content than that from the *sinensis* variety. For example, juice from the Indian summer variety had about twice the levels of saturated and omega 7 (palmitoleic acid) fatty acids. Furthermore, juice from the Indian summer variety contained about twice the vitamin A of *sinensis*. Juice from the *sinensis* variety had over twice the vitamin C content of that from Indian summer. Indian summer and *sinensis* are the most abundant and commercially viable varieties in Canada [59].

Palmitoleic acid is the key source of Omega 7's amazing skin support properties. Omega 7 repairs skin and restores moisture to dry and fragile mucous membranes. It is a strong emollient, a substance that soothes and moisturizes the skin and promotes tissue regeneration. It helps maintain natural lubrication of mucous membranes in the mouth, eyes and digestive tract.

## Seabuckthorn Juice Sensory Attributes

The SB juice was a bright orange colour, opaque with some surface oil, pulpy with a very tart fruity flavour and a distinctive aroma. Sensory differences existed between Indian summer and *sinensis* varieties. The Indian summer juice was a darker red orange while *sinensis* juice was orange. Juice from the Indian summer variety was tarter and less sweet than that from *sinensis*. These varietal sensory differences could provide flexibility when formulating products with SB juice.

## Seabuckthorn Beverage Formulation Considerations

Beverages containing 30, 35 and 45% SB juice were prepared and evaluated. The SB juice was very tart (Indian summer pH 2.7), not very sweet (10.9 °Brix) and strongly flavoured, thus a sweetener was required and 30% SB juice was considered the maximum level for beverage palatability. The SB juice contained a substantial amount of pulp and a small amount of oil which rapidly separated from the juice and the beverage even after high shear mixing. The SB juice and the SB beverage exhibited browning with heat exposure. Minimal heat treatment is recommended to preserve product colour and limit the loss of heat sensitive nutrients such as vitamin C. Indian summer juice produced a brighter coloured slightly more appealing beverage than *sinensis* juice.

## Seabuckthorn Beverage Nutritional Profile

Figure 5 shows the Canadian nutrition facts panel for the SB beverage. A 250 mL beverage serving provides an adult with 240% of the daily value of vitamin C and 15% of the daily value of vitamin A.

**Nutrition Facts**
**Valeur nutritive**
Serving Size 250 mL / Portion
Servings Per Container
Portions par contenant

| Amount<br>Teneur | % Daily Value<br>% valeur quotidienne |
|---|---|
| Calories / Calories 240 | |
| Fat / Lipides 1 g | 2 % |
|    Saturated / saturés 0.4 g<br>   + Trans / trans 0 g | 2 % |
| Cholesterol / Cholestérol 0 mg | 0 % |
| Sodium / Sodium 15 mg | 1 % |
| Carbohydrate / Glucides 58 g | 19 % |
|    Fibre / Fibres 0 g | 0 % |
|    Sugars / Sucres 51 g | |
| Protein / Protéines 0.4 g | |
| Vitamin A / Vitamine A | 15 % |
| Vitamin C / Vitamine C | 240 % |
| Calcium / Calcium | 4 % |
| Iron / Fer | 4 % |

Figure 5. Seabuckthorn beverage nutrition facts panel according to the Guide to Food Labelling and Advertising [60].

According to the Guide to Food Labelling and Advertising [60], the following nutrient content claims can be made for the SB beverage: "excellent source" of vitamin C and "good source" of vitamin A. Although SB juice is rich in health promoting antioxidants, health claims for antioxidants are currently not allowed in Canada. However, the nutritional profile of the SB beverage would still position it favorably in the functional beverage category.

## Dried Seabuckthorn Pulp Nutritional Composition

The nutritional composition of dried SB pulp from the Indian summer and *sinensis* varieties is shown in Table 9. SB pulp from the Indian summer variety had about twice the vitamin A, saturated fatty acids, monounsaturated fatty acids and total fat compared to *sinensis*. Polyunsaturated fatty acids were also higher in the Indian summer pulp.

*Sinensis* pulp contained about twice the vitamin C and protein of Indian summer and more fiber. These differences in nutritional composition between the varieties could be an important consideration when developing functional foods containing dried pulp.

## Dried Seabuckthorn Pulp Sensory Attributes

Dried seabuckthorn pulp had an orange colour, distinctive aroma, very tart fruity flavour, fibrous texture and a slightly gritty/powdery mouth feel if ground. Indian summer pulp is tarter and redder than *sinensis* pulp. The strong tart flavour of the dried SB pulp could limit its use but the attractive colour could create formulation opportunities.

## Seabuckthorn Energy Bar Nutritional Profile

The Canadian nutrition facts panel for the SB energy bar is shown in Figure 6. A 30-g serving of the energy bar provides 2g fibre, 1g omega 3 fatty acids, 2g omega 6 fatty acids and 15% of an adult's daily value for vitamin C.

**Table 9. Nutritional composition of dried seabuckthorn pulp from two varieties**

| Nutrients | Indian Summer | *Sinensis* |
|---|---|---|
| Protein (g/100g) | 6.80 | 11.90 |
| Fat (g/100g) | 23.53 | 13.73 |
|    Saturated | 8.85 | 4.87 |
|    Monounsaturated | 11.12 | 6.21 |
|    Polyunsaturated | 3.56 | 2.53 |
|    Omega 3 | 0.65 | 0.51 |
|    Omega 6 | 2.91 | 2.02 |
|    Omega 7 | 8.63 | 4.58 |
| Fibre (g/100g) | 31.00 | 39.60 |
| Vitamin C (mg/100g) | 442 | 743 |
| Vitamin A (IU/100g) | 8212 | 4397 |

Source: Food Development Centre, Manitoba, Canada.

According to Health Canada's Guide to Food Labelling and Advertising, the following nutrient content claims can be made for the SB energy bar: "source" of fibre, "source" of omega 3 and 6 fatty acids, "source" of vitamin C, "source" of iron, low sodium, low cholesterol, low in saturated fat and trans fat free. The SB energy bar addresses many current nutrition concerns thus creating opportunities for it as a health and wellness product.

## Fruit Fractions of Seabuckthorn

Seabuckthorn fruit fractions are processed by freeze drying and air drying (Figure 7). Freeze drying (lyophilisation) is the process of removing water from a product by sublimation.

Freeze drying is an attractive option for drying heat sensitive high-value products. Convection air drying is the most basic and effective method widely used in industries. Equipment such as tray dryer can be used (e.g. Proctor and Schwartz Dryer). The nutrient composition of dried SB fruit is shown in Table 10.

## Extraction of Oils from Puree, Skin and Seed Fractions

Supercritical fluid extraction (SFE) is the preferred process used for extracting seabuckthorn oils at FDC, Portage la Prairie, Manitoba. Supercritical fluid is a material (gas or liquid) used in a state above its critical temperature and pressure. SFE is a process which utilizes unique properties of material above its critical conditions to extract soluble components from the raw materials (Figure 8). Carbon dioxide is normally used as a supercritical fluid. SFE process parameters are i) gas ($CO_2$), ii) temperature 40° and 50° C, iii) pressure 200-400 bar, iv) flow rate 50 and 70 g/min, and v) ground seeds. The size of pilot scale SFE equipment at FDC is $2 \times 5$ L.

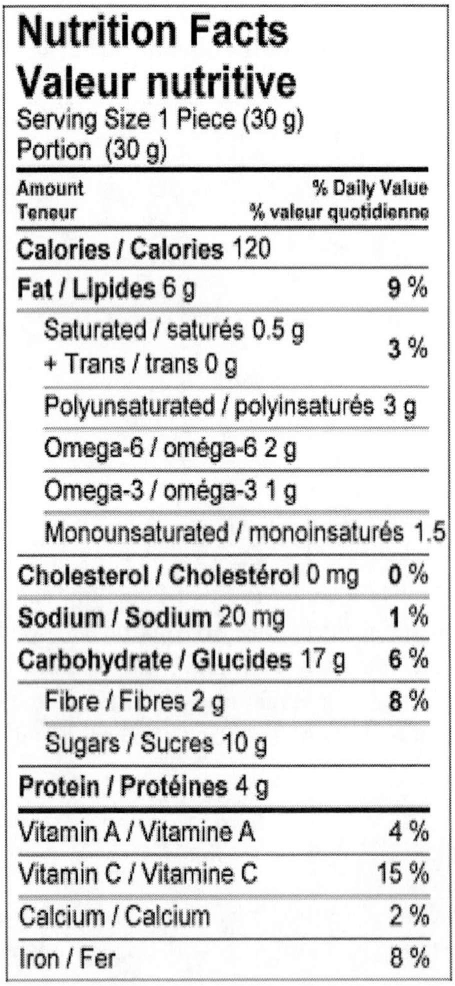

## Nutrition Facts
## Valeur nutritive

Serving Size 1 Piece (30 g)
Portion (30 g)

| Amount<br>Teneur | % Daily Value<br>% valeur quotidienne |
|---|---|
| Calories / Calories 120 | |
| Fat / Lipides 6 g | 9 % |
| Saturated / saturés 0.5 g<br>+ Trans / trans 0 g | 3 % |
| Polyunsaturated / polyinsaturés 3 g | |
| Omega-6 / oméga-6 2 g | |
| Omega-3 / oméga-3 1 g | |
| Monounsaturated / monoinsaturés 1.5 | |
| Cholesterol / Cholestérol 0 mg | 0 % |
| Sodium / Sodium 20 mg | 1 % |
| Carbohydrate / Glucides 17 g | 6 % |
| Fibre / Fibres 2 g | 8 % |
| Sugars / Sucres 10 g | |
| Protein / Protéines 4 g | |
| Vitamin A / Vitamine A | 4 % |
| Vitamin C / Vitamine C | 15 % |
| Calcium / Calcium | 2 % |
| Iron / Fer | 8 % |

Figure 6. Nutrition facts panel for the seabuckthorn energy bar according to the Guide to Food Labelling and Advertising [60].

**Table 10. Proximate profile of seabuckthorn dried fruit fractions**

| Content (%) | Puree | Skin | Seeds |
|---|---|---|---|
| Moisture | 18.2 | 9.2 | 6.6 |
| Protein | 4.5 | 7.3 | 30.7 |
| Oil | 16.5 | 12.1 | 12.4 |
| Ash | 2.4 | 2.3 | 2.3 |
| Carbohydrates | 58.3 | 69.1 | 48.0 |

Source: Food Development Centre, Manitoba, Canada.

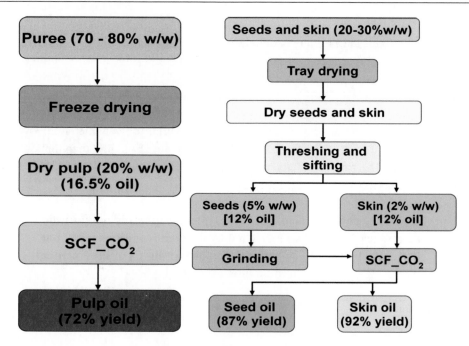

Figure 7. Schematic process flowchart for seabuckthorn fruit fractions. SCF = supercritical fluid process developed and used at Food Development Centre, Manitoba, Canada.

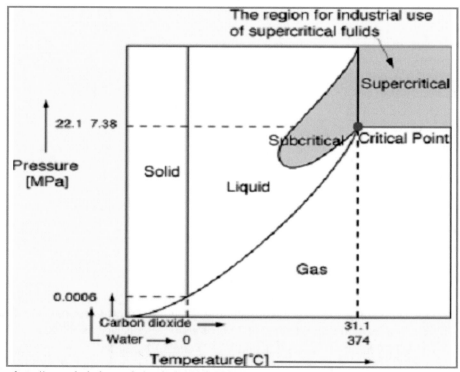

Source: http://www.kobelco.co.jp/eneka/p14/sfe01.htm.

Figure 8. Phase diagram showing region of importance for extraction.

Based on the fatty acid compositions, seabuckthorn seed oil obtained by SC-CO$_2$ under different temperatures and pressures contained similar fatty acid profile. Generally, the fatty acid profile of seabuckthorn seed oil extracted by SC-CO$_2$ and solvent extraction methods are similar. It contains about 5.5-6.5% of palmitoleic acid ($\omega$7), 10.5-12.0% of palmitic acid, 15-17.5% of oleic acid, 31-32.31-32% of linoleic acid ($\omega$6) and 29-32% linolenic acid ($\omega$3) as shown in Table 11. These findings corroborate the results of Yang and Kallio [53] who reported the fatty acid composition of seabuckthorn seed oil by solvent method. However, the linolenic acid content of the SC-CO$_2$-extracted oil was about 2% higher than that obtained by solvent extraction. The total $\omega$-3 fatty acid from SC-CO$_2$-extracted oil was higher than that from solvent extraction.

**Table 11. The fatty acids (%) and alpha tocopherols composition of seabuckthon seed oil extracted by different conditions (200 bar 40 °C, 300 bar 40 °C, 400 bar 40 °C, 300 bar 40 °C) of supercritical and Soxhlet extraction**

| Component Name | 200/40 | 300/40 | 400/40 | 300/50 | Soxhlet Extraction |
|---|---|---|---|---|---|
| Myristic Acid C14:0 | 0.24 | 0.28 | 0.3 | 0.33 | 0.23 |
| Myristoleic Acid C14:1, $\omega$-5 | 0.13 | 0.13 | 0.13 | 0.14 | |
| Palmitic Acid C16:0 | 10.62 | 11.15 | 10.96 | 10.98 | 11.60 |
| Palmitoleic Acid C16:1, $\omega$-7 | 6.15 | 6.25 | 6.40 | 6.62 | 5.41 |
| Heptadecanoic Acid C17:0 | 0.29 | 0.45 | 0.38 | 0.40 | 0.23 |
| Heptadecenoic Acid C17:1 | 0.29 | 0.30 | 0.30 | 0.31 | |
| Stearic Acid C18:0 | 2.51 | 2.56 | 2.48 | 2.49 | 3.17 |
| Oleic Acid C18:1, $\omega$-9 | 15.2 | 15.35 | 14.94 | 15.01 | 17.40 |
| Linoleic Acid C18:2, $\omega$-6 | 31.86 | 31.39 | 31.37 | 31.41 | 32.02 |
| Gamma Linolenic Acid C18:3 | 0.13 | 0.10 | 0.13 | 0.13 | |
| Linolenic Acid C18:3, $\omega$-3 | 31.76 | 31.1 | 31.82 | 31.41 | 29.23 |
| Arachidic Acid C20:0 | 0.4 | 0.40 | 0.40 | 0.40 | 0.46 |
| Eicosenoic Acid C20:1, $\omega$-9 | 0.18 | 0.18 | 0.18 | 0.18 | 0.23 |
| Eicosadienoic Acid C20:2 | 0.06 | 0.06 | | | |
| Behenic Acid C22:0 | 0.1 | 0.11 | 0.10 | 0.1 | |
| Omega 3 Fatty Acids | 31.76 | 31.1 | 31.82 | 31.41 | 29.23 |
| Omega 6 Fatty Acids | 32.05 | 31.9 | 31.5 | 31.54 | 32.02 |
| Trans Fatty Acids | 0.08 | 0.11 | 0.11 | 0.09 | 0.10 |
| Alpha Tocopherols | 180.4 | 260.2 | 237.5 | 201.3 | |

Source: Food Development Centre, Manitoba, Canada.

The fatty acids composition of three fractions of final oil products are shown in Table 12. The seabuckthorn seed oil was extracted at 300 bar at 40 °C, collected at 120 bar at 45 °C for fraction 1 (F1), 90 bar at 40 °C for fraction 2 (F2) and 50 bar at 35 °C for fraction 3 (F3). Fraction 3 had slightly higher myristic acid (C14:0), myristoleic acid (C14:1, $\omega$-5) and eicosadienoic acid (C20:2) contents compared to those of fractions 1 and 2. The $\alpha$-tocopherol was much higher in F1 than those of F2 and F3 while $\beta$-carotene content was higher in F1 and F2. At present, there is no known information on seabuckthorn seed oil collected by different fractions. Based on these findings, it is possible to concentrate certain nutrients in seabuckthorn oil by supercritical fluid extraction.

**Table 12. The fatty acids (g/100g), alpha-tocopherol, vitamin A and beta-carotene contents of three fractions of seabuckthorn seed oil extracted at 300 bar at 40 °C**

| Component Name | F1 | F2 | F3 |
|---|---|---|---|
| Myristic Acid C14:0 | 0.28 | 0.24 | 0.58 |
| Myristoleic Acid C14:1, ω-5 | 0.04 | 0.03 | 0.12 |
| Pentadecanoic Acid C15:0 | 0.13 | 0.12 | 0.18 |
| Palmitic Acid C16:0 | 10.93 | 10.39 | 11.84 |
| Palmitoleic Acid C16:1, ω-7 | 6.39 | 5.38 | 6.37 |
| Heptadecanoic Acid C17:0 | 0.47 | 0.39 | 1.11 |
| Heptadecenoic Acid C17:1 | 0.31 | 0.25 | 0.33 |
| Stearic Acid C18:0 | 2.54 | 2.66 | 2.59 |
| Oleic Acid C18:1, ω-9 | 15.33 | 15.78 | 15.12 |
| Linoleic Acid C18:2, ω-6 | 31.52 | 32.33 | 31.32 |
| Gamma Linolenic Acid C18:3, ω-6 | 0.12 | 0.13 | |
| Linolenic Acid C18:3, ω-3 | 31.11 | 31.40 | 29.15 |
| Arachidic Acid C20:0 | 0.39 | 0.43 | 0.38 |
| Eicosenoic Acid C20:1, ω-9 | 0.18 | 0.20 | 0.16 |
| Eicosadienoic Acid C20:2 | 0.06 | 0.06 | 0.28 |
| Behenic Acid C22:0 | 0.10 | 0.11 | 0.13 |
| Omega 3 Fatty Acids | 31.11 | 31.4 | 29.15 |
| Omega 6 Fatty Acids | 31.7 | 32.5 | 31.6 |
| Trans Fatty Acids | 0.10 | 0.10 | 0.10 |
| Alpha Tocopherols (IU/100g) | 259.7 | 79.8 | 87.1 |
| Vitamin A (IU/100g) | 823 | 555 | 806 |
| Beta Carotene (IU/100g) | 14276 | 16224 | 7864 |

Source: Food Development Centre, Manitoba, Canada.

**Table 13. Profile of oils from dried fruit fractions of seabuckthorn**

| | Oils | | |
|---|---|---|---|
| Component | Puree | Skin | Seed |
| % Total | | | |
| Saturated FAs | 36.07 | 34.22 | 12.13 |
| Monounsaturated FAs | 46.98 | 44.62 | 19.09 |
| Polyunsaturated FAs | 14.44 | 16.75 | 67.17 |
| Omega-3 | 1.80 | 3.45 | 31.97 |
| Omega-6 | 12.64 | 13.30 | 35.15 |
| Omega-7 | 37.16 | 34.21 | 2.04 |
| Omega-9 | 3.17 | 4.22 | 15.18 |
| Ratio of omega-3: omega-6 | 1:7 | 1:3 | 1:1 |
| Total carotenoids (ppm) | 456 | 207 | 95 |
| Lutein (ppm) | 116 | 109 | 95 |
| Vitamin E (mg/100g) | 259.3 | 159.9 | 199.6 |
| Total sterols (mg/100g) | 868 | 1130 | 1152 |

FAs = Fatty acids. Source: Food Development Centre, Manitoba, Canada.

**Table 14. Proximate composition of seabuckthorn defatted cakes**

| Content (%) | Puree | Skin | Seeds |
|---|---|---|---|
| Moisture | 16.0 | 9.3 | 5.9 |
| Protein | 10.4 | 8.6 | 37.3 |
| Oil | 5.4 | 2.2 | 0.4 |
| Ash | 2.7 | 2.6 | 2.4 |
| Carbohydrates | 65.5 | 77.3 | 54.0 |

Source: Food Development Centre, Manitoba, Canada.

Defatted puree contains 10% protein. Puree oil contains mostly monounsaturated fatty acids (Table 13) and its major fatty acids are C16 fatty acids – palmitoleic and palmitic acids. The most abundant vitamin in puree oil is the group of carotenoids. Defatted seeds contain 37% protein (Table 14). Seed oil contains high level of unsaturated C18 fatty acids with α-linolenic and linoleic acids in a perfect ratio of 1:1.

## Seabuckthorn Products Developed at the Food Development Centre, Manitoba: Seabuckthorn Infused Fruit

Some of the SB products developed at Food Development Centre (FDC), Manitoba include infused SB fruit (Figure 9). SB fruit was infused with apple juice concentrate and dried. The final infused fruit product contains whole fruit which is rich in seed oil and fibre. Infused SB fruit is a potential ingredient for nutritional bar enrichment. It has strong aroma, tart fruity flavor, appealing orange/red color and chewy dried fruit texture. It can also be coated with chocolate and marketed as candies.

## Seabuckthorn Juice Products

SB juice is an excellent material for developing beverages, blended beverages, jam, juice [61], fruit leather and fruit jelly [62]. SB juice mixed with apple juice concentrate produced a pleasant beverage with high nutritional value [62]. However, the jam product contained almost no vitamin C, due to vitamin C degradation during heat treatment. Some SB productprototypes developed at FDC are shown in Figure 10. SB mixed fruit jelly was prepared by blending SB juice with papaya, watermelon or grapes in varying proportions to obtain an acceptable level of total soluble solids (TSS) and acidity in the final product [63]. Among the stated blends, SB-grape jelly exhibited good organoleptic characteristics with high sensory score.

The shelf stability of the jelly samples was evaluated at ambient temperature and at 37 °C for a period of 6 months. The physicochemical properties of SB-grape jelly blend such as TSS, reducing sugar, acidity and browning significantly increased during storage at 37°C. Total sugars, vitamin C, vitamin E, total phenols, total carotenoids and total anthocyanins decreased significantly during storage at 37°C.

Figure 9. Infused seabuckthorn fruits (Indian summer).

Beverage      Jam      Wine      Puree

Figure 10. Images of seabuckthorn beverage, jam, wine and puree prototypes produced at FDC.

SB-grape jelly blend remained acceptable up to 6 months of storage under ambient temperature when stored in polyethylene terephthalate bottles. The microbial load of stored jelly under stated conditions was found to be within acceptable limits.

Figure 11. An image of spray dried seabuckthorn juice powder.

## Seabuckthorn Juice Powder

The natural liquid state of SB juice limits its use in dry food formulations, nutraceuticals and cosmetics. Therefore, a free-flowing SB juice powder will find wide application in commercial products. SB juice powder is more convenient and stable than its juice during prolonged storage. Low moisture content greatly reduces microbial activity without the need for freezing or refrigeration.

Spray drying (used in drying SB juice) transforms a fluid into a dry powder in a single operation at low temperature and short time compared to other drying processes while retaining the natural nutrients, color and flavour of the hydrated product. An image SB juice powder produced at the FDC, Manitoba is shown in Figure 11.

## Seabuckthorn Pulp Products

Dried SB pulp contains high amount of fibre, vitamin C and iron. Other ingredients in the nutritional bar formulation can be used to balance strong tart SB flavour. Dried SB (Indian summer) pulp of up to 10% [62] can be used in the formulation of nutritional bar (Figure 12).

Figure 12. Nutritional bar contains seabuckthorn pulp.

## Seabuckthorn Pulp and Seed Separation

Wet fruit seeds and skin were spread onto perforated drying trays (10 mesh or 1.91 mm perforation size) giving a drying layer of approximately 10 mm.

The wet cake was dried at 50°C for 48 hrs in a ventilated drying oven (Gas Fired Variable Circulation Laboratory Dryer, Proctor and Schwartz Corp., Philadelphia, PA).

The dried seed and skin were carefully removed from the drying trays and empties into an industrial mixer in approximately 2 kg batches. An industrial mixer (Hobart Cutter Mixer, HCM 300, Hobart Corp., Troy, OH) equipped with a plastic, two-blade attachment with 1140 rpm served as a threshing unit to gently separate seeds from pulp and remove the white seed skins encapsulating the seeds. The mixer was operated for short time intervals of 1-2 min. This was done to ensure that seeds did not become damaged during threshing.

A vibratory screen separator LS 24S444 (SWECO, Sweco Canada Inc., Toronto, ON) equipped with a stackable arrangement of three screens was assembled for the separation of seeds from pulp.

Screens were arranged (top and bottom layer screen openings of 6-mesh or 3.35 mm and 10-mesh or 1.91 mm, respectively) to collect three fractions including debris with pulp, seeds and skin (pulp). When necessary, the seeds were further cleaned using compressed air to remove residual pulp that was not removed by mechanical separation. The dried pulp from two SB varieties is shown in Figure 13.

In a review on the medicinal and nutritional bioactive properties of seabuckthorn fractions, Li [64] outlined some findings from clinical trials as shown in Tables 15 and 16.

### Table 15. Clinical findings on the health benefits of seabuckthorn fractions

| Health-related conditions | Supporting evidence on bioactivity of plant molecules |
|---|---|
| Liver fibrosis | Thirty liver cirrhosis patients treated with seabuckthorn extract showed marked reduction in serum levels of laminin (LN), hyaluronic acid (HA), collagen types III and IV, total bile acid (TBA) compared to those in control group (20 cirrhosis patients). Seabuckthorn shortened the duration for normalization of amino-tranferases [65]. |
| Hypertension | Isometric exercise may significantly increase the heart rate, blood pressure and plasma catecholamine concentration in hypertensive patients. Zhang *et al.* [66] examined the effect of total flavones of *Hyppophae* (TFH) extracted from seabuckthorn on sympathetic nerve activity of essential hypertensive patients. After 8 weeks of treatment, 35 patients in TFH group did not show altered resting heart rate, plasma catecholamine concentration and blood pressure after exercise. However, the same isometric exercise greatly increased the heart rate, blood pressure and noradrenaline concentration in calcium antagonist nifedipine group (33 patients). In verapamil ER group (20 patients), the plasma catecholamine level did not change after treatment, but it was significantly increased after isometric exercise. |
| Hypertension and chronic cardiac insufficiency | Xiao *et al.* [67] used an immunohistochemical protocol to assess the efficacy of total flavonoids of *Hyppophae* (TFH) to inhibit the activation of NF-κ B in stretched cardiac myocytes. Evidence showed that the NF-κ B was activated by stretching cardiac myocytes in 10 hrs. However, the activation was partially and completely inhibited at three levels (1:400, 1:200, 1: 100) of TFH. Thus, the use of TFH might provide potential means of improving myocardial function by inhibiting activation of NF-κ B. |
| Cardiovascular homeostasis | Seabuckthorn berry extract (at oral dose of 500 mg daily) was studied for 3 months on various electro-physiological and neurochemical parameters following cold stress among positive cold stress responders [68]. Results indicated that the average differences in cardiovascular responses such as systolic and diastolic blood pressure, and pulse rate (which increased after cold presser test) decreased after a 3-month oral administration of extract; indicating that seabuckthorn berry enhances stress tolerance capacity and better adaptation towards stress. |

**Table 16. Clinical findings on the health benefits of seabuckthorn fractions continued**

| Health-related characteristics | Supporting evidence on bioactivity of plant molecules |
| --- | --- |
| Mucous membranes | Antioxidatvie properties of seabuckthorn oils are mainly due to its high content of tocopherols, tocotrienols and carotenoids. This is explained with respect to the suppression of malondialdehyde formation (a product of lipid peroxidation). Seabuckthorn oil was used in the treatment of 5 patients with chronic vaginal inflammation. Patients received 3 g oral capsules of seabuckthorn oil (contains omega-7, a mixture of oils from seed and berry soft parts) daily for 12 weeks. Data indicated that 3 patients with severe vaginal inflammation showed marked improvement when treated with seabuckthorn oil [69]. |
| Platelet aggregation | The impact of supercritical $CO_2$-extracted seabuckthorn berry oil (SBO) on some risk factors of cardiovascular disease in 12 healthy normolipidemic men was evaluated [70]. The experimental group consumed SBO while the control group consumed fractionated coconut oil randomly at 5g per day for 4 weeks. Intake of SBO clearly reduced the rate of adenosine-5′-diphosphate-induced platelet aggregation and maximum aggregation. SBO is beneficial in treating individuals with increased tendency to blood clotting. |
| Coronary heart disease | Increasing evidence support the hypothesis that free radical-mediated oxidative processes contribute to atherogenesis. Reports supporting the ability of antioxidant nutrients to affect *in vitro* cell response and gene expression provides insights in several mechanisms involved in the bioactivity of antioxidants. Eccleston *et al.* [42] assessed the effect of intake of seabuckthorn juice (SBJ) or placebo on plasma lipids, LDL oxidation, platelet aggregation and plasma soluble cell adhesion protein concentration in 20 healthy males for 8 weeks. Results indicted an increase in plasma HDL-C (20%) and triacylglycerol levels (17%). Also, SBJ intake resulted in a moderate reduction in the susceptibility of LDL to oxidation |
| Dermatological disease | Yang *et al.* [22] studied 49 patients with atopic dermatitis who received 5g of seabuckthorn seed oil, pulp oil or paraffin oil daily for 4 months. Groups treated with pulp oil and paraffin oil had improved atopic dermatitis. |
| Gastric ulceration | A clinical trial of 468 ulcer patients treated by laser irradiation plus choline blocking agents with adjuvant α-tocopherol antioxidants from seabuckthorn oil provided evidence supporting antioxidant addition. Clinical finding was corroborated by biochemical findings (vitamin E and malonic dialdehyde concentrations), electron microscopic, and amino acids studies [71] |

Figure 13. Dried pulp from *sinensis* (left) and Indian summer (right).

# CONCLUSION

Seabuckthorn being termed the super-crop is an understatement because its health promoting attributes and commercial value are numerous. Its fruit can yield juice rich in vitamin C and functional oils high in fat soluble vitamins A and E, sterols and essential fatty acids. Seabuckthorn leaves could be dried for tea blends or used as raw materials for designer bioactives. Its "waste" may be processed into high value animal feed. Seabuckthorn is a viable food crop with valuable applications.

# REFERENCES

[1]     Rousi, A. The genus *Hippophae* L.: A taxonomic study. *Annales Botanici Fennici*, 1971, 8, 177-227.

[2]     Bailey, L.H.; Bailey, E.Z. *Hortus Third. A concise dictionary of plants cultivated in the United States and Canada*. MacMillan Pub. Co. Inc., 1978.

[3]     Small, E. Perspectives of the Crop Potential. In: Li, T.S.C.; Beveridge, T.H.J. *Sea Buckthorn: A New Medicinal and Nutritional Botanical*. Agriculture and Agri-Food Canada, Publication 10320E, 2007, 7-10.

[4]     Er, J. The important role of seabuckthorn development in improving ecological environment of West China. *The global Seabuckthorn Research and Development*, 2003, 1, 1-2.

[5]     Bernath, J.; Foldesi, D. Sea buckthorn (*Hipppophae rhamnoides* L.): A promising new medicinal and food crop. *Journal of Herbs, Spices, Medicinal Plants*, 1992, 1, 27-35.

[6]     Li, T.S.C. Next generation of new botanical. In: Li, T.S.C.; Beveridge, T.H.J. (Eds.). *Sea Buckthorn: A New Medicinal and Nutritional Botanical*. Agriculture and Agri-Food Canada, Publication 10320E, 2007, 11-14.

[7]     Guliyev, V.B.; Gui, M.; Yildirim, A. *Hippophae rhamnoides* L.: Chromatographic methods to determine chemical composition, use in traditional medicine and pharmacological effects. *Journal of Chromatography B. Analytical, Technological, Biomedical and Life Sciences*, 2004, 812, 291-307.

[8]     Rosch, D.; Bergmann, M.; Knorr, D.; Kroh-Lothar, W. Structure antioxidant efficiency relationships of phenolic compounds and their contribution to the antioxidant activity of seabuckthorn juice. *Journal of Agricultural and Food Chemistry*, 2003, 51, 4233-4239.

[9]     Utioh, A. Supercritical $CO_2$ extraction of seabuckthorn fruit oil. Data from Food Development Centre, Portage La Prairie, Manitoba, Canada; Paper presented at National Conference on Seabuckthorn, New Delhi, India, November, 2010.

[10]    Health Canada. Nutraceuticals/functional foods and health claims on foods. Policy Paper. Therapeutic Products Programme and the Food Directorate from the Health Protection Branch. Food Directorate of Health Canada, Ottawa, Canada, 1998, 3.

[11]    Ge, X.Y.; Shi, G.F.; Zhang, Y.M.; Wang, T.B. Medical application of seabuckthorn. *Shanxi Medical Research* (seabuckthorn edition), 1985, 2, 9-14 (in Chinese).

[12]    Yang, B.; Kallio, H. Composition and physiological effects of seabuckthorn (*Hippophaë*) lipids. *Trends in Food Science and Technology*, 2002a, 13, 160-167.

[13] Ranjith, A.; Kumar, K.S.; Venugopalan, V.V.; Arumughan, C.; Sawhney, R.C.; Singh, V. Fatty acids, tocols, and carotenoids in pulp oil of three sea buckthorn species (*H. rhamnoides, H. salicifolia, H. tibetana*) grown in the Indian Himalayas. *Journal of the American Oil Chemists' Society*, 2006, 88, 359-364.

[14] Gao, X.; Ohlander, M.; Jeppsson, N.; Bjork, L.; Trajkovski, V. Changes in antioxidant effects and their relationship to phytonutrients in fruits of seabuckthorn (*Hippophae rhamnoides* L.) during maturation. *Journal of Agricultural and Food Chemistry*, 2000, 48, 1485-1490.

[15] Zadernowski, R.; Naczk, M.; Rubinskiene, M.; Szalkiewicz, M. Composition of phenolic acids in seabuckthorn (*Hippophae rhamnoides* L.) berries. *Journal of the American Oil Chemists' Society*, 2005, 82, 175-179.

[16] Arimboor, R.; Venugopalan, V.V.; Sarinkumar, K.; Arumughan, C.; Sawhney, R.C. Integrated processing of fresh Indian sea buckthorn (Hippophae rhamnoides) berries and chemical evaluation of products. *Journal of the Science of Food and Agriculture*, 2006, 86, 2345-2353.

[17] Zu, Y.; Li, C.; Fu, Y.; Zhao, C. Simultaneous determination of catechin, rutin, quercetin, kaempferol and isorhamnetin in the extract of seabuckthorn (*Hippophae rhamnoides* L.) leaves by RP-HPLC with DAD. *Journal of Pharmaceutical and Biomedical Analysis*, 2006, 41, 714-719.

[18] Velioglu, Y.S.; Mazza, G.; Gao, L.; Oomah, B.D. Antioxidant activity and total phenolics in selected fruits and vegetables and grain products. *Journal of Agricultural and Food Chemistry*, 1998, 46, 4113-4117.

[19] Wolf, D.; Wegert, R. Development of cultivars and growing techniques for sea buckthorn. In: *Cultivation and Utilization of Wild Fruit Crops*. Bernhard Thalacker Verlag GmbH and Co., 1993, 23-29.

[20] Chen, Y.; Jiang, Z.; Qin, W.; Ni, M.; Li, X.; He, Y. Chemistry and Industry of Forest Products, 1990, 10, 163-175 (in Chinese).

[21] Berezhnaya, G.A.; Ozerinina, O.V.; Yeliseev, I.P.; Tsydendambaev, V.D.; Vereschagin, A.G. *Plant Physiology and Biochemistry*, 1993, 31, 323-332.

[22] Yang, B.; Kallimo, K.O.; Mattila, L.M.; Kallio, S.E.; Katajisto, J.K.; Peltola, O.J. Effects of dietary supplementation with sea buckthorn *(Hippophae rhamnoides)* seed and pulp oils on atopic dermatitis. *Journal of Nutritional Biochemistry*, 1999, 10, 622-630.

[23] Tolkachev, O.N.; Sheichenko, O.P. In: Singh, V. (Ed.). *Biochemistry and Pharmacology*, Vol. II. Delhi: Daya Publishing House, 2006, 159-167.

[24] Arimboor, R.; Venugopalan, V.V.; Sarinkumar, K.; Arumughan, C.; Sawhney, R.C. Integrated processing of fresh Indian seabuckthorn (*Hippophae rhamnoides*) berries and chemical evaluation of products. *Journal of the Science of Food and Agriculture*, 2006, 86, 2345-2353.

[25] Kampa, M.; Alexaki, V.I.; Notas, G.; Nifli, A.P.; Nistikaki, A.; Hatzoglou, A.; Bakogeorgou, E.; Kouimtzoglou, E.; Blekas, G.; Boskou, D.; Gravanis, A.; Castanas, E. Antiproliferative and apoptotic effects of selective phenolic acids on T47D human breast cancer cells: Potential mechanisms of action. *Breast Cancer Research*, 2004, 6, R63-R74.

[26] Arimboor, R.; Sarin Kumar, K.; Arumughan, C. Simultaneous estimation of phenolic acids in sea buckthorn (*Hippophae rhamnoides*) using RP-HPLC with DAD. *Journal of Pharmaceutical and Biomedical Analysis*, 2008, 47, 31-38.

[27] Xu, Q.; Chen, C. Effects of oil of *Hippophae rhamnoides* on experimental thrombus formation and blood coagulation system. *Research and Development of Natural Products*, 1991, 3, 70-73 (in Chinese).

[28] Li, Y.; Wang, L. Preliminary analysis of the clinical effects of sea buckthorn oil capsule and sea buckthorn Saimaitong capsule (containing mixture of sea buckthorn seed oil and Chinese herbs) on ischemic apoplexy. *Hippophae*, 1994, 7, 45-47.

[29] Beveridge, T.; Li, T.S.; Oomah, B.D.; Smith, A. Seabuckthorn products: Manufacture and composition. *Journal of Agricultural and Food Chemistry,* 1999, 47, 3480-3488.

[30] Velioglu, Y.S.; Mazza, G.; Gao, L.; Oomah, B.D. Antioxidant Activity and Total Phenolics in Selected Fruits, Vegetables, and Grain Products. *Journal of Agriculture and Food Chemistry*, 1998, 46, 4113-4117.

[31] Li, Z.R.; Tan, S.Z. A clinical observation on the effects of oral supplementation of sea-buckthorn oil on patients with malignant tumor under chemotherapy. *Hippophae*, 1993, 6, 41-42.

[32] Ring, J.; Ruzicka, T.; Przybilla, B. The pathophysiology of atopic eczema: Synopsis. In: Ruzicka, T; Ring, J; Przybilla, B. (Eds.). *Handbook of Atopic Eczema.*, Berlin: Springer-Verlag, Berlin, Germany. 1991, 330-331.

[33] Johansson, A.K.; Korte, H.; Yang, B.; Stanley, J.C.; Kallio, H.P. Seabuckthorn berry oil inhibits platelet aggregation. *Journal of Nutritional Biochemistry*, 2000, 11, 491- 495.

[34] Jiang, Y.; Zhou, Y.; Bi, C.; Li, J.; Yang, J.; Yu, Z.; Hu, Z.; Zhao, S. Research on the clinical effects of sea buckthorn oil on hyperlipaemia. *Hippophae*, 1993, 6, 23-24.

[35] Calzada, C.; Bruckdorfer, K.R.; Rice-Evans, C.A. The influence of antioxidant nutrients on platelet function in healthy volunteers. *Atherosclerosis*, 1997, 128, 97-105.

[36] Ge, H. GC-MS analysis of sterols in seabuckthorn pulp oil. *Hippophae*, 1992, 5, 7-15.

[37] Zhao, J.; Zhang, C.Y.; Xu, Y.; Huang, G.Q.; Xu, Y.L.; Wang, Z.Y.; Fang, S.D.; Chen, Y.; Gu, Y.L. The antiatherogenic effects of components isolated from pollen typhae. *Thrombosis Research*, 1990, 57, 957-966.

[38] Field, F.J.; Born, E.; Mathur, S.N. Effect of micellar beta-sitosterol on cholesterol metabolism in CaCo-2 cells. *Journal of Lipid Research*, 1997, 38, 348-360.

[39] Jones, P.J.; MacDougall, D.E.; Ntanios, F.; Vanstone, C.A. Dietary phytosterols as cholesterol-lowering agents in humans. *Canadian Journal of Physiology and Pharmacology*, 1997, 75, 217-227.

[40] Budijanto, S.; Ito, M.; Furukawa, Y.;Kimura, S. Effects of various dietary fatty acid ethyl esters on plasma cholesterol and lipoprotein metabolism in rats. *Journal of Clinical Biochemistry and Nutrition*, 1992. 13, 13-22.

[41] Colquhoun, D.M.; Humphries, J.A.; Moores, D.; Somerset, S.M. Effects of a macadamia nut enriched diet on serum lipids and lipoproteins compared to a low fat diet. *Food Australia*, 1996, 48, 216-222.

[42] Eccleston, C.; Yang, B.; Tahvonen, R.; Kallio, H.; Rimbach, G.H.; Minihane, A.M. Effects of an antioxidant-rich juice (sea buckthorn) on risk factors for coronary heart disease in humans. *Journal of Nutritional Biochemistry*, 2002, 13, 346-354.

[43] Geetha, S.; Ram, M.S.; Singh, V.; Ilavazhagan, G.; Sawhney, R.C. Antioxidant and immunomodulatory properties of seabuckthorn (*Hippophae rhamnoides*) - an in vitro study. *Journal of Ethnopharmacology*, 2002, 79, 373-378.

[44] Xing, J.; Yang, B.; Dong, Y.; Wang, B.; Wang, J.; Kallio, H.P. Effects of sea buckthorn (*Hippophae rhamnoides* L.) seed and pulp oils on experimental models of gastric ulcer in rats. *Fitoterapia*, 2002, 73, 644-650.

[45] Dawson, L. E.; Gartner, R. Lipid oxidation in mechanically deboned poultry. *Food Technology*, 1983, 37, 112-116.

[46] Al-Najdawi, R.; Abdullah, B. Proximate composition, selected minerals, cholesterol content and lipid oxidation of mechanically and hand-deboned chickens from the Jordanian market. *Meat Science*, 2002, 61, 243-247.

[47] Mielnik, M.B.; Aaby, K.; Skrede, K. Commercial antioxidants control lipid oxidation in mechanically deboned turkey meat. *Meat Science*, 2003, 65, 1147-1155.

[48] Püssa, T.; Pällin, R.; Raudsepp, P.; Soidla, R.; Rei, M. Inhibition of lipid oxidation and dynamics of polyphenol content in mechanically deboned meat supplemented with sea buckthorn (*Hippophae rhamnoides*) berry residues. *Food Chemistry*, 2008, 107, 714-721.

[49] Li, T.S.C. Documentation of seabuckthorn publications supporting human health and wellness. In Li, T.S.C. and Beveridge, H. J (Eds.). *Seabuckthorn: A New Medicinal and Nutritional Botanical*. Agriculture and Agri-Food Canada, 2007..

[50] Xu, X.; Xie, B.; Pan, S.; Yang, E.; Wang, K.; Cenkowski, S.; Hadamaka, A.; Rao, S. A new technology for extraction and purification of proanthocyanidins derived from sea buckthorn bark. *Journal of the Science of Food and Agriculture,* 2006), 86, 486-492.

[51] Guan, T.; Cenkowski, S.; Hydamaka, A. Effect of drying on the nutraceutical quality of sea buckthorn (*Hippophae rhamnoides* L. ssp. sinensis) leaves. *Journal of Food Science,* 2005, 70(9), E514-E518.

[52] Li, T.S.C. Next Generation of New Botanical Seabuckthorn (*Hippophae rhamnoides* L.). In: Proceedings of the 3rd International Seabuckthorn Association Conference, Quebec City, Canada, August 12-16, 2007,1-2.

[53] Yang, B.; Kallio, H. P. Fatty acid composition of lipids in sea buckthorn (*Hippopha rhamnoides* L.) berries of different origins. *Journal of Agricultural and Food Chemistry,* 2001, 49(4), 1939-1947.

[54] Yang, B. R., and Kallio, H. (2006). Analysis of triacylglycerols of seeds and berries of sea buckthorn (*Hippophae rhamnoides*) of different origins by mass spectrometry and tandem mass spectrometry. *Lipids,* 41(4), 381-392.

[55] Yang, B.; Kallio, H. Effects of harvesting time on triacylglycerols and glycerophospholipids of sea buckthorn (*Hippophae rhamnoides* L.) berries of different origins. *Journal of Food Composition and Analysis,* 2002b,15(2), 143-157.

[56] USDA, 2011. http://www.ars.usda.gov/Services/docs.htm?docid=8964.

[57] Wang, H.; Utioh, A.. Evaluation of processing and nutritional attributes of seabuckthorn fruit fractions of Indian Summer and sinensis varieties. 3rd International Seabuckthorn Association Conference. Quebec City, Canada, August 12-16, 2007.

[58] Beveridge, T.; Harrison, J.E.; Drover, J. Processing effects on the composition of sea buckthorn juice from *Hippophae rhamnoides* L. cv. Indian Summer. *Journal of Agricultural and Food Chemistry,* 2002, 50(1) 113-116.

[59] Li, T.S.C. The range of medicinal plants influencing mental and physical performance. In: David H. Watson (Ed.) Performance functional foods. Woodhead Publishing Ltd. Cambridge, England, 2003, 38-60.

[60] Health Canada. Guide to Food Labelling and Advertising and Amendments. In: 2003 Guide to Food Labelling and Advertising. http://www.inspection.gc.ca/english/fssa/labeti/guide/toce.shtml.

[61] Beveridge, T.; Li, T.S.C.; Oomah, D.; Smith, A. Seabuckthorn products: Manufacture and composition. *Journal of Agricultural and Food Chemistry,* 1999, 47(9), 3480-3488.

[62] Meseyton, J.; Hudson, L.; Wang, H.; Utioh, A. Utilization of seabuckthorn fruit pulp and juice as functional food ingredients. 3rd International Seabuckthorn Association Conference, Quebec, August 12-16, 2007.

[63] Selvamuthukumaran, M.; Khanum, F.; Bawa, A.S. Development of sea buckthorn mixed fruit jelly. *International Journal of Food Science and Technology,* 2007, 42(4), 403-410.

[64] Li, T.S.C. Seabuckthorn therapeutic values. In: Li, T.S.C. and Beveridge, T.H.J. (Eds.), *Seabuckthorn: A New Medicinal and Nutritional Botanical.* Agriculture and Agri-Food Canada Publication 10320E, 2007, 24-38.

[65] Gao, Z.L.; Gu, X.H.; Cheng, F.T.; Jiang, F.H. Effect of sea buckthorn on liver fibrosis: a clinical study. *World Journal Gastroenterology,* 2003, 9, 1615-1617.

[66] Zhang, X.; Zhang, M.; Gao, Z.; Wang, J.; Wang, Z. Effect of total flavones of *Hippophae rhamnoides* L. On sympathetic activity in hypertension. *Hua Zi Yi Ke Da Xue Xue Bao* 2001, 32, 547-50.

[67] Xiao, Z.; Peng, W.; Zhu, B.; Wang, Z. The inhibitory effect of total flavonoids of *Hippophae* on the activation of NF-kappa B by stretching cultured cardiac myocytes. *Sichuan Da Xue Xue Bao Yi Xue Ban* 2003, 34, 283-5.

[68] Dubey, G.P.; Agrawal, A.; Dixit, S.P. Role of sea buckthorn (*Hippophae rhamnoides*) in the maintenance of cardiovascular homeostasis following cold stress. *Journal of Natural Remedies,* 2003, 3, 36-40.

[69] Erkkola, R.; Yang, B. Sea buckthorn oils: Towards healthy mucous membranes. *AGRO Food industry hi-teck.* May/June 2003, 5.

[70] Johansson, A.K.; Korte, H.; Yang, B.; Stanley, J.C.; Kallio, H.P. Sea buckthorn berry oil inhibits platelet aggregation. *Journal of Nutritional Biochemistry,* 2000, 11, 491-5.

[71] Degtiareva, I.I.,; Toteva, Ets;. Litinskaia, E.V.; Matvienko, A.V.; Iurzhenko, N.N.; Leonov, L.N.; Khomenko, E.V.;Nevstruev, V.P. Degree of lipid peroxidation and vitamin E level during the treatment of peptic ulcer. *Klin Med.* (Mosk), 1991, 69, 38-42.

# INDEX

**B**

## D

## E

## F

## G

## J

## K

## L

molecular dynamics, 146
molecular mass, 43, 51, 56, 72
molecular mobility, 141
molecular weight, 9, 50, 51, 54, 68, 84, 111, 148
molecules, 9, 13, 29, 56, 66, 114, 136, 183, 184
mollusks, 141
Mongolia, 164, 165
monomers, 51
monounsaturated fatty acids, 174, 180
Moon, 29, 40, 44
morphine, 3, 28, 63
mortality, 117
motif, 71
motion sickness, 3
MR, 28, 29, 33
mRNA, 8, 115, 119, 127
mucosa, 9, 39, 126
mucous membrane, 173, 189
mucous membranes, 173, 189
multiple myeloma, 126
mung bean, 51, 59
muscle relaxant, 47
mutagenesis, 128
mutant, 27
mutation, 144
mycelium, 43
myocardial ischemia, 41
myocardial necrosis, 25
myocardium, 101

**N**

NAD, 132, 146, 158
National Institutes of Health, 119
National Research Council, 1, 25
natural compound, 120
natural food, 170
nausea, 3, 25, 26
negative effects, 113
neovascularization, 101
nephritis, 96, 107
nerve, 42, 47, 183
nervous system, 52, 63, 65
Netherlands, 76
neuroblastoma, 42, 118, 126
neurodegeneration, 31
neurodegenerative diseases, 112
neurogenesis, 36
neuronal cells, 19, 44
neurons, 8, 31, 47
neuropeptides, 73
neuroprotection, 20
neurotoxicity, 35, 36, 46, 47

neutral, 167
neutral lipids, 167
neutrophils, 41, 69
New Zealand, 82
nitric oxide, 16, 28, 29, 46, 65, 70, 71, 118, 119, 127
nitric oxide synthase, 29, 46, 70, 71, 118, 119
nitrogen, 51, 54, 65, 164
NK cells, 70
NMR, 82
nodules, 164
non-polar, 60, 149
North America, 10, 164
NRC, 25
Nrf2, 29, 30
nucleotide sequence, 68
nutraceutical, 40, 163, 164, 188
nutrient, 50, 135, 174, 175
nutrients, 106, 170, 173, 179, 182, 184, 187
nutrition, 50, 111, 151, 153, 154, 163, 173, 174, 175

**O**

obesity, 3, 26, 38, 63, 64, 112, 131, 133
OH, 41, 46, 65, 66, 67, 82, 99, 100, 143, 182
oil, 4, 5, 6, 26, 28, 29, 30, 31, 51, 52, 56, 60, 91, 92, 96, 97, 107, 118, 155, 159, 163, 165, 166, 167, 168, 169, 170, 173, 178, 179, 180, 184, 185, 186, 187, 189
oilseed, 52
oleic acid, 163, 171, 178
oligomers, 104
omega-3, 179
opacity, 21, 48
opioid activities, 49, 72
opioids, 62, 63
opportunities, 103, 174, 175
orbit, 65
organ, 4, 62
organic solvents, 133, 147, 148
organism, 73, 135
organs, 2, 4, 6, 7, 21
oriental medicine, 35
ornithine, 113
osteoporosis, 20, 45
ovarian cancer, 27, 121
overweight, 63, 98, 108
ox, 87, 149
oxidation, 37, 38, 65, 99, 100, 109, 119, 138, 141, 144, 156, 168, 169, 171, 184, 188
oxidation products, 99, 100, 141
oxidative damage, 34, 35, 65, 117, 122, 156
oxidative stress, 10, 16, 19, 27, 31, 35, 83, 84, 119, 120, 122

vasodilation, 47
vegetables, 84, 186
vegetative reproduction, 164
vein, 4, 28, 42, 64, 122
versatility, 50
very low density lipoprotein, 119
viral infection, 70
viruses, 69
viscera, 21
vision, 9, 10, 12, 16, 21
vitamin A, 173, 174, 179
vitamin C, 38, 165, 166, 167, 170, 173, 174, 175,
   180, 182, 185
Vitamin C, 11, 170, 171, 172, 175
vitamin E, 100, 109, 143, 165, 166, 167, 170, 180,
   184, 189
vitamins, 23, 62, 163, 165, 166, 172, 185
vitiligo, 6
VLDL, 83, 118, 119, 133, 137
vomiting, 2, 3, 4, 5, 6, 7, 14, 17, 21, 22, 25, 26

water, 5, 9, 19, 23, 33, 37, 38, 41, 42, 44, 51, 55, 84,
   97, 138, 140, 143, 144, 147, 149, 164, 165, 175
well-being, 8, 10
wellness, 1, 2, 24, 163, 175, 188
wheat germ, 62
wood, 158, 164
woodland, 133
workers, 115
worldwide, 164, 165
worms, 141

## X

xenografts, 95, 107

## Y

yield, 84, 148, 170, 172, 185
young women, 86, 90

## W

waste, 140, 185

## Z

zinc, 54